Philip Witting is Principal Lecturer in Computer Engineering at The Polytechnic of Wales. He gained his BSc in Electrical and Electronic Engineering from the University of Birmingham in 1968 and his MTech in Systems Engineering from Brunel University in 1974. After graduation, Mr Witting worked for ICI Ltd, Plastics Division as an instrumentation engineer and from 1969 to 1981 was on the staff of the Control Engineering Group at Hatfield Polytechnic. He has undertaken consultancy work for a number of Government Departments, industry and the Open University. He is a Member of the Institution of Electrical Engineers and has served on a number of institution committees. Currently, he is Chairman of Committee C6II – Microprocessor Education and Government Liaison.

The Hatfield Polytechnic Computer Science Series

Fundamentals of Microprocessor Systems

Philip A Witting

Chartwell-Bratt, England
Studentlitteratur, Sweden

For Jacqueline and Abigail

Foreword
by Sir Norman Lindop MSc, CChem, FRSC.

It is a particular pleasure for me to introduce this series of books, which is designed to provide a coherent set of undergraduate texts in computer science. All the contributors to the series have been associated in one way or another with Information Sciences at The Hatfield Polytechnic, and the texts are based upon modules of the Honours degree course in Computer Science — a full-time course on the sandwich pattern which has evolved over the past 15 years.

One of the main features of the Hatfield computer science courses is that they provide a set of broadly-based studies, not unduly biased towards any particular aspects or applications though including many specialist topics and achieving a high final academic standard. It is intended that the modules upon which this series of books is based form a graduated set, from basic foundation studies up to advanced texts.

The development of computing and of computer science at Hatfield has been exciting and spectacularly successful and it is gratifying to present to a wider public some of the fruits of that experience.

Preface

There are many books on microprocessors and yet none seems to include sufficient information to inform adequately someone about to take part in his first development project. Some books cover particular topic areas well and to considerable depth while others cover a much broader spectrum often giving insuffcient detail to be of practical use. This book is designed to fill the gap between the two extremes. It will prove useful both to those professionally involved in microprocessor-based system design and also as a course text at undergraduate and postgraduate levels.

The topic areas covered may be broadly divided into two classes. The first includes those subjects which need to be thoroughly understood before any useful design work may be undertaken; these are dealt with in considerable detail. The second group of topics is dealt with in rather less detail and serves a twofold purpose. It provides an awareness of the wider issues and techniques which are relevant to microprocessor-based systems and also sets out the necessary introductory material so that those who need to pursue these matters further may approach the relevant specialist texts with some confidence.

In selecting material for inclusion in this book, I have been influenced by a number of considerations.

* Microprocessors are computing machines and so the theory applicable to computers in general has been included. However, those aspects which are primarily applicable to large machines have been omitted, unless they are likely to be implemented in microprocessors in the near future.

* Designers of microprocessor-based systems are using software to replace functions which would traditionally be achieved solely by hardware. They are, therefore, very concerned about the software issues as well as hardware. Both of these subject areas are covered thoroughly.

* The majority of microprocessors are embedded within systems with a view to achieving the most cost-effective solution to a problem. Consequently consideration must be given to those factors which affect the cost of a completed product. These include the problems of system development, of ensuring its reliable operation and of servicing it when it does go wrong.

* Microprocessors are widely used in "communications" of one sort or another and therefore some background information on communications techniques will be required by most designers.

Chapters 1 to 8 are concerned with the basic techniques used in the design of microprocessor-based systems.

Chapter 9 is designed to illustrate the theory developed in the first eight Chapters by examining in some detail the Motorola 6800 processor. This Chapter is paralleled by Appendix A for those readers who are more interested in the Intel 8080/8085 processors.

Chapters 10 and 11 are specifically concerned with the types of peripheral equipment likely to be encountered in typical microprocessor application areas. These include control applications, logic circuit replacement, instrumentation systems, data communications and microcomputers.

Chapter 12 covers the issues raised by the use of multiple microprocessors in systems since this type of solution is becoming more common and is often easier to implement than an equivalent single processor solution.

Chapter 13 on memory management has been included because modern microprocessors are capable of supporting very large amounts of memory and the software techniques which this makes possible rely on the facilities provided by memory management systems.

Chapter 14 is complementary to Chapter 9 and illustrates the way in which interfacing problems are solved in microprocessor systems by reference to the Motorola 6800 family of devices. Again this chapter is parallelled by Appendix B for those readers who are more interested in the Intel 8080/8085 family.

Chapters 15 and 16 together cover the very important issues of hardware and software design and maintenance. The decisions taken on these matters during a project can profoundly affect the economic success of a system.

Chapters 17 and 18 are devoted to special types of microprocessor; their capabilities and uses, and the demands which they make during the system development phase.

This book is the product of several years' experience with undergraduate and short-course students. Many people, not least the students themselves, have contributed to its final content and form. I would, however, like to place on record my particular thanks to a number of people to whom I am especially indebted:

To my former colleagues in the Control Group at Hatfield Polytechnic who indulged and encouraged my interest in computer systems and computer control of systems.

To Professor A C Davies of the City University who has patiently spent many hours discussing computer matters with me, especially in connection with bit-slice processors.

To my wife, Jacqueline, who coped with our removal to Wales and the typing of this manuscript and still managed to end up smiling.

P A W
Radyr, South Glamorgan

Acknowledgements

Acknowledgement is gratefully given to the following people for permission to make use of material first published elsewhere:

IEE (Electronics and Power) for Figures 10.31, first published in Ref 18 and for material in Table 18.2 first published in Ref 57.

Peter Peregrinus Ltd for Tables D1 and D2 which contain material first published in Ref 69.

Tektronix Ltd for Figures 16.2 and 16.3 which are based on similar items in their literature.

Advanced Micro Devices Ltd for figures 18.5, 18.6, 18.11, 18.14, 18.15, and Tables 18.5, 18.6, 18.7, and 18.8, which owe their parentage to similar material appearing in Ref 59 and for the blank master table supplied with the AMD 2900 evaluation kit and used as the basis for constructing Fig 18.31.

Zilog (UK) Ltd for Figure 13.2 which is based on similar item in Ref 36.

Open University for Figures 1.1, 2.1, 2.2, 2.3, and 2.4 which are based on similar items in Unit 2 of the course TM221 – 'The Digital Computer'. Also for permission to use, in Chapters 9 and 14, material originally written by the author for Unit 15 of the same course.

Mrs. J. Bacon for figure 12.5 which is based on a similar item in Ref 32.

McGraw Hill Inc for figures 16.10, 16.11, 16.12, which are reprinted from Electronics March 3 1977. Copyright © 1977, McGraw Hill Book Company Inc. All rights reserved.

Intel Corporation (UK) Ltd for Figures 12.10, and 12.11 which are based on material in Ref 30. Also for Figures A5, A6, B2, B5-B7, B9-B12, B14, B15, B17, B18, B20-B23 and for one table in each of sections A4, B2, and B4.1 all of which are based on material in Ref 66.

Hewlett Packard Ltd for Figure 12.7 which is based on a similar item in Ref 29.

Motorola Ltd (Semiconductor Products Sector) for Figures 9.1, 9.2, 9.3, 9.7, 9.10, 14.2, 14.4, 14.5, 14.10, 14.12, 14.13, 14.14, 14.15, 14.16, 14.17, 14.18, 14.20, Tables 14.1, 14.2, 14.3, 14.4, and another small table in Section 14.2.1.1, all of which are based on material in Ref 14.

GPIB is a trademark of Hewlett-Packard
MULTIBUS is a trademark of Intel Corporation

Contents

1. Introduction

Microprocessors are, at one and the same time, electronic components and computing devices and this dual personality has tended to heighten the mystery and suspicion surrounding them. In fact, the development of microprocessors is due to two separate events which occurred some thirty-five years ago, namely the successful operation of the first stored program computer and the discovery of the transistor effect. These two events resulted in the establishment of the semiconductor and the computer industries which, for 20 years, pursued their relatively independent paths. Notwithstanding this independence, it is true to say that both industries were acutely aware of each other, requirements in one stimulating developments in the other. The major breakthrough came at the end of the 1960s when it became both technically feasible and economically desirable to construct the essential elements of a computer as a single semiconductor component. Having once achieved this, the further sophistication of the available devices has continued at an almost frightening pace and it is literally true that a design can be obsolete before the designer has finished his work.

1.1 A Historical Review

Computing machines were first proposed in the 17th Century, primarily as aids for mathematicians, by Pascal (1642) and Leibniz (1694). These were manually controlled machines and the name most closely associated with the early development of self-controlled computing machinery is that of Charles Babbage (1835). Unfortunately progress was slow since all of the proposed designs were of a mechanical nature and the standard of work necessary to produce a workable machine exceeded that which was practicable at the time. However, there was a requirement, particularly in the USA, for data sorting machines to be used in connection with the national census and Herman Hollerith succeeded in obtaining a contract from the United States Government for the development of such a machine. The analysis of the US census of 1896 was completed very rapidly thanks to the successful operation of this sorting machinery which processed punched cards onto which the data contained in each census return had been encoded. Thus the two primary uses for modern computers, computation and data manipulation, were well established by the beginning of the 20th Century. At the same time another worker, George Boole (1859), was establishing the theoretical basis for the design of logic circuits, the essential building blocks of modern computing machinery.

By the time of the Second World War, mechanical and electronic techniques had advanced sufficiently to permit working computers to be built. These were special purpose machines designed for specific tasks, such as gun aiming and code breaking (COLOSSUS - 1943). These devices were very expensive and their general usefulness limited since it required a major re-design of the hardware to change its function.

The major conceptual breakthrough at this time was the realisation that all tasks, no matter how complex, may be broken down into a sequence of relatively simple operations. This is illustrated in Figure 1.1 for the calculation

$$(A + B * C) + D$$

although the principle is not restricted to arithmetic calculations alone.

It turned out that the repertoire of functions was not large and that each function could easily be implemented in electronic (valve) hardware. Unfortunately, most useful tasks require very many elementary operations and so the amount and cost of a useful set of equipment was enormous. Also valve equipment was not very reliable and so it proved very difficult to keep such a large mass of equipment working. Reprogramming of this type of computer is a relatively simple, though hardware-oriented, operation. It simply involves changing the connections between the various functional blocks. The problem of cost and reliability was solved by constructing a single, multi-purpose piece of

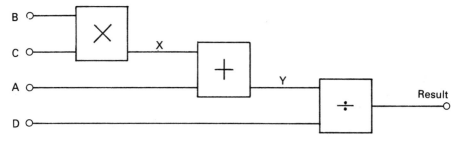

Figure 1.1: Steps in the Computation of (A+B*C)÷ D

equipment which could, given the appropriate control input
(instruction), carry out any of the elementary functions.
This was called the Arithmetic and Logic Unit (ALU). The
control signals had to be stored as did the intermediate
answers (x, y in Figure 1.1) so that the complete calculation
could be carried out successfully by sequentially obeying the
specified instructions. The credit for establishing the
general principles on which such a computer could be
constructed goes to Burks, Goldstein and Von Neumann in their
paper, "Preliminary Discussion of the Logical Design of an
Electronic Computing Instrument" (1946).

After the end of the war, a large number of research teams
was engaged in projects to solve the various practical
problems presented by the sequential processor concept. In
due course, these problems of storage and sequencing were
solved and the first successful operation of an electronic
stored-program computer took place in June 1948 at Manchester
University. A very important point to note is that the task
carried out by the computer was no longer determined by the
hardware interconnection of units but rather by the
instructions stored:- the program. To carry out the problem
illustrated in Figure 1.1 would require a sequence something
like:

                multiply B by C
                add   X to A
                divide   Y by D

Further research work was supported, amongst others, by J
Lyons and Company resulting in the first commercial
application in the United Kingdom of computers for payroll
calculations etc. in 1954. This machine, manufactured by
Lyons Computers, later by English Electric, was called LEO
(Lyons' Electronic Office).

The development of computers in the USA was considerably
stimulated by the space programme with its requirement for
compact and reliable electronics. This need was met by the
adoption of transistors for the fabrication of computer
circuits and resulted in considerably reduced size and
improved reliability. The first transistor-based computer was
produced in 1956 and no new valve-based machines were
designed after 1958.

With the increasing reliability and miniaturisation of electronics the ALU was considerably enhanced by the addition of non-elementary functions (such as multiplication). These required many elementary operations if they were to be performed by a program but if performed by a special-purpose electronic circuit could be carried out very much faster. This factor, combined with an increase in the intrinsic speed of the electronic circuits, caused a very rapid advance in the power and the utility of computers.

The increased power and reliability was put to work not only for data processing but also for the automation of factories, notably chemical plants. The first computer to be used in a chemical plant was at Texaco's Port Arthur refinery in 1959 where it performed a monitoring function. The first instance of a computer assuming control of a chemical plant was at ICI's Fleetwood Plant in 1962. The computer used was a Ferranti Argus machine.

The developments in electronic devices continued to be applied to computers during the 1960s resulting in yet smaller, faster and cheaper machines. One notable event was the establishment of the Digital Equipment Corporation PDP8 series in 1964. This is widely regarded as establishing the mini-computer concept and it is interesting because the designers used the latest electronics not to produce greater computing power but rather to produce the same power as had been available a decade earlier from "mainframe" computers but with much reduced cost and size. This exercise was repeated some five years later by Intel when they designed the world's first microprocessor.

1.2 The Birth of the Microprocessor

By the late 1960s, it was common practice for semiconductor manufacturers to produce complex, custom-designed circuits for other firms. This was necessary since the number of generally saleable circuits of high complexity is small and so manufacturers could not therefore use their manufacturing capacity fully by producing general purpose circuits "on spec". The custom design procedure, although aided by computers, was economic only if the production run for the finished device was large. This factor limited the number of applications in which large-scale integrated circuits could be used. Thus Intel hit upon the idea of producing a general purpose circuit which could be readily configured to fit many applications by the addition of some defining program.

This was exactly the solution achieved by the early computer designers in their attempt to escape from the special-purpose computing machines. The first offering from Intel was indeed a very small scale computer, the 4004 (1971). It was soon followed by the 8008, 4040 and the 8080. Other companies such as Texas Instruments, National Semiconductor, Motorola and

Ferranti soon followed suit.

In order to fit a computer into the constraints imposed by semiconductor technology, it was necessary:

(i)   To use a transistor technology which used the minimum area of semiconductor

(ii)   To simplify the design and eliminate many features that were commonplace in "conventional" computers.

Thus Intel trod the same path as Digital Equipment Corporation in bringing the facilities offered back to those existing a decade or more before in order to achieve a considerable cost and size reduction.

In simplifying the computer, certain necessary functions were hived off to be realised in separate circuit packages. Thus a simple but complete system consisted of about four integrated circuit packages (excluding power supplies etc). This is referred to as a "4-chip set".

Developments since the arrival of the first microprocessors in 1972 have been to improve semiconductor technology so that both circuit speed and circuit complexity are again rising rapidly. The other, complementary, trend is the incorporation of external circuits onto the main microprocessor chip to give a single-chip microprocessor. Typical costs of mid-range microprocessors are now in the order of £ 2 - $ 5 when bought in 100,000 piece lots and about £ 10 - $ 15 in one-off quantities.

1.3 The Application of Microprocessors

As originally conceived, the microprocessor is a replacement for custom-designed integrated circuits and it is in this role that the majority of applications are still to be found. In this area the special-purpose, integrated circuit replaces a multitude of general-purpose integrated circuits. In so doing it provides reduced assembly costs and improved reliability, smaller packaging and reduced power requirements.

Although microprocessors are very widely used in relatively simple applications to replace large arrays of logic, it is perhaps inevitable that the computational abilities of these devices should be used to enhance the performance of equipment. This has always been possible by using minicomputers but, as has been pointed out above, the cost of minicomputers combined with their relatively large size has usually meant that such applications are not viable. Thus the availability of microprocessors has contributed very considerably to the development and improvement of

instrumentation and other systems where the computational
power can be used to provide greater accuracy and ease of use.

The above two categories may be broadly described as embedded
applications. The microcomputing components are buried within
the system in such a way that the end user is barely aware of
their existence. In addition to these applications, however,
there exists a wide range of situations in which the
microprocessor is very visible. These are where the
microprocessor is used to fabricate a small computer - a
microcomputer. Such applications may possibly be amongst the
most important because, although they do not necessarily
provide the greatest sales of microprocessor components, they
have made computers generally available at very low cost.
They have contributed immensely to the de-mystification of
computers and to the general public acceptance and
understanding of their use in both large and small systems.

2. The Sequential Processor

There are a number of ways in which data may be processed in order to produce the solution to some defined problem. For instance, a special purpose logic circuit could be designed to process the input data. Such an approach is not, however, of sufficient generality to produce a versatile computational machine. By contrast a simple pocket calculator may be used for a wide variety of purposes, but it is not fast because it requires manual input of key-strokes to sequence its operations. The main qualities associated with a computer are that it should operate rapidly (which means with the minimum of human intervention) and be capable of being rapidly reorganised to carry out a wide variety of tasks.

Thus the essential features which distinguish a computer from other forms of data processor are that it is:

(i) Automatic

(ii) Reprogrammable

The second feature is one of the most important properties of a computer. Because the device is to operate automatically and is also to be capable of performing various tasks, the specification of the particular task to be undertaken must be stored within the machine in some way which is only semi-permanent. This leads to the requirement that the device be:

(iii) Stored program

As discussed in Chapter 1, all problems are capable of being decomposed into elementary steps. Since it is impractical to provide enough computational units to solve any realistic problem by simply interconnecting a number of basic "building blocks", each step is taken in turn and processed by the same general-purpose hardware unit. This hardware unit is controlled by the stored program so that at each stage of the computation the hardware is carrying out the correct processing task. Virtually all modern computers, be they "mainframe" or microprocessor, make use of this very basic sequential approach to data processing.

2.1 The Evolution of a Sequential Processor Architecture

The sequential processor approach succeeds in solving many problems but not without generating some of its own. Because it solves every problem in a stepwise fashion, the sequential processor is slower than some methods of processing (e.g. special-purpose logic). Also, because the machine has to be "organised", there is a considerable overhead of organisational hardware needed to ensure correct operation. This leads to a relatively complex structure which, fortunately, may be evolved in a number of relatively simple stages.

The principal idea underpinning the sequential processor concept is that every process can be broken down into a number of elementary processes which, when performed IN THE CORRECT SEQUENCE, will produce the desired result. The more complex the problem, the more stages will be required and the longer it will take, but even so the solution merely involves the use, in the correct sequence, of a number of standard processes each of which can be undertaken by a relatively simple module of hardware.

For instance, consider the arithmetic process:

$$A = [(B + C) / D] + E$$

This may be broken down into elementary processes as shown in Figure 2.1.

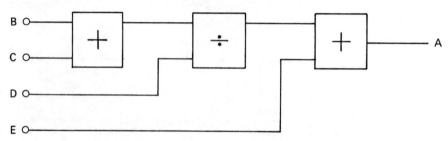

Figure 2.1: Decomposition of a simple problem

This structure involves two addition-type modules and a single division module. Clearly a large problem will involve very many stages of computation and the system could become uneconomic.

Notice too, however, that the programming of this processor involves merely the specification of the order in which various processes will be carried out.

It involves an ANALYSIS OF THE LOGIC of the processing task but it does not involve the complete solution of the problem for all possible inputs.

An economy in hardware can be achieved if, instead of having very many special-purpose processors, we construct one general-purpose device capable of all the necessary operations (arithmetic unit). Such a device could be used in place of processor (i) in Figure 2.1, the answer computed and the result (called a partial result) stored for subsequent use. Later the general-purpose processor could be re-configured automatically as a divider and using both D and the partial result could produce a second partial result for storage, thus replacing processor (ii). Finally it could be configured as an adder and replace processor (iii) in the addition of the second partial result and E to give the final answer.

To carry out the above process a number of additional units will be required. First, a temporary storage unit is needed for the partial results. This device is commonly called a register. In fact this particular register (there are many in a typical computer) is called the accumulator. Also required is a control unit to ensure that the correct operation is being carried out and a clock to ensure that all the various tasks performed by the control unit (e.g. transferring the accumulator from input to output) are carried out at the appropriate time. Figure 2.2 shows the general sequence of events for the calculation

$$[(B + C) / D] + E$$

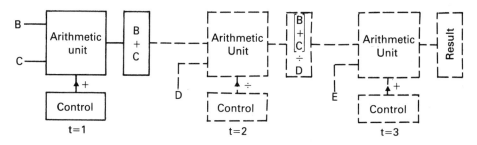

Figure 2.2: Sequential Use of a General Purpose Arithmetic Unit

While Figure 2.2 shows how the sequential processor is configured for this particular problem, it does not make clear the structure of the processor itself.

This is shown in Figure 2.3.

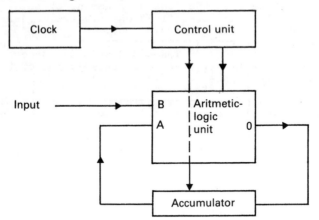

Figure 2.3: Practical Interconnection Scheme

Notice that the control unit is shown controlling both the arithmetic-logic unit and the accumulator. The name arithmetic-logic unit has been adopted since, in general, these devices can perform both arithmetic and logical processes. Figure 2.3 does not make clear how the control unit is told what to do, nor how data is put into or out of the machine.

The control unit will be given commands in sequence and it is in response to these commands that it configures the arithmetic-logic unit and the accumulator etc. These commands will be held in a command store, where they have been placed by the user. This sequence of commands is the STORED PROGRAM, and the commands stored are called the INSTRUCTIONS. These instructions are stored, like all other data in the computer, in binary digital format. To ensure that the program is executed in the proper sequence, the command store (better called the PROGRAM STORE) has a SEQUENCE CONTROL REGISTER associated with it.

The data for the computation has to be obtained from somewhere and two sources of data are possible:

(i)   Internal storage

(ii)   The outside world, via input peripherals

Similarly, there must be output peripherals to allow the communication of results to the user, and also it is necessary to be able to store results in memory. These requirements are all brought together in the structure shown in Figure 2.4.

10

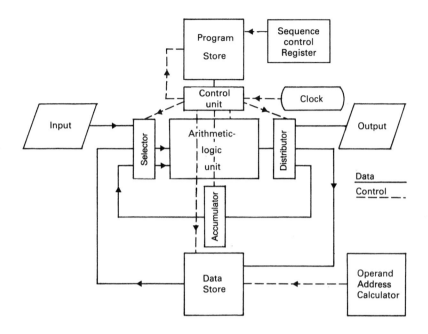

Figure 2.4: Complete Sequential Processor Structure

Notice that the control unit plays a central role in the operation of the machine and has connections to most parts. The structure shown in Figure 2.4, with its separate program store and data store, is termed a HARVARD ARCHITECTURE.

There is one major drawback to the structure of Figure 2.4. The partitioning of storage between program and data is wasteful because there are some processes which require very short programs but much data and others that require long programs and very little data. Thus the structure of Figure 2.4 must have storage adequate for all eventualities, but it is highly unlikely that any particular process will use all of the available storage. An improved structure therefore will combine these two stores. This is then termed a PRINCETON ARCHITECTURE. Inevitably this structure also has a drawback. Since the program must be capable of modifying data, it will also be able to modify the instructions if these reside in the same store. Thus there is a very real possibility of the program destroying itself under fault conditions. Despite this most computers use the Princeton architecture although some recent machines have returned to the Harvard structure.

The highly interconnected structure of Figure 2.4 with almost every module being connected to every other is very expensive to implement. A much more economical solution is to provide only one or two lines of "communication" to which all devices are connected. Thus any module can communicate with any other module, but only one "conversation" can be carried out at any one time. This may seem restrictive, and it does result in some slowing of the machine but it is generally very successful. The situation very much resembles that in a telephone system where many thousands of subscribers share only a few lines between, say, London and Manchester. It is the function of the control unit to decide which units are able to use the 'lines of communication'.

At this point, it is almost possible to draw the complete structure of a simple sequential processor. However, before doing this, it is important to understand how data and instructions are stored, retrieved and transmitted within a computer.

Both data and instructions are stored within a computer as a collection of binary digital numbers; the number of symbols used in the representation is called the word length and the greater the word length, the more accurately data can be represented but the more costly the machine is likely to be.

A data item can be transmitted around the computer in two ways:

> (i) serially: each symbol of a word is sent individually in a strict time sequence.

> (ii) in parallel: all symbols of a word are sent at the same time.

Serial transmission involves only a single wire but it is slow since one time slot is required for each symbol in the word. Parallel transmission requires as many wires as there are symbols, but transmission occupies only one time slot.

The speed advantage of parallel transmission is the dominant factor and virtually all computers use parallel transmission for the shared internal communication link(s). These multi-wire links are called DATA BUSES or DATA HIGHWAYS.

The structure used in Figure 2.4 may be revised to permit the use of a single data bus for all communications and this is shown in Figure 2.5. Notice that both the operand addressing unit and the sequence control register (commonly called the program counter) both have access to the store unit since both data and instructions reside in the same store. A commonly used name for the storage unit is MEMORY. The correct data is extracted from memory by specifying its address and there is usually a register association with the memory unit into which the correct address is written prior to a READ or WRITE operation. This is the memory address register (MA) shown in Figure 2.5. There is also an Instruction Register (IR) to hold the instruction throughout its execution.

In a practical sequential processor, the address of an operand is usually specified, in part at least, by the

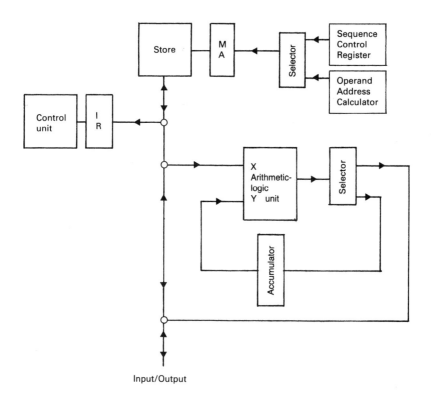

Figure 2.5: Bus-Oriented Sequential Processor

instruction and so it is necessary for the operand addressing unit to have access to the output of the memory. Thus this unit cannot be isolated as shown in Figure 2.5. The operand addressing unit is, in fact, a simple arithmetic unit. In advanced processors, it is often implemented as a separate unit but in simpler systems the ALU itself is frequently used to perform this function. Again this simplification of the hardware results in a certain inefficiency and a corresponding slowing of the overall operation of the processor.

Most of the time, the sequence controller simply steps through instructions one at a time. However, much of the power of a computer is associated with its ability to vary the order in which instructions are obeyed depending on the results of previous calculations. For this reason, the sequence register cannot be implemented as a simple counter. It may have to be reloaded with new data obtained either from the memory or from the output of the arithmetic-logic unit. It, too, therefore requires access to the main bus of the computer.

Finally, it is necessary in practice to have a temporary storage register associated with the X input of the ALU. Incorporating all of these modifications into the structure shown in Figure 2.5 results in the final simple computer structure shown in Figure 2.6.

The various logic symbols shown in Figure 2.6 are described in Appendix C. In particular, it should be noted that the registers used in Figure 2.6 will be of the "master-slave" type described in Appendix C-4.

The structure shown in Figure 2.6 may seem a little strange. However, its operation should become clear after studying the details of the operation of a selection of instructions in Section 2.3. It will suffice at this stage to note that the operation of a computer is cyclic, each instruction requiring one or more machine cycles for its execution. Every instruction will involve a first cycle during which the instruction to be obeyed is obtained from memory. This is the FETCH cycle. Following this, it will often be necessary to extract from memory details about which operand is to be used. This will require a second machine cycle. Depending on the way in which the operand is to be accessed (the addressing mode) one or more additional machine cycles may be needed in order that the exact location in memory (address) of the operand can be computed by the ALU. Finally one or more machine cycles will be required to actually access the operand and to carry out the necessary manipulations with it. A typical microprocessor will contain all of the elements shown in Figure 2.6 with the exception of the memory. Thus memory and input/output circuitry have to be added externally - although special "single-chip" microprocessors will include these items as explained in Chapter 17.

In order that memory may be added externally, the addressing information (contained in the memory address register) must be made available to it. Figure 2.7 shows the general arrangement of a microprocessor-based system. The data bus corresponds to the main spinal bus of Figure 2.6 while the address bus is the output of the memory address register and the control bus consists of signals originating in the control unit of Figure 2.6 which need to be made available to external memory etc.

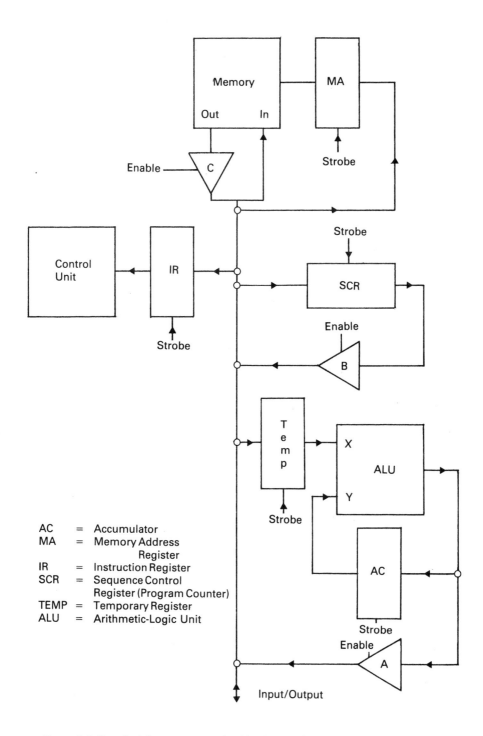

AC   = Accumulator
MA   = Memory Address
            Register
IR   = Instruction Register
SCR = Sequence Control
            Register (Program Counter)
TEMP = Temporary Register
ALU = Arithmetic-Logic Unit

Figure 2.6: Practical Arrangement of a Simple Bus-Oriented Sequential Processor

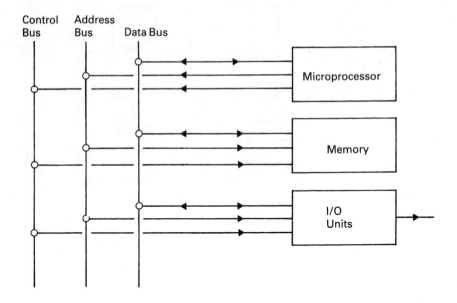

Figure 2.7: A Typical Microprocessor-based System

2.2 Fundamental Operations Required in a Computer

An important influence on the usefulness of a computer is the range of operations which have been provided by the designer. There is a basic minimum of arithmetic and logical operations which must be provided in order that the full range of processing tasks may be carried out. However, designers frequently include other non-fundamental operations so that the machine is easier to use and is more efficient. These will be obtained by combining the fundamental operations in hardware. Thus multiplication which could be implemented as a sequence of simple addition instructions may in fact be provided as a single instruction. When implemented as a single instruction, it is bound to execute more rapidly since the sequencing will be carried out by hardware and not by fetching a large number of elementary program instructions. The price paid for this speed and convenience is, of course, an increase in the complexity of the hardware, notably the control unit. The precise range of instructions provided will be a compromise between cost, speed and ease of use chosen by the designer to suit the particular application area of the computer.

The remainder of this section will be concerned with the basic minimum, rather than the typical, range of ALU operations. In practice, a considerably wider range is usually available and the reader is referred to Chapter 9 and to Appendix A where two typical microprocessor instruction sets are reviewed.

The fundamental operations to be provided may be categorised:

(i)   Arithmetic operations
(ii)   Logical operations
(iii) Machine control instructions
(iv)   Program control instructions

The basic minimum that must be provided in the arithmetic class of instructions is ADDITION. From this subtraction may be formed by first negating one of the operands. This is simply achieved by first complementing the operand (a logical operation) and then adding one to the result (Section 3.5.2). Once addition and subtraction have been established, it is relatively simple to implement multiplication and division as repeated addition and subtraction operations.

Logical operations must, as outlined above, include the COMPLEMENT function [1 $\longrightarrow$ 0, 0 $\longrightarrow$ 1] plus one other basic logical operation such as AND or OR. It is one of the basic axioms of logic circuit design that these two operations are all that is needed to implement any function, although the availability of other operations is usually a great help.

The repertoire of machine control instructions is necessarily related to the facilities offered by the particular machine but would normally include such operations as HALT, TURN INTERRUPTS ON/OFF etc.

Program control instructions are most important. Basically these instructions re-load the sequence control register with a new value, thus causing a completely new sequence of instructions to be executed. These are called BRANCH or JUMP instructions. Two main categories of such instructions may be identified, namely

        JUMP   (without the intention of returning to
                         the current instruction sequence)
    and

        JUMP TO SUBROUTINE

The first 'JUMP' instruction simply causes the sequence control register to be re-loaded with a new value which is in some way specified by the instruction. The old value of the sequence register is completely lost and return to the original sequence of instructions is, in general, impossible (Figure 2.8a).

The 'JUMP TO SUBROUTINE' instruction, however, is used when it is required to return to the original sequence at a later time. In this case, it is necessary to preserve the current contents of the sequence control register so that it may be restored later. The method of preserving the sequence register will be discussed later; it is sufficient to note at this point that there is a 'RETURN FROM SUBROUTINE' instruction which recovers the old value of the sequence

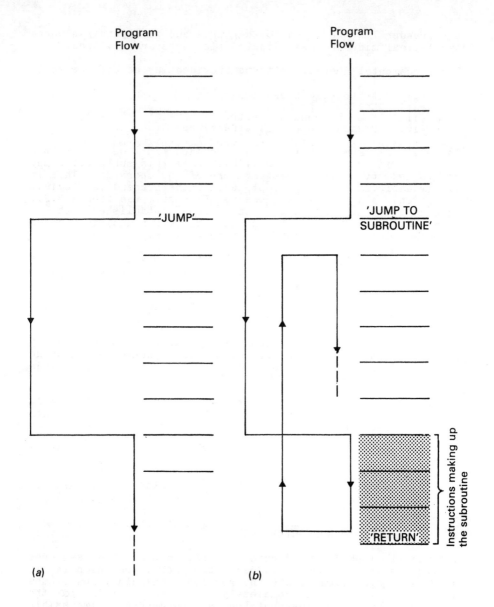

Figure 2.8: Jump-Type Instructions

control register and restores it; this is a special type of jump instruction (Figure 2.8b).

It will be seen that the jump to subroutine causes a subsequence of instructions to be executed. This is most useful when the same sequence of instructions has to be obeyed several times at different points in the program. Typically a subroutine might be used to carry out such operations as multiplication etc. in a machine that did not have the necessary hardware provision to carry out this operation.

The most powerful feature of all jump-type instructions is that they can be made CONDITIONAL. All machines incorporate hardware to detect certain conditions pertaining to the result of an operation. For instance, is it negative/positive, zero/non-zero, is there an overflow/no overflow etc. These conditions are stored in a hardware register called a 'Condition Code Register' (not shown in Figure 2.6).

Conditional jump instructions may be used to inspect the contents of any particular condition code and to jump or not to jump depending on the result of the test.

> For example, the instruction 'JUMP IF ZERO' would execute the specified jump if it was found that the result of the last operation had set the 'zero' condition code; otherwise execution would continue in a sequential fashion.

It is these conditional jump instructions which give the computer its basic decision-making capability. All of the jump-type instructions (JUMP, JUMP TO SUBROUTINE and RETURN) may be made conditional.

2.3 Stack Operation

It was noted above that the 'JUMP TO SUBROUTINE' instruction must preserve the contents of the sequence control register so that it is possible to return to the calling sequence. It would be possible to save this information in a special memory location, but this would be inconvenient since any attempt to call a second subroutine from within the first (which is quite common) would overwrite the first return address. An alternative strategy (used, for instance, in PDP8 computers) is to reserve a memory location within the subroutine for this purpose. This overcomes the former objection unless, of course, the subroutine calls itself!

The most common method of obtaining subroutine linkage in modern machines is by the use of a STACK. A stack is a LAST-IN-FIRST-OUT (LIFO) store which operates exactly like a pile of cups. The last item placed on the pile must be the first one off. Stack operation will be illustrated by an example in

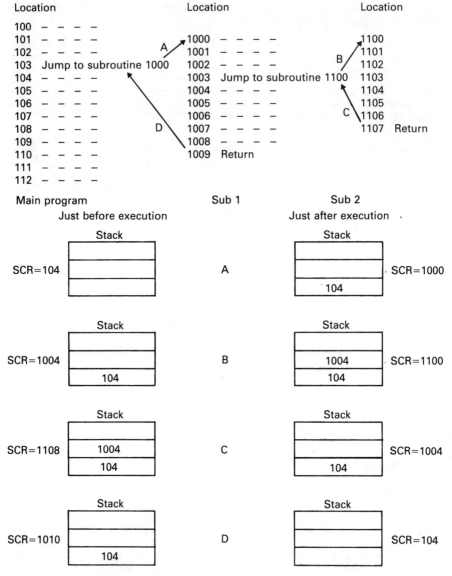

Figure 2.9: Stack Operation for Subroutine Linkage

which the main program calls a subroutine (SUB1) and in due course SUB1 calls a second subroutine (SUB2). This is termed subroutine nesting. The situation is illustrated in Figure 2.9.

It will be noticed that, during execution, the sequence control register always points to the next sequential instruction. Provided that the subroutines are exited in the reverse order of entry, the correct value of sequence control register will always be available at the top of the stack irrespective of the depth of the nest. The 'JUMP TO SUBROUTINE' instruction puts the current sequence control register value on the stack and then jumps to the specified address while the RETURN instruction retrieves the top value from the stack and places it in the sequence control register. It is clearly not correct to JUMP from SUB2 to SUB1 (as distinct from RETURNing).

The operation of putting data on the stack is called 'PUSHing' while retrieving data is called 'POPping' or 'PULLing'.

Although some machines may incorporate a special piece of hardware for the stack, this is unusual. The more normal method is to use part of the main memory for stacking data. The next available address for use is indicated by a special hardware register called the STACK POINTER. This would appear in the architecture of Figure 2.6 as another register connected to the main bus in a fashion similar to that employed for the sequence control register. After the storage on the stack has been accomplished, the content of the stack pointer is incremented to point to the next free location. This procedure is best illustrated by studying the values assumed by the memory locations and the pointer before and after a push of a single data item to the stack and the pull of a single item from the stack (Figure 2.10). The conventions covering stack pointer usage given above are not invariable. In some computers the stack pointer is decremented when data is placed on the stack. Also, the stack pointer may indicate the last item on the stack rather than the next free location.

For the 'PULL' instruction, the stack pointer must be decremented before it is used to extract data. Notice that items are not erased from memory, they are simply placed outside the stack due to the change in the pointer and will subsequently be overwritten by 'PUSH' instructions.

Initial contents of accumulator = 50
Initial contents of stack pointer = 100

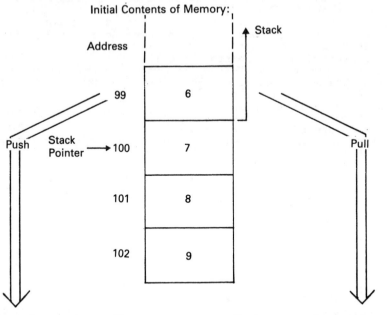

Final contents of accumulator = 50
Final contents of stack pointer = 101

Final contents of memory:

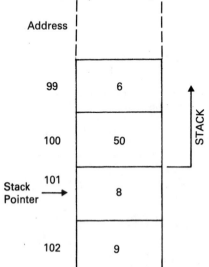

Final contents of accumulator = 6
Final contents of stack pointer = 99

Final contents of memory:

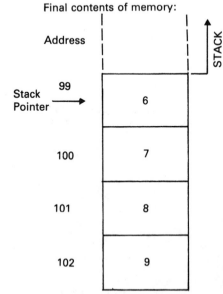

Figure 2.10: Simple Stack Operations

2.4 The Implementation of Some Simple Instructions

A better understanding of the operation of the simple computer shown in Figure 2.6 will be obtained if the detailed data flow during the execution of a few simple instructions is examined. This exercise will be carried out in this section.

The format of an instruction will be discussed in detail in a later Chapter. For the present purpose, it is sufficient to distinguish those instructions which perform operations on a single piece of data from those which require two. In the former case, we will assume that this data is already located in the accumulator. The latter group of instructions include addition, subtraction etc and we will assume that one operand is already in the accumulator and that the second operand is held somewhere in memory. Such instructions are termed memory-reference instructions.

For the purpose of the following examples, we will assume that the designer of our computer has decided that all single operand (non-memory reference) instructions will occupy a single memory location, the contents of which will specify the operation to be performed (operation code).

Two operand (memory reference) instructions will occupy two sequential locations in memory. In the first will be a code specifying the operation to be performed (operation code) and in the second will be a number representing the address of the second operand (operand address) (see Figure 2.11).

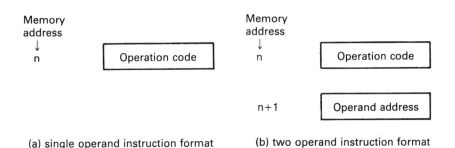

(a) single operand instruction format

(b) two operand instruction format

Figure 2.11: Layout of One- and Two-Word Instructions

The movement of data during an instruction is best expressed in the form of a table using a simple shorthand to indicate the source and destination of data.

e.g.   (SCR) ——————————→ MA

This indicates that the CONTENTS of the sequence control register is loaded into the memory address register. On completion of this exercise, the contents of the memory address register are identical to that of the sequence control register.

Similarly

$$(memory) \longrightarrow MD$$

This indicates that the contents of memory are transferred to the memory data register. Which memory contents ? The contents of the location whose address is stored in the MA register.

The notation given here is termed "bracket-and-arrow". It is simple to understand provided one remembers that "()" are to be read as "the contents of" and "⟶" is read as "is transferred to". These rules apply very strictly so · "((MA))" would be read as "the contents of the contents of...".

2.4.1 IMPLEMENTATION OF A 'LOAD' INSTRUCTION

The purpose of this instruction is to transfer the contents of some specified memory location into the accumulator. The instruction is a memory reference instruction and has the format:

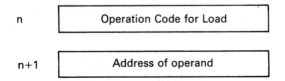

We will assume that the SCR is initially loaded with the address of the instruction (i.e. n). The execution of the instruction is in three distinct parts; first, the instruction itself must be read into the IR and decoded; secondly, the specified operand must be located and finally the specified instruction must be carried out. Steps 1 and 2 set up the memory ready to read the first word of the instruction while 3 - 6 use the ALU to update the SCR so that it points to the next sequential program location (i.e. n+1). The memory is then read (step 7) at the address specified by MA (i.e. n). This location contains the instruction operation code which is directed into the instruction register (step 8).

Steps 9 - 16 are virtually a repeat of the first eight steps and achieve the fetching of the second word of the instruction. This is not an operation code and so is not

Step	Actions Taken		Data flow
1	Enable driver B		$(SCR) \rightarrow MA$
2	Strobe MA		
3	Enable driver B		$(SCR) \rightarrow Temp$
4	Strobe 'Temp'		
5	Open X I/P, Signal ALU 'Increment' Enable driver A	Instruction	$(Temp) + 1 \rightarrow SCR$
6	Strobe SCR		
7	Read memory, enable driver C	Fetch	$(Mem) \rightarrow IR$
8	Strobe IR		
9	Enable driver B		$(SCR) \rightarrow MA$
10	Strobe MA		
11	Enable driver B	Address	$(SCR) \rightarrow Temp$
12	Strobe 'Temp'		
13	Open X I/P, Signal ALU 'increment' Enable driver A	Operand	$(Temp) + 1 \rightarrow SCR$
14	Strobe SCR		
15	Read memory, enable driver C	Obtain.	$(Mem) \rightarrow Temp$
16	Strobe temp		
17	Open X I/P, Signal ALU 'ADD', Enable driver A		$(Temp) + 0 \rightarrow MA$
18	Strobe MA		
19	Read memory, enable driver C	Execute	$(Mem) \rightarrow Temp$
20	Strobe 'Temp'		
21	Open X I/P, Signal ALU 'ADD',		$(Temp) + 0 \rightarrow ACC$
22	Strobe ACC		

Table 2.1: Sequence Table for 'LOAD' instruction

directed to the instruction register but is routed to the 'temporary' register.

Steps 17 - 22 actually execute the instruction. Initially, the address of the operand is in the 'TEMP' register. This is transferred to the memory address register by adding zero to it in the ALU (this is the only way of getting the contents of TEMP back onto the bus - steps 17 and 18). This memory address is then read and the required data obtained and put into TEMP (steps 19 - 20) subsequently (steps 21 and 22). The contents of TEMP are placed in the accumulator.

On completion of the last step of this (or any other) instruction, the control unit automatically starts to fetch another instruction.

2.4.2 IMPLEMENTATION OF A 'JUMP' INSTRUCTION

This also is a memory reference instruction which transfers program control from the next instruction to some other instruction which is held at a specified location. This simply involves re-loading the SCR with the address of this new instruction.

The first 16 steps (Table 2.2) are identical to the LOAD instruction since the JUMP is also a two-word instruction. On completion of step 16, the address to be jumped to (target address) is in the 'TEMP' register. Remember that on completion of an instruction, the control unit automatically goes to the location specified by the SCR to get the next instruction. It will be clear, therefore, that all that is required of a jump instruction is to transfer the contents of TEMP into the SCR, thus loading it with the target address.

2.4.3 IMPLEMENTATION OF A 'COMPLEMENT' INSTRUCTION

The operation "complement" is provided within the ALU. It merely involves changing all of the ones in a binary number to zero and all the zeros to ones. Thus the COMPLEMENT instruction will require only one operand and, by our convention, this will be in the accumulator. Hence "complement" will occupy only one memory location.

Since this is a one-word instruction, only the operation code needs to be fetched. This is achieved by steps 1 - 8 (Table 2.3) as with the previous two instructions. Once this is done the control unit detects that the current instruction is a one-word instruction and executes it as shown in steps 9 and 10.

Note that all three examples have started with the same eight stages. This, of course, is necessary because, until the instruction is actually in the IR, the control unit is unable

n	Operation Code for Jump

n+1	Address of instruction to be jumped to

Step	Actions Taken		Data flow
1	Enable driver B	Instruction	$(SCR) \rightarrow MA$
2	Strobe MA		
3	Enable driver B		$(SCR) \rightarrow Temp$
4	Strobe 'Temp'		
5	Open X I/P, Signal ALU 'Increment', Enable driver A		$(Temp) + 1 \rightarrow SCR$
6	Strobe SCR		
7	Read memory, Enable driver C	Fetch	$(Mem) \rightarrow IR$
8	Strobe IR		
9	Enable driver B	Target Address	$(SCR) \rightarrow MA$
10	Strobe MA		
11	Enable driver B		$(SCR) \rightarrow Temp$
12	Strobe 'Temp'		
13	Open X I/P, Signal ALU increment Enable driver A		$(Temp) + 1 \rightarrow SCR$
14	Strobe SCR		
15	Read memory, Enable driver C	Obtain	$(Mem) \rightarrow Temp$
16	Strobe 'Temp'		
17	Open X I/P, Signal ALU 'ADD', Enable driver A	Execute	$(Temp) + 0 \rightarrow SCR$
18	Strobe SCR		

Table 2.2: Sequence Table for 'JUMP' Instruction

	Operation Code for Complement

Step	Actions Taken		Data flow
1	Enable driver B		$(SCR) \rightarrow MA$
2	Strobe MA	Instruction	
3	Enable driver B		$(SCR) \rightarrow Temp$
4	Strobe 'Temp'		
5	Open X I/P, Signal ALU 'Increment', Enable driver A		$(Temp) + 1 \rightarrow SCR$
6	Strobe SCR		
7	Read memory, Enable driver C	Fetch	$(Mem) \rightarrow IR$
8	Strobe IR		
9	Open Y I/P, Signal ALU 'Complement',	Execute	$(\overline{ACC}) \rightarrow AC$
10	Strobe ACC		

Table 2.3: Sequence Table for a 'COMPLEMENT' Instruction

to decode it and decide on the appropriate action. These first stages are termed the FETCH CYCLE of the computer and they are to be found at the start of every instruction.

Notice that both of the two-word instructions have their fetch cycle followed by a second set of eight steps which are virtually identical to the fetch sequence except that the data is deposited in the 'TEMP' register. This sequence of 16 steps will be termed an EXTENDED FETCH CYCLE.

Following the fetch or extended fetch cycle, the computer is able to execute the required instruction. The number of steps involved in this EXECUTE cycle depends on the operation being carried out. The operation of a computer's control unit may be shown pictorially in what is known as a state diagram. A simplified state diagram for the computer discussed above is shown in Figure 2.12. This shows very clearly how the machine enters a fetch cycle immediately the current instruction execution is complete.

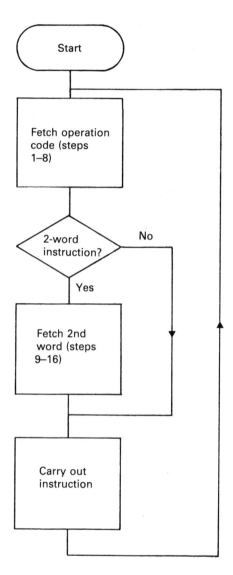

Figure 2.12: Simplified State-Diagram for a Computer

2.5 Programming a Computer

Before a computer can be used, it must have the necessary instructions loaded into its memory. The sequence control register is then set to the address of the first instruction and the machine allowed to run.

In order to get to this stage, two tasks must be undertaken:

(i)   The sequence of steps needed to achieve the desired objective must be decided upon.

(ii) These steps must be encoded into the machine-readable binary form which will drive the control unit.

The basic structure and logic of the task is usually expressed in the form of a program flowchart. This consists of standard symbols representing processes, decisions etc. and provides a convenient pictorial representation of the processing task. The most commonly used symbols are shown in Figure 2.13.

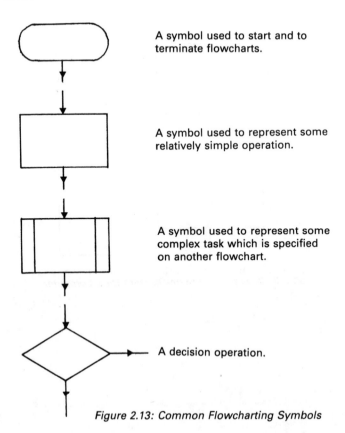

A symbol used to start and to terminate flowcharts.

A symbol used to represent some relatively simple operation.

A symbol used to represent some complex task which is specified on another flowchart.

A decision operation.

Figure 2.13: Common Flowcharting Symbols

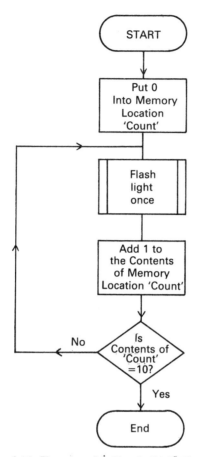

Figure 2.14: Flowchart for Simple 'Light-Flashing' Program

An example of how these symbols may be combined is shown in Figure 2.14 which is the flowchart for a program which flashes a light ten times. The operation of flashing the light once is assumed to be relatively complex.

Once the structure of the solution has been found, all that remains to be done is to write out the elementary operations that will achieve it. Although the computer can only recognise the binary patterns representing instructions (machine code) it is not usual for programmers to generate their programs in this form since the process is very prone to error. Therefore in the initial stages, each machine instruction is represented as a meaningful group of letters (a mnemonic) such as MPY for multiply, JZ for Jump-if-zero etc.

Furthermore, memory locations are given names (called labels) and these are chosen to be helpful in reminding the

```
START:    CLA                 ; clear accumulator (=0)
          STO    COUNT        ; store accumulator in 'count' i.e. put zero into count
LOOP:     JSB    FLASH        ; jump to subroutine 'flash'
          LOAD   COUNT        ; get value of 'count'
          INC                 ; increment it
          STO    COUNT        ; put new value back
          SUB    TEN          ; subtract contents of memory location 'ten' from accu-
                              ; mulator
          JNZ    LOOP         ; if not zero go round again
          HLT                 ; if zero, finished so halt.
COUNT:                        ; space location used to keep a tally
TEN:      10                  ; location used to hold the constant 10
FLASH:    ____
          ____                ; subroutine to flash light once
          ____
          ____
```

Figure 2.15: 'Light-Flashing' Program Written in Mnemonic Assembly Language

programmer of the significance of these locations or the information in them. In this way, a fairly readable program is generated. Figure 2.15 shows how the program of Figure 2.14 might appear in the MNEMONIC ASSEMBLY LANGUAGE of some fictitious computer.

Once written, these readable program instructions are converted into machine code either by hand (for very short programs) or by a computer. The topic of computer languages and program writing is covered in much more detail in Chapter 15, it is mentioned here simply to complete the reader's understanding of how sequential processors are operated.

2.6 A Short Glossary

Computer technology, perhaps more than most other disciplines, abounds in jargon words. A number have already been used without too much explanation and hopefully without causing too much confusion. It seems appropriate, however, to define formally a few of the more common words used in connection with computer systems.

ARCHITECTURE:

An architectural description of a computer will describe the arrangement of the various functional blocks within a computer and also the way in which they are interconnected.

BINARY:

The binary digital system uses only two symbols 0 and 1. This is the system used exclusively in digital computers. It is used because the two states are very easily distinguished and this makes the chance of an undetected error occurring very low - the system is "robust". The two states are typically represented by voltage levels of less than 0.8 and greater than 2.4 giving a margin for error of 1.6 volts. The two levels can also be thought of as being the states ON/OFF or the states TRUE/FALSE of logic. The circuits used to manipulate these variables can respond very rapidly since they only have to move between two levels. This leads to rapid operation of the processor and is another reason for the use of binary digital representation. Notice that since there are only two symbols, a data item made up of two symbols can only represent one of $2^3 = 8$ possible combinations. To achieve 1000 combinations, each data item would have to consist of ten symbols since $2^{10} = 1024 \sim 1000$. In general, for the same number of combinations the binary system requires 3.3 times as many symbol positions as the denary system.

DATA:

Data items are the formalised representation of facts and ideas. The formalised rules themselves are unimportant to this definition (though very important if one is attempting to glean the information carried by the data items). Thus the same ideas can easily be expressed in any agreed manner e.g. French/English/German. As we shall see later even such a simple idea as the magnitude of some variable can be expressed in a number of different ways within a computer and the particular choice may well be dictated by convenience (e.g. binary/ BCD). In a strict sense a program, as written on paper or punched into paper tape is data. It is a representation of the programmer's ideas as to how a particular processing task may be executed.

DATA PROCESSOR:

A data processor is a device which will perform a process or processes on data items. Thus a calculator is clearly a data processor; so also is a radio set or a tape recorder.

DIGITAL:

The term digital implies that the data is represented by a symbol, or combination of symbols drawn from a restricted set of possibilities. Thus the height of a river could take on any value between zero and some maximum value. However, the representation of that height will usually be in the form of a combination of symbols drawn from the set 0123456789. Consider the specific case of the height being 10 1/3 feet: the height can be represented using 3, 5 or 7 digits respectively.

$$10.3 \qquad (a)$$
$$10.333 \qquad (b)$$
$$10.33333 \qquad (c)$$

Notice that none of the representations is exact (in this case) and that the larger the number of symbols used, the closer the written number approaches the actual height.

Clearly the maximum height that can be represented using 3 symbols (a) is 99.9 and the least is 00.0. The step between each representation is 0.1 and the total number of height values that can be represented is 1000. This is easily predicted since there are three symbols in the group and each can take on ten different values hence 10^3 combinations are possible. This is the denary digital system.

FIRMWARE:

This is a relatively new term which has come into prominence with the advent of microprocessors and their associated technology. It is used to describe devices which, while themselves being hardware (transistors etc.) are used as permanent or semi-permanent carriers of programs. This definition will become clearer towards the end of the book.

HARDWARE:

This is the term used to describe the machinery of a computer. Such items as memory, the central processor, lineprinters etc would be classed as hardware.

PERIPHERALS:

A computer, as specified above, is useless unless it is possible to input data and to output data. This is done using peripheral devices. Typical of such devices are: VDUs, teleprinters and also numerous other more specialised devices.

PROCESSING:

Is the execution of a number of operations on data. Such operations are normally co-ordinated so as to achieve a desired goal.

PROGRAM:

A program represents the co-ordination of a number of simple processes (each specified by a computer instruction) to achieve some defined overall goal.

SOFTWARE:

This term is used to cover such items as the programs used in a computer, the manufacturer's documentation, circuit diagrams etc.

34

3. Data Representation and Number Systems

As has already been mentioned, data within computers is represented in binary digital form. The number of digits used varies from computer to computer but is typically 32 or 36 digits in a large computer, 12, 16 or 24 in a minicomputer and 4, 8, 12 or 16 in microprocessors. The term used for each 'binary digit' which makes up the data representation is BIT. Thus a piece of data will be said to consist of (say) 12 bits.

The largest number of bits which any given computer can handle as a single entity is termed its WORD LENGTH. Thus the statements made above could have been re-written as:-

"large computers have word lengths of 32 or 36 bits while minicomputers typically employ word lengths of 12, 16 or 24 bits and in microprocessors the word length can be 4, 8, 12 or 16 bits".

The fact that a computer has a word length of 16 bits does not preclude the use of more, or less, bits to represent data. It is usually less convenient to do this unless special instructions and/or hardware are included in the system. For instance, the word length of the PDP-11 is 16 bits, but all machines are equipped with instructions that enable half-words of 8 bits to be manipulated. In addition, it is possible to purchase the facility of manipulating two words as a single 32-bit data item.

There are special jargon words for subdivisions of the computer word.

BYTE:

A single 8-bit section of a computer word. Thus a 16-bit word can be divided into 2 bytes, a 24-bit word into 3 bytes. This is particularly convenient since it corresponds to the amount of space required to store a single alphanumeric character.

NIBBLE:

This is a relatively recent term used to describe a 4-bit section of a word.

It is mostly used in the microprocessor field where the most common word length is 8-bits and the half-word is 4-bits. A nibble is just sufficient space for the storage of a single denary digit when the latter is represented in BCD format (see later).

3.1 Coding of Binary Numbers

It is clearly impractical to write out 12- and 16-bit numbers as a string of ones and noughts; to do so is to invite errors. The human brain can, however, recognise groups of about five characters with fair accuracy. Thus, when it is necessary to communicate a binary pattern to a human recipient it is usual to employ a simple code which serves to reduce the number of characters used. This is achieved by collecting the binary pattern into groups of 3 or 4 bits and then representing each group by a single character.

    e.g.   1101000010000001

    becomes   1101 0000 1000 0001

    which is coded   D 0 8 1 (see section 3.1.2)

There are two important methods of coding binary data: OCTAL and HEXADECIMAL.

3.1.1 OCTAL CODE

To code a binary number into octal, it is first split up into groups of three bits and then each group is replaced by a single symbol according to Table 3.1.

Thus the number   001111010000

is coded   001 111 010 000

i.e.   1   7   2   0

It will become clear from a later section that the right-hand column above is simply the denary representation of the

36

3-bit group	Octal character
000	0
001	1
010	2
011	3
100	4
101	5
110	6
111	7

Table 3.1: Octal Coding of Binary Numbers

binary number in the left-hand column.

If the number does not divide exactly into groups of three bits, then up to two leading zeros may be added to complete the left-hand group.

e.g.   1101000010000001

is grouped (00)1 101 000 010 000 001

extra zeros

and the octal number is :-

                1   5   0   2   0   1

This representation of a 16-bit number is a little cumbersome but it is used by Digital Equipment Corporation. Most other manufacturers prefer to use the more compact hexadecimal system.

3.1.2 HEXADECIMAL CODE

This coding method is similar in principle to octal except that the bits are collected into groups of four and then substitution is made from Table 3.2.

In this case, up to three leading zeros may be added to complete the most significant group.

A number of possibilities exist for the types of data that can be represented by a computer word; these include:

    textual variables
    logical (Boolean variables)
    computer instructions
    numerical variables

Each of the above four categories will appear, when stored in memory, as a string of binary digits. It is impossible, merely by inspecting the pattern, to determine the category

4-bit group	Hexadecimal Code
0000	0
0001	1
0010	2
0011	3
0100	4
0101	5
0110	6
0111	7
1000	8
1001	9
1010	A
1011	B
1100	C
1101	D
1110	E
1111	F

Table 3.2: Hexadecimal Coding of Binary Numbers

into which the word in question should be fitted. Further, without this information it is impossible to extract the information carried by the word. It is very important to be clear about this.

3.2 Textual Variables

Textual variables are those which represent the usual alpha-numeric characters A→Z, 0→9, a→z and certain punctuation and other marks. To establish a "set" of textual variables, it is simply necessary to list all the possible characters (62 plus punctuation etc.) and then to write against each one a binary code. These codes can then be stored to represent the characters concerned. It is, of course, useful if all programmers and manufacturers use the same code. There are a number of different "standard" codes in existence, but the one most commonly used is the ASCII code which is set out below. A number of the so-called "control codes" have been omitted.

The hexadecimal codes have been obtained by putting an additional 0 on the front of each code. Since these codes are frequently used in conjunction with 8-channel paper tape, it is common practice to extend the code to 8-bits in this way. Alternatively the code is sometimes extended using a '1'. Using this latter convention, the ASC11 8-bit representation for

        A becomes   1100 0001 (C1)

        C becomes   1100 0011 (C3)   etc.

Character	Code	Hexadecimal Equivalent	Character	Code	Hexadecimal Equivalent
A	1000001	41	a	1100001	61
B	1000010	42	b	1100010	62
C	1000011	43	c	1100011	63
D	1000100	44	d	1100100	64
E	1000101	45	e	1100101	65
F	1000110	46	f	1100110	66
G	1000111	47	g	1100111	67
H	1001000	48	h	1101000	68
I	1001001	49	i	1101001	69
J	1001010	4A	j	1101010	6A
K	1001011	4B	k	1101011	6B
L	1001100	4C	l	1101100	6C
M	1001101	4D	m	1101101	6D
N	1001110	4E	n	1101110	6E
O	1001111	4F	o	1101111	6F
P	1010000	50	p	1110000	70
Q	1010001	51	q	1110001	71
R	1010010	52	r	1110010	72
S	1010011	53	s	1110011	73
T	1010100	54	t	1110100	74
U	1010101	55	u	1110101	75
V	1010110	56	v	1110110	76
W	1010111	57	w	1110111	77
X	1011000	58	x	1111000	78
Y	1011001	59	y	1111001	79
Z	1011010	5A	z	1111010	7A
			@	1000000	40
!	0100001	21	?	0111111	3F
''	0100010	22	[	1011011	5B
#	0100011	23	\	1011100	5C
$	0100100	24	]	1011101	5D
%	0100101	25	↑	1011110	5E
&	0100110	26	←	1011111	5F
'	0100111	27	space	0100000	20
(	0101000	28	carriage		
)	0101001	29	return	0001101	0D
*	0101010	2A	line feed	0001010	0A
+	0101011	2B	0	0110000	30
,	0101100	2C	1	0110001	31
−	0101101	2D	2	0110010	32
.	0101110	2E	3	0110011	33
/	0101111	2F	4	0110100	34
:	0111010	3A	5	0110101	35
;	0111011	3B	6	0110110	36
<	0111100	3C	7	0110111	37
=	0111101	3D	8	0111000	38
>	0111110	3E	9	0111001	39

Table 3.3: 7-bit ASCII Codes with Hexadecimal Equivalents

A slightly more useful way of using the last bit is to use it as a PARITY BIT. The purpose of a parity bit is to aid in the detection of errors. Bearing in mind that a '1' is represented by a hole in paper tape, it is easy to see how errors can arise due to extra holes being put into the tape.

The parity system simply requires that the number of '1's in any code is either an even number (even parity) or is an odd number (odd parity). When the character is received the number of 1s is checked and if the number is not correct (odd/even) for the system being used, an error is assumed. Unfortunately, if two errors occur, the system assumes that no errors have occurred.

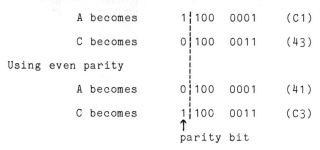

Using odd parity

      A becomes   1 100 0001   (C1)

      C becomes   0 100 0011   (43)

Using even parity

      A becomes   0 100 0001   (41)

      C becomes   1 100 0011   (C3)
                   ↑
              parity bit

Error detection and correction is discussed more fully in Chapter 10.

If a paper tape is read into the computer, it is very wasteful to store one 7-bit character per word, so several will be joined together in one word.

    2 per 16-bit word
    3 per 24-bit word
    4 per 32-bit word
    5 per 36-bit word

For instance, if the two characters AT were received, and stored together in a 16-bit computer word, the word would be (assuming a 0 is added to the left-hand side of each character to make 8 bits)

    01000001 01010100   Binary word
       A   T   Textual meaning
      41   54   Hexadecimal coding of 16-bit binary
                       word

As an alternative to the ASCII encoding scheme, there exists the EBCDIC scheme. This is quite commonly used but is not as well accepted as the ASCII system. The EBCDIC coding scheme is given, for reference, in Table 3.4. The EBCDIC (Extended Binary Coded Decimal Interchange Code) is primarily used by IBM equipment.

Character	Code	Hexadecimal Equivalent	Character	Code	Hexadecimal Equivalent
A	11000001	C1	a	10000001	81
B	11000010	C2	b	10000010	82
C	11000011	C3	c	10000011	83
D	11000100	C4	d	10000100	84
E	11000101	C5	e	10000101	85
F	11000110	C6	f	10000110	86
G	11000111	C7	g	10000111	87
H	11001000	C8	h	10001000	88
I	11001001	C9	i	10001001	89
J	11010001	D1	j	10010001	91
K	11010010	D2	k	10010010	92
L	11010011	D3	l	10010011	93
M	11010100	D4	m	10010100	94
N	11010101	D5	n	10010101	95
O	11010110	D6	o	10010110	96
P	11010111	D7	p	10010111	97
Q	11011000	D8	q	10011000	98
R	11011001	D9	r	10011001	99
S	11100010	E2	s	10100010	A2
T	11100010	E3	t	10100011	A3
U	11100100	E4	u	10100100	A4
V	11100101	E5	v	10100101	A5
W	11100110	E6	w	10100110	A6
X	11100111	E7	x	10100111	A7
Y	11101000	E8	y	10101000	A8
Z	11101001	E9	z	10101001	A9
			@	01111100	7C
!	01011010	5A	?	01101111	6F
''	01111111	7F	[	01001010	4A
#	01111011	7B	\	———	——
$	01011011	5B	]	01011010	5A (alternative to!)
%	01101100	6C	↑	01101010	6A
&	01010000	5C	←	01001100	4C?
'	01111101	7D	space	01000000	40
(	01001101	4D	carriage return	00001011	0B
)	01011101	5D	line feed	00100101	25
*	01011100	5C	0	11110000	F0
+	01001110	4E	1	11110001	F1
,	01101011	6B	2	11110010	F2
−	01100000	60	3	11110011	F3
.	01001001	49	4	11110100	F4
/	01100001	61	5	11110101	F5
:	01111010	7A	6	11110110	F6
;	01011110	5E	7	11110111	F7
<	01001100	4C	8	11111000	F8
=	01111110	7E	9	11111001	F9
>	01101110	6E			

Table 3.4: 8-bit EBCDIC Codes with Hexadecimal Equivalents.

Tables 3.3 and 3.4 include the major characters. However, there are a number of less important characters, and also control characters defined for EBCDIC and ASCII which have not been included.

3.3 Logical Variables

A logical, or Boolean, variable is one which can only take on one of two values: True or False. Such variables can, therefore, be represented exactly by a single bit and hence a 16-bit computer word can represent 16 such variables..

A particular use for such variables is to indicate the status of some item of equipment, for instance whether a light is ON or OFF, or whether a piece of equipment is functioning or has failed.

To illustrate this usage, consider a microprocessor with a 4-bit word length (e.g. Intel 4004 or 4040).

If this device is to be used to control a traffic light, it might well have one word in its memory dedicated to storing data about the status of the traffic lights. Thus one possible allocation of the bits in this STATUS WORD would be

Thus if the word contained 1100, it would indicate that the lights have with the red traffic light on.

The manipulation of logical variables is most efficiently carried out in processors equipped with "bit manipulation" instructions. In the absence of such instructions, the examination of one particular bit in a data word is rather a cumbersome procedure. For example, to check whether the orange light is on would require the following steps:

(i) Load status word into the accumulator

(ii) Form the logical AND of the accumulator and the MASK word 0010

(iii) Test the result for zero.

As a consequence, many programmers devote a whole word to the storage of a single logical variable, perhaps defining the following convention:

    True = 1111 1111
    False = 0000 0000

This is, of course, rather inefficient in terms of storage space.

3.4 Computer Instructions

It has already been noted that computer instructions like any other variables are stored as patterns of binary digits. Indeed, neither the user nor the computer itself can detect whether any particular word is intended to be an instruction, text, data or a Boolean variable. In fact, the computer will ASSUME that the first item it reads from memory during a fetch cycle is an instruction and proceed accordingly. If, by some mischance, it is not an instruction, the control unit will attempt to decode and obey it. Thus a computer could end up by obeying its own operands !

All instructions have to contain sufficient information to indicate which operation is to be performed. Some instructions will, in addition, have to specify operands also. In terms of the number of operands required, instructions may be classified as follows:

Operation Type	Number of Operands	Form of Operation	Number of addresses to be specified
dyadic	2	(source 1). operation. (source 2)⟶ (Destination)	3
monadic	1	(source 1) $\xrightarrow{\text{operation}}$ (Destination)	2
niladic	0	control (eg No-Operation)	0

Each instruction will consist of a string of bits. A number of bits will be grouped together to form a FIELD and each field will be used for a specific purpose such as specifying the address of an operand, or the type of instruction to be executed. Since there are many ways of calculating an operand address (see Chapter 5) the address field may be divided into two sub-fields, one to specify the addressing mode and another to provide numeric information for use in the calculation. Figure 3.1 shows the various possibilities for different classes of instruction.

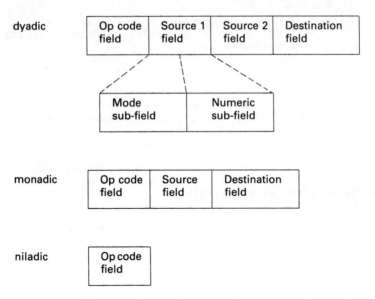

Figure 3.1: Addressing Information in various classes of Instruction

Clearly a great deal of information is contained within an instruction and a consequently large number of bits are needed for its representation. It is common practice to assume that, in dyadic instructions, the source-2 address and the destination address are identical, thus saving one field and making the format of monadic and dyadic instructions identical. In many small machines, especially microprocessors, a further simplifying assumption is usually made. Namely, that the source-2/destination address is one of the machine registers.

Even with these simplifying assumptions, it is often necessary to use more than one word of storage for each instruction. Often several different lengths of instruction will be implemented in one machine and microprocessors typically employ instructions which range from one 8-bit word to four 8-bit words in length.

The width of each field in an instruction is governed by the number of options which the designer wishes to implement and the layout of an intruction can have considerable influence on the complexity of the computer control unit.

3.5 Numerical Variables

There is clearly a requirement to represent numerical variables in a computer. The only difference between the denary system of numbers which is common in everyday usage and the binary system used in computers is the number of different symbols available. Nevertheless, binary numbers are constructed using the same principles as denary numbers.

To write a set of denary numbers in ascending order, it is simply necessary to write out each of the individual symbols in ascending order until they are all used. Then the symbols are written out again with the first available symbol on the left also. When this group is completed the symbol on the left is replaced by the next highest one and the process repeated. The same process is used for binary numbers except that, as there are only two symbols, the build-up of digits used is more rapid.

When using denary notation, counting is carried out to base 10 (because there are 10 different symbols). Thus each place in the number has a significance 10 times greater than that of the place immediately to the right. Thus we have, in common speech, hundreds, tens, units etc. and any specific number is interpreted accordingly.

Thus   4   2   3   5

$$10^3 \qquad 10^2 \qquad 10^1 \qquad 10^0 \longleftarrow \text{significance of digit position}$$

$$10^0 = 1 \text{ (units)}$$

$$10^1 = 10 \text{ (tens)}$$

$$10^2 = 100 \text{ (hundreds)}$$

$$10^3 = 1000 \text{ (thousands)}$$

Hence this number is   4 thousands
                         2 hundreds
                         3 tens
                         5 units

i.e. number = $4 \times 10^3 + 2 \times 10^2 + 3 \times 10^1 + 5 \times 10^0$

A similar argument can be used for binary numbers except that the "base" used is now 2 because there are only two symbols. Thus the significance of the places is as shown below.

$$\begin{array}{cccc} 1 & 0 & 1 & 1 \\ 2^3 & 2^2 & 2^1 & 2^0 \end{array}$$

Hence this number is

$$1 \times 2^3 + 0 \times 2^2 + 1 \times 2^1 + 1 \times 2^0$$

but $2^3 = 8$ denary (written 8_{10})

$$2^2 = 4_{10}$$

$$2^1 = 2_{10}$$

$$2^0 = 1_{10}$$

Thus the number is $8_{10} + 2_{10} + 1_{10} = 11_{10}$

This fact can be verified by writing out the first 11 binary numbers alongside the first 11 denary numbers.

0	0000
1	0001
2	0010
3	0011
4	0100
5	0101
6	0110
7	0111
8	1000
9	1001
10	1010
11	1011

It is usual to include leading '0's in binary numbers up to the word length of the computer in use.

It will be clear from the foregoing, that it is not always obvious whether a number is a binary number, or octal, or hexadecimal. To clear away any misunderstanding, a subscript will be used wherever the meaning is not obvious (or, for ease of layout, the base will follow the number in brackets).

$$nn_2 \qquad nn(2) \qquad \text{binary}$$

$$nn_8 \qquad nn(8) \qquad \text{octal}$$

46

$$\begin{array}{lll} nn_{10} & nn(10) & decimal \end{array}$$

$$\begin{array}{lll} nn_{16} & nn(16) & hexadecimal \end{array}$$

3.5.1 UNSIGNED BINARY INTEGERS AND BINARY FRACTIONS

Consider an 8-bit binary word. The largest number that could be represented is

$$1111\ 1111 = 2^7 + 2^6 + 2^5 + 2^4 + 2^3 + 2^2 + 2^1 + 2^0$$

$$= 128_{10} + 64_{10} + 32_{10} + 16_{10} + 8_{10} + 4_{10} + 2_{10} + 1_{10} = 255_{10}$$

i.e. $(2^n)-1$ where n = word length.

This is not a very large number and it would be impractical for most calculation purposes. Even a 16-bit machine can only represent numbers as high as $(2^{16})-1 = 65,535$ which is not always sufficient.

Numbers represented in this way are termed binary integers. To construct a useful number representation system, it is necessary to find a way of representing negative numbers and fractions. Before proceeding with this matter, though, two more jargon terms must be defined.

The leftmost digit is the one with the greatest significance or value. It is called the MOST SIGNIFICANT BIT (MSB). Similarly the right hand bit is termed the LEAST SIGNIFICANT BIT (LSB).

Implicit in the binary number (255) illustrated above is the fact that the LSB has a weight of 2^0. This implies that the "binary point" is just to its right.

1111 1111.

There is no fundamental reason for this assumption; it is certainly not built into the hardware. We could assume that the point is placed as shown below

$$1\quad 1\quad 1\quad 1\quad .\quad 1\quad 1\quad 1\quad 1$$

$$2^3\quad 2^2\quad 2^1\quad 2^0\qquad 2^{-1}\quad 2^{-2}\quad 2^{-3}\quad 2^{-4}$$

and the value then represented is

$$8_{10} + 4_{10} + 2_{10} + 1_{10} + 1/2_{10} + 1/4_{10} + 1/8_{10} + 1/16_{10}$$

$$= 15.9375_{10}$$

A programmer may assume the binary point lies at any fixed position provided he is consistent throughout his program. He will normally fix the point so that all the numbers he needs to represent can be accommodated.

Often the binary point is chosen to be on the extreme left so that only fractional variables are represented. This is convenient where multiplication is to be used, since if numbers greater than one are multiplied they can soon exceed the capacity of the word length, while fractions merely become smaller.

3.5.2 SIGNED NUMBERS

One way of representing signed numbers is to allocate the MSB as a sign bit so that '1' in this position indicates a negative number and '0' is a positive one (sign-and-magnitude representation).

e.g. for an 8-bit word

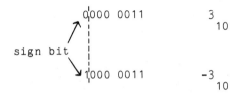

$$0000\ 0011 \qquad 3_{10}$$

sign bit

$$1000\ 0011 \qquad -3_{10}$$

This is not very convenient for hardware design purposes and results in two representations for zero.

$$1000\ 0000 \qquad -0$$

$$0000\ 0000 \qquad +0$$

The most common scheme for integrating the representation of positive and negative binary numbers is the 2s complement notation.

To see how the complement system works, consider a 2-denary-digit counter which resets itself each time it reaches 99.

00,01,02,......98,99,00,01,..... etc.

Now if negation is considered to be counting backwards from zero then

$$99 = -1$$
$$98 = -2 \text{ etc.}$$

Obviously if this convention is adopted, it is not possible to represent both 99 and -1 using only two denary digits.

To prove that this system works, add -2 to +6

```
i.e.      6          06
        - 2          98
                    _____
                    (1)04   obtained using the usual arithmetic rules
```

The (1) is, in fact, lost since we can only represent two
digits; thus the answer is 04 as expected. This complement
notation for denary arithmetic is called 10s complement. The
binary equivalent is called 2s complement. In binary
notation, for an 8-bit word, the number scheme works out as
follows:

```
0000 0000       0(10)     |
1111 1111      -1(10)     |   Counting downwards
1111 1110      -2(10)     ↓

     .
     .
0000 0001       1(10)     |
0000 0010       2(10)     |
0000 0011       3(10)     |
0000 0100       4(10)     |   Counting upwards
0000 0101       5(10)     |
0000 0110       6(10)     ↓
```

```
e.g.      +6        0000   0110
          -2        1111   1110
                   _____
                   (1)0000   0100    =     4      (ignoring the carry
                                          10      from the most
                                                  significant column)
```

A quick way of obtaining the 2s complement negative from the
binary representation of its positive is:

```
          (1)  complement (i.e. 1->0  0->1) each bit
          (2)  add one
```

e.g.

```
    +2       0000 0010
                          )  complement
             1111 1101
        +    0000 0001
             _____
             1111 1110
             ============
```

This is the method used by computer hardware to negate a
number. A slightly easier method for pencil-and-paper
computation is the algorithm:

"write down the number from the least significant bit up to,
and including, the first 1. Then write down the complement of
the remaining digits."

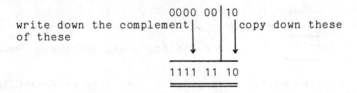

write down the complement
of these

copy down these

0000 00 | 10

1111 11 10

The complete range of numbers represented in 2s complement notation using a 4-bit word is:

0000	0
0001	1
0010	2
0011	3
0100	4
0101	5
0110	6
0111	7
1000	-8
1001	-7
1010	-6
1011	-5
1100	-4
1101	-3
1110	-2
1111	-1

The table was compiled by writing out the binary codes then filling in the numbers starting from the top with 0 and the bottom with -1 and writing an entry at each end in turn until the table was completed.

Notice that:

(i)   there are equal numbers of positive (including zero) and negative numbers

(ii)   the number range is $-2^{(n-1)} \leqslant x \leqslant 2^{(n-1)}-1$ where n is the word length (4)

(iii)   all negative numbers have the MSB=1; all positive numbers have the MSB=0

(iv)   that the 2s complement notation requires that the word length be specified. For instance, in a 4-bit word, -2(10) is represented as 1110 whereas, using an 8-bit word, it would be 1111 1110

The example in (iv) above raises the question of how, in general, a 2s complement number may be extended to include extra bits. For instance, when converting a number from single precision to double precision - see Section 3.5.3. Clearly a positive number merely requires that the appropriate number of leading zeros be added. Less obviously negative numbers (i.e. those with a '1' in the most significant place) require that the appropriate number of leading 1s be added.

50

Thus the general rule is that the number should be extended to the required number of digits by replicating the sign bit.

The 2s complement binary representation is a true "weighted code" unlike the sign-and-magnitude convention in which the sign bit does not have any numerical significance. In fact, in the 2s complement system, each of the bits has the same weighting as in the ordinary unsigned system EXCEPT THAT THE SIGN ASSOCIATED WITH THE MOST SIGNIFICANT BIT IS NEGATIVE.

Thus this number is

$$-2^7 + 2^6 + 2^5 + 2^4 + 2^3 + 2^2 + 2^1$$

$$= -128_{10} + 64_{10} + 32_{10} + 16_{10} + 8_{10} + 4_{10} + 2_{10} = -2_{10}$$

Note that, in 2s complement binary fractions, the binary point is assumed to come after the sign bit as shown below.

```
0. 1 1 0   =   +3/4

complement  ⎤
            ⎬  usual negation rule
and add 1   ⎦

1. 0 1 0   =   -3/4
```

This implies a weighting on each bit (including the sign bit) of

```
1.   0   1   0

  0    -1   -2   -3
-2 .+ 2   +2   +2
```

Thus the number range for binary fractions of word length n is:

$$-1 \leqslant x \leqslant 1 - 1/2^{(n-1)}$$

3.5.3 MULTI-PRECISION INTEGERS

When the number range required is too large for the word length, then it is possible to use two consecutive words in memory for storage. The most significant bit of the "Hi" word will be the sign bit, the "Lo" word will not have a sign bit.

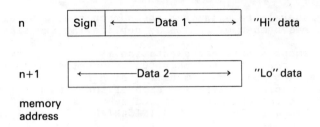

These two words effectively form a single, double-length word:-

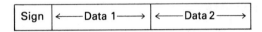

In this way, a 16-bit machine can handle integers in the range

$$-2^{31} \leqslant x \leqslant 2^{31}-1$$

where 2^31 is about 2,100,000,000.

It is not as simple to perform arithmetic on multi-precision integers as it is on single precision ones. Some computers have hardware in the ALU especially for this purpose while in other machines it is necessary to write special (time consuming) software subroutines. Many microprocessors have special instructions to help in the writing of these routines because double precision working is very often necessary for arithmetic in these short-word machines.

3.5.4 FLOATING POINT NUMBERS

Sometimes, especially in scientific calculations, it is necessary to express a wider range of numbers than is possible, even with double- or triple-precision working. In such circumstances, floating point numbers must be used. In denary terms, these numbers are of the form

$$mm \times 10^{e}$$

where e is the exponent and mm is a denary fraction, in the range -1.0 <= mm <= 1.0, called the mantissa.

e.g.
$$.011 = .11 \times 10^{-1} \qquad \begin{array}{l} e=-1 \\ mm=.11 \end{array}$$

$$.11 = .11 \times 10^{0} \qquad \begin{array}{l} e=0 \\ mm=.11 \end{array}$$

Thus it can be seen that the exponent, e, serves to keep
track of where the decimal point is in any given number.
Since these numbers keep track of the position of the point,
there is no need to fix it and it can be allowed to float.

Binary floating point numbers take the form:

$$mm \times 2^{e}$$

where mm is a 2s complement binary fraction (often double
precision) and e is a 2s complement binary integer (often
single precision or less). A floating point number might be
typically stored in three consecutive words.

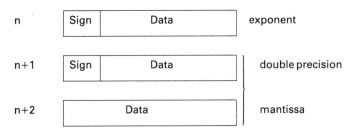

Again, manipulation of such numbers is more complex even than
double precision numbers. It may be carried out by special
hardware within the processor, or by a set of (very time
consuming) subroutines.

3.5.5 BINARY CODED DECIMAL

Sometimes, when the output of a system has to be interfaced
to simple, human-readable, output devices such as 7-segment
displays it is convenient to do all arithmetic in a denary-
compatible form as this minimises the problem of converting
from binary numbers to some other form later. BCD
representation is widely used for this purpose.

When using BCD, each denary digit is represented by its
equivalent binary code. This of course requires 4 bits.

Thus the number 4 0 1 2 would be represented in a 16-bit word
by four groups of 4 bits:-

         0100   0000   0001   0010
          4   0   1   2

This is somewhat wasteful of storage since 4 bits are being
used to represent the digits 0 $\rightarrow$ 9 whereas they are capable
of storing 0 $\rightarrow$ 15.

Clearly 2s complement notation cannot be used for this system.

Also addition etc. is not possible with an ordinary binary
adder unless certain corrections are made by software.

Since microprocessors are widely used in applications requiring BCD (cash registers, car parks, lifts etc) they often have a special "Decimal Adjust" instruction to help in the task of correction.

3.6 Special Binary Codes

A number of binary codes which are non-weighted find applications in digital systems. Two of these, the offset binary code and the Gray code, will be discussed in this Section.

3.6.1 OFFSET BINARY

This code is frequently used by analogue-digital and digital-analogue convertors. The offset binary representation of a number is determined by adding $2^{(n-1)}$ to that number (where n is the word length of the binary representation) and then representing the resulting number in the usual way. This is best seen by considering the offset binary representation of the numbers -8 to +7 using a 4-bit word shown in Table 3.5.

OFFSET BINARY	NUMBER	2s COMPLEMENT
1111	7	0111
1110	6	0110
1101	5	0101
1100	4	0100
1011	3	0011
1010	2	0010
1001	1	0001
1000	0	0000
0111	-1	1111
0110	-2	1110
0101	-3	1101
0100	-4	1100
0011	-5	1011
0010	-6	1010
0001	-7	1001
0000	-8	1000

Table 3.5
Comparison of Offset Binary Code and 2s Complement Binary Code

Conversion from offset binary to 2s complement is simply achieved by adding 1000 to the offset binary representation. Conversion in the reverse direction is achieved in the same way.

When dealing with computers with a word length which is longer than the offset binary code being provided (say) by the analogue-digital convertor, a slightly different and more general conversion routine is needed.

If m-bit offset binary is to be converted to n-bit, 2s complement (n > m) it is necessary to add a constant to the offset binary. The constant needed has 1s in the most significant n-m+1 places.

e.g. to convert 12-bit offset binary to 16-bit 2s complement, add 1111 1000 0000 0000 to the offset binary.

To convert back to offset binary, the 2s complement of this number must be added, i.e. 0000 1000 0000 0000.

3.6.2 GRAY CODE

Gray code is a special binary code, constructed so that only one bit changes between adjacent codes. A 4-bit Gray code sequence is shown in Table 3.6.

NUMBER	GRAY CODE	BINARY CODE
0	0000	0000
1	0001	0001
2	0011	0010
3	0010	0011
4	0110	0100
5	0111	0101
6	0101	0110
7	0100	0111
8	1100	1000
9	1101	1001
10	1111	1010
11	1110	1011
12	1010	1100
13	1011	1101
14	1001	1110
15	1000	1111

Table 3.6: Comparison of Gray Code and Unsigned Binary Code

This code is particularly favoured for encoding the output of digital transducers that utilise coded tapes or wheels and mechanical pick-offs. Clearly the alignment of the mechanical pick-off may be imperfect, thus resulting in the detection of a wrong code. With Gray code, the error is never greater than +/- 1 whereas, with binary code, considerable errors are possible.

This may be illustrated using Table 3.6. Consider a system in which the code for 7 should be being received. However, the detector for the most significant bit is displaced some way towards the higher codes due to manufacturing tolerances. As a result, the character received using Gray code will be 1100 which is the Gray code for 8 and so the error is +1.

However, the character received using binary code will be 1111 which is the binary code for 15 and so the error is +8.

In order to convert Gray code to unsigned binary, the

following algorithm may be used:-

"start at the most significant bit and write down all bits up
to and including the first '1'. Then invert all bits up to
and including the next '1', then write down all bits up to
and including the next '1'... continue until all bits have
been scanned".

For example:

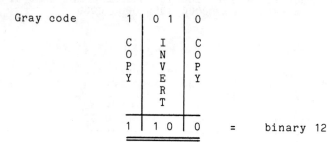

Gray code	1	0 1	0
	C O P Y	I N V E R T	C O P Y
	1	1 0	0

= binary 12

The algorithm to convert from binary to Gray code is:-

"start at the most significant bit. Write down up to and
including the first '1'. Invert up to and including the next
'0', write down up to and including the next '1', invert up
to and including the next '0'... continue until finished".

4. Binary Arithmetic Processes

The manipulation of numerical quantities represented as binary numbers must be one of the major tasks of any programmer. The various formats in which binary numbers may appear have been discussed in Chapter 3. In this Chapter, the details of how these representations may be manipulated will be presented. The methods will mainly be of interest to machine code level programmers since the operations discussed are virtually invisible to users of high level languages such as BASIC and Pascal. However, an appreciation of the processing required can be of great help to high level language programmers who have to decide, for instance, whether to use real (floating point) or integer variables.

4.1 Addition and Subtraction of Unsigned Binary Numbers

Binary addition is exactly analogous to ordinary denary addition except that the radix is 2 instead of 10. This has a number of consequences.

    (i) There are only two symbols, 0 and 1.
    (ii) A carry is generated from a given column when the total in that column reaches 2.

This is best illustrated by a simple example:

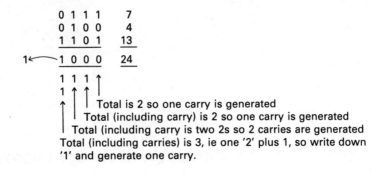

```
        0 1 1 1      7
        0 1 0 0      4
        1 1 0 1     13
   1←──1 0 0 0      24
        1 1 1 ↑
        1 ↑ ↑ ↑
        ↑ │ │ │
        │ │ │ └ Total is 2 so one carry is generated
        │ │ └ Total (including carry) is 2 so one carry is generated
        │ └ Total (including carry is two 2s so 2 carries are generated
        Total (including carries) is 3, ie one '2' plus 1, so write down
        '1' and generate one carry.
```

A normal arithmetic unit would permit only the addition of two numbers. Notice that, in the example, there is a carry generated from the most significant column and so the result is five digits long. In practice, a computer has a. defined word length (in the above example, 4 bits) and it is impossible to represent answers which cannot be contained in this space. Thus the above answer would appear as 1000 = 8 which is, of course, wrong.

When such an overflow condition occurs the programmer must decide what action is to be taken. The carry from the most significant bit is used to set a hardware flip-flop, called the CARRY FLAG, in the computer and instructions will exist which permit the programmer to check the contents of the carry flag and to proceed accordingly.

Subtraction follows the same general principles as denary subtraction except that a "borrow" from one column to the next is worth 2, not 10. Consider the example:

```
     ┌②
     1 1 0 1                13
     1 0 1 1 -              11 -
     ─────────             ────
     0 0 1 0                 2
       1 ↑
         ↑ one from 0 'won't go' so generate a borrow (worth 2)
         │ one from 2=1
         Restore the borrow on the bottom line, 1-1=0
```

A second example will indicate a possible error condition.

```
   ┌②┌②
   0 1 0 1                 5
   1 0 1 1 -              11 -
   ─────────             ────
   1 0 1 0                -6
 1     1
 ↑
 borrow from non-existent column
```

58

In most computers, a borrow from a non-existent column during subtraction is treated in a similar way to a carry out of the most significant place during addition. The error is indicated by the carry flag (which is referred to as the borrow flag under these circumstances). It is the programmer's responsibility to check for this error condition and to act appropriately.

4.2 Addition and Subtraction of 2s Complement Signed Binary Numbers

The attraction of 2s complement arithmetic is that it may be carried out according to the normal rules of binary arithmetic and thus the same hardware as is used for unsigned numbers may also be used for this purpose. However, the range of numbers that may be represented is different:

$$-2^{n-1} \leqslant x \leqslant 2^{n-1} - 1$$

and the carry flag is no longer a useful way of checking for the validity of the result, as may be seen from the following examples of addition.

(A)	0 1 0 0	(+4)
	0 1 0 0	(+4)
	1 0 0 0	(−8) ×

(B)	1 1 0 0	(−4)
	1 1 0 0	(−4)
	1 1 0 0 0	(−8) √

(C)	0 1 1 1	(+7)
	0 1 1 1	(+7)
	1 1 1 0	(−2) ×

(D)	1 0 0 0	(−8)
	1 0 0 0	(−8)
	1 0 0 0 0	(0) ×

(E)	0 1 1 1	(+7)
	1 0 0 0	(−8)
	1 1 1 1	(−1) √

(F)	0 0 1 0	(+2)
	0 0 0 1	(+1)
	0 0 1 1	(+3) √

(G)	0 1 1 1	(+7)
	1 0 1 1	(−5)
	1 0 0 1 0	(+2) √

From the above, it will be seen that the generation of a carry is not correlated with an erroneous result. Note also that all of the original operands were legal 4-bit, 2s complement numbers.

A little thought will show that, if both of the operands are in range then, if they are of different sign, it is impossible for the result to be out of range. The problem only arises when both operands are of the same sign.

It is self-evident that, if both operands are of the same sign, then the result, if valid, must also have this sign. Inspection of the above examples will confirm that in all cases of error the sign bit is different from that of the operands. This observation forms the basis of a method of detecting 2s complement overflow.

Figure 4.1 Flowchart for software detection of 2s complement overflow.

The procedure shown in Figure 4.1 may be implemented in software or hardware. However, when the processor is equipped with an OVERFLOW FLAG in addition to the carry flag, the hardware used to implement the overflow flag is based on a somewhat simpler principle. This involves comparing the carry into the most significant column and the carry out from it, (C(n) and C(n+1) respectively in Figure 4.2).

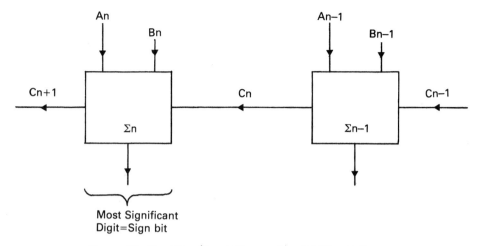

Figure 4.2: Most Significant Stages of an Addition Unit

Three cases must be considered:

(i)   Both operands positive $A(n) = 0$ $B(n) = 0$

Clearly, irrespective of the value of $C(n)$, $C(n+1)$ will be zero. However, $\Sigma(n)$ must also be zero to give a positive answer and so $C(n)$ must be zero for no overflow.

i.e.

$$C_{n+1} = 0$$
$$C_n = 0$$
            Correct result

$$C_{n+1} = 0$$
$$C_n = 1$$
            Overflow

(ii)   Both operands negative: $A(n) = 1$ $B(n) = 1$

Clearly, irrespective of $C(n)$, $C(n+1)$ will be ONE. However, $\Sigma(n)$ must also be one to give a negative answer and so $C(n)$ must be one for no overflow.

i.e.

$$C_{n+1} = 1$$
$$C_n = 1$$
⎫ Correct result

$$C_{n+1} = 1$$
$$C_n = 0$$
⎫ Overflow

(iii) Operands of different sign: $A(n) = 1$ $B(n) = 0$
            or $A(n) = 0$ $B(n) = 1$

A little thought will show that in both cases $C(n) = C(n+1)$.
The result is, of course, always correct.

i.e.

$$C_{n+1} = 1$$
$$C_n = 1$$
⎫ Correct result

$$C_{n+1} = 0$$
$$C_n = 0$$
⎫ Correct result

An inspection of the above three cases will reveal that
overflow has occurred if $C(n)$ is not equal to $C(n+1)$ and so a
simple "exclusive-or" gate may be used to generate the 2s
complement overflow flag (Figure 4.3).

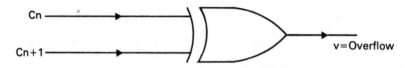

Figure 4.3: Generation of 2s Complement Overflow Flag

In the case of 2s complement subtraction, the same circuitry will also function as an overflow indicator. This occurs because the hardware of a subtractor is identical to that of an adder except for a negation unit on one of the operands (Figure 4.4).

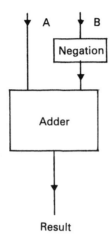

Figure 4.4: Implementation of Subtraction

4.3 Multiplication of Unsigned Binary Numbers

A simple method of multiplication is the "repetitive addition" method.

i.e. 5 x 5 = 5 + 5 + 5 + 5 + 5 = 25

similarly, in binary numbers this would be:-

```
        101
        101
        101
        101
        101
       ─────
      11001  = 1x2  + 0x2  + 0x2  + 1x2  + 1x2   =  25
       ─────
       1111
        1 1
         1
```

$11001 = 1 \times 2^0 + 0 \times 2^1 + 0 \times 2^2 + 1 \times 2^3 + 1 \times 2^4 = 25$

It is very easy to write a program to do this but, as it will be readily appreciated, the above process is likely to be rather time consuming.

As an alternative, it is possible to use the more common method of multiplication.

```
      101    multiplicand
      101    multiplier
    ─────
      101
     0000
    10100
    ─────
    11001    result
    ═════
```

The process is a simple one; the multiplier is scanned from the least significant bit upwards. The multiplicand is added to the total if the multiplier bit is 1 and then the multiplicand is shifted left one place (i.e. multiplied by 2) so that it has the correct significance for the next multiplier bit position to be examined.

As a rule, computers can only cope with two operands at once and so it is normal for a running total to be accumulated rather than the large addition shown above. Secondly, it is usually more convenient to move the accumulated sum to the right rather than moving the multiplicand to the left in order to obtain the correct relative positions for the next addition. This revised method is shown in Figure 4.5.

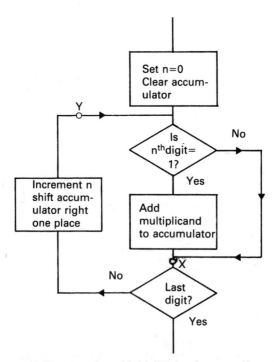

Figure 4.5: Flowchart for a Multiplication Program (See also Figure 4.6)

The operation of this can be seen by considering the values of n and the accumulator at points x and y in the process each time they are passed.

At start		Acc	000	n=1
at x	(first pass)	Acc	= 101	n=1
at y	(first pass)	Acc	= 0101	n=2
at x	(second pass)	Acc = 0101 + 0000 = 0101		n=2
at y	(second pass)	Acc	= 00101	n=3
at x	(third pass)	Acc = 00101 + 10100 = 11001		n=3

The routine does not reach y a third time since n=3 and the process is terminated. So final answer=11001   as before

It will be observed that the final answer contains more bits than the original numbers. This can cause problems because the computer only has a fixed number of bits in its word. Consider the above example carried out by a machine with a word length of three bits, assuming the numbers to be integers.

The input, showing the binary points, is 101. and 101.

The output is 11001.

If we shorten the answer to three bits so that it can be stored by throwing away the two LEAST SIGNIFICANT bits, we have

$$\boxed{110} \quad 01.$$

but the binary point is now no longer in the standard position and further arithmetic with this number will give wrong answers since it will be interpreted as 110 (i.e. 6).

Conversely, it is clearly wrong to throw away the two most significant bits.

Had the numbers been binary fractions, the situation would have been rather better since the multiplication of two fractions produces a smaller number. Also the binary point is associated with the most significant bit so removing the least significant bits does not involve any ambiguity about the position of the binary point.

With the same bit pattern, the input would be .101 = 5/8

Now 5/8 x 5/8 is 25/64 and

```
        .101
        .101
        ──────
        .000101
        .00000
        .0101
        ──────
```
$$.011001 = 0 \times 2^{-1} + 1 \times 2^{-2} + 1 \times 2^{-3} + 0 \times 2^{-4} + 0 \times 2^{-5} + 1 \times 2^{-6}$$

$$= 1/4 + 1/8 + 1/64$$

$$= 25/64$$

Truncating this answer to three bits gives:

.011   001

This still retains the binary point in its correct position and the apparent answer is .011 = 24/64 which is reasonably close to the correct answer and is as near as it is possible to get with three bits. In general, the answer could be in error by as much as .000111 = 7/64 and rounding errors such as this must be carefully watched by those who write computer programs.

Notice that this fractional answer is not simply obtained by moving the binary point to the front of the previous integer answer as this would give:

.11001

which is twice the correct answer.

The reason for this is quite simple; the movement of the binary point on each of the multiplier and multiplicand is equivalent to a multiplication by $2^{(-3)}$. Thus the result must be multiplied by $2^{(-6)}$. In the example given above this would yield:

$$11001. \times 2^{-6} = .011001$$

The reason for the apparent inconsistency is the fact that multiplying two 3-bit numbers should yield a 6-bit answer. This would indeed have been the case if, as might have happened, there had been a carry from the most significant place of the addition.

Thus the algorithm shown in Figure 4.5 needs to be corrected so that the right shift occurs at point x (Figure 4.6).

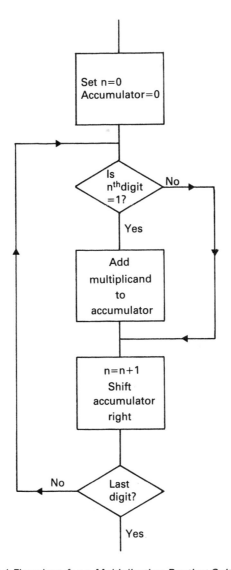

Figure 4.6: Corrected Flowchart for a Multiplication Routine Suitable for Integers and Fractions

4.4 Signed Binary Multiplication

Probably the easiest way of achieving a signed binary multiplication in 2s complement notation is to convert all numbers to positive and then carry out an unsigned multiply, correcting the sign of the result at the very end.

Alternatively, the correct answer may be obtained automatically by noting that the significance of the most significant bit is minus. Thus the shifted multiplicand should be subtracted from the accumulated sum if the most significant bit of the multiplier is 1 (i.e. negative multiplier).

For example:

```
        0101    (+5)
        1011    (−5)
        ──────
        0101
       01010
      000000
```

001111 − − − − Partial sum before dealing with
                multiplier sign bit
0101000 − − − − Due to sign bit, so SUBTRACT

borrow   1100111 =−25

This procedure works equally well for the multiplication of two negative numbers. Note how the numbers in the result have to be sign-extended in this case. This was not needed previously since the multiplicand was positive and sign extension would merely have added non-significant leading zeros.

```
              1011    (−5)
              1011    (−5)
              ──────
sign        ⎰ 1111011
extension   ⎱ 1110110
              0000000
```

1110001 − − − − Partial sum before dealing with
                multiplier sign bit
1011000 − − − − Due to sign bit, so SUBTRACT

0011001 =25

The sign extension is taken care of automatically in the shift-and-add algorithms shown in Figures 4.5 and 4.6 provided that ARITHMETIC shifts are used.

The modified algorithm for 2s complement numbers is shown in Figure 4.7.

Notice that in Figure 4.7, the shift has been put back into the return loop. This is necessary because one less right shift is needed for signed numbers as compared with unsigned numbers as the weights of corresponding bits differ by a factor of 2.

```
        −2
         2
         ↓
        .1 0 1 1    unsigned
        1.0 1 1     signed
           ↓
          −1
          2
```

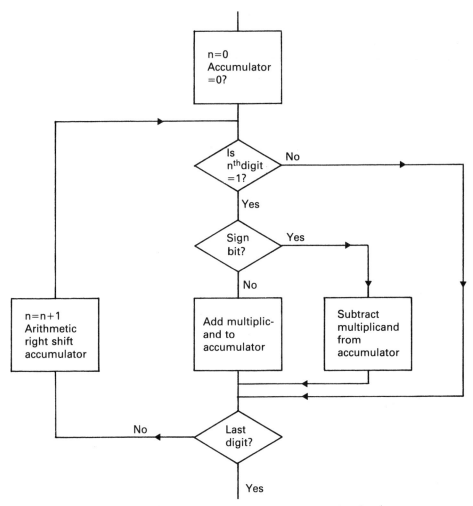

Figure 4.7: Flowchart for a Signed Multiplication Program

4.5 Unsigned Binary Division

Binary division may be carried out using the "pencil and paper" method. This is particularly easy since the divisor will go into the dividend either once or not at all. The fact that it "will not go" may be detected by subtracting the divisor from the dividend and looking for a borrow.

Usually the divisor will be n bits long and the dividend 2n bits. The result of the division is an n-bit quotient and an n-bit remainder.

The process may be illustrated by dividing 101 (i.e. 5) into 011010 (26).

69

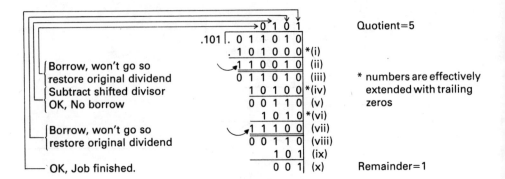

The algorithm for carrying out this process is shown in Figure 4.8.

With division, there is always the danger that the result may be so large that it cannot be represented by the n bits allocated. The occurrence of this overflow situation may be detected by a carry being generated during the left shifting of the result (an example would be 25 / 2 giving a quotient of 12 which cannot be accommodated in three bits).

The algorithm shown above is called the RESTORING METHOD since the dividend is restored to its former value if a subtraction fails.

An alternative algorithm, the NON-RESTORING METHOD avoids this inefficiency. Let the divisor be given the symbol D and the dividend (or remainder of dividend) be given the symbol R. In the restoring method the following actions are taken:

a) Form $\qquad$ R - D

b) Subtraction fails
   so add D back in $\qquad$ R - D + D = R

c) Shift divisor right
   one place $\qquad$ D $\longrightarrow$ D/2

d) Subtract new divisor $\qquad$ R - D/2

RESTORING METHOD

Steps a - c above represent one iteration in the division. In the non-restoring method this final result is achieved in two steps as follows:

a) Form $\qquad$ R - D

b) Subtraction fails
   so shift divisor
   right one place $\qquad$ D $\longrightarrow$ D/2

c) Add new divisor in $\qquad$ R - D + D/2
   $\qquad$ = R - D/2

NON-RESTORING METHOD

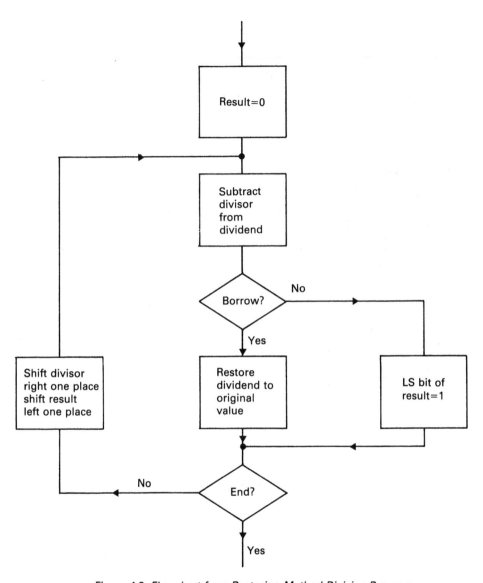

Figure 4.8: Flowchart for a Restoring Method Division Program

Using this method the previous division may be re-worked. The Roman numerals refer to the line numbers in the restoring method example.

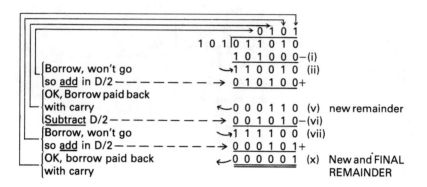

A flowchart for this method is shown in Figure 4.9.

If a 2m-bit number is being divided by an m-bit number, the finish condition occurs when n=m. Note also that, in the above example, every failure is followed by a success. This need not be so (try 001010 / 101); the algorithm in Figure 4.9 will cope with this situation.

If in Figure 4.9, the final operation was a failure then either

    (i)   the least significant bit should be set

            OR

    (ii)   the remainder should be restored to its value before the unsuccessful test.

This stage has not been shown in Figure 4.9. It would be placed after the exit decision (xiii) on the "yes" branch.

The latter course would be the normal one since it results in a position remainder.

As will be appreciated from the above, division is rather more complex and time consuming than multiplication.

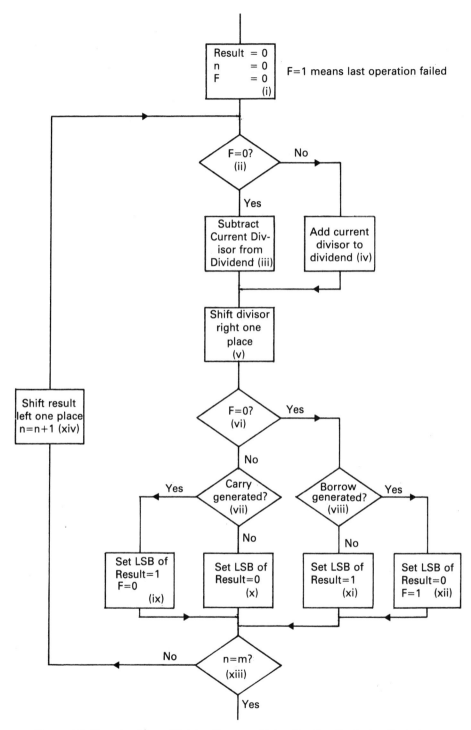

Figure 4.9: Flowchart for a Division Program Using the Non-Restoring Technique

4.6 Signed Binary Division

Probably the most convenient way of achieving a signed division is to convert both numbers to positive and then to use the division algorithm described previously, accounting for the sign of the answer separately.

Alternatively, the division may be carried out directly on 2s complement numbers using the previously described algorithm modified as follows:

(A) When the signs of the divisor and dividend (or remainder of dividend) are the same then the addition/subtraction operations apply as before. If the signs are different then addition is replaced by subtraction [block (iv)], subtraction is replaced by addition [block (iii)].

(B) An operation is considered to have failed if the sign of the resulting number is different from the sign of the dividend (or the last partial dividend formed during a successful operation).

Thus block (viii) becomes "are signs of dividend (or remainder of dividend) and current resulting number different?" and block (vii) becomes "is the sign of the current resulting number the same as that of the last successfully formed dividend (or partial dividend)".

(C) The quotient is, on completion, negated if the signs of the divisor and dividend are different.

4.7 Multi-Precision Addition and Subtraction

Multi-precision arithmetic is required when the number range possible within one computer word is insufficient for the computation in hand. This is a fairly common situation with microprocessors, most of which only support arithmetic on 8-bit words.

In this section, only double-precision arithmetic will be considered, but the principles are readily extended to triple or quadruple-precision. Further, consideration will be limited to addition and subtraction since, as has been shown in previous sections, these operations can be combined to permit division and multiplication.

A multi-precision word is formatted as shown in Figure 4.10.

Notice that only the most significant word has a sign bit, all of the remaining words being unsigned. A multi-precision quantity is stored in several adjacent memory words. The address of the multi-precision quantity being taken as either that of the most significant word or that of the least

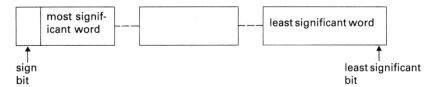

Figure 4.10: Format of a Multi-Precision Word

significant word. The first assumption seems more logical, but in practice the second is usually more convenient since most processes operate on the least significant word first.

Because, by definition, an ALU can only operate on a pair of words at once, the addition of two double-precision quantities has to be carried out in two stages (see Figure 4.11).

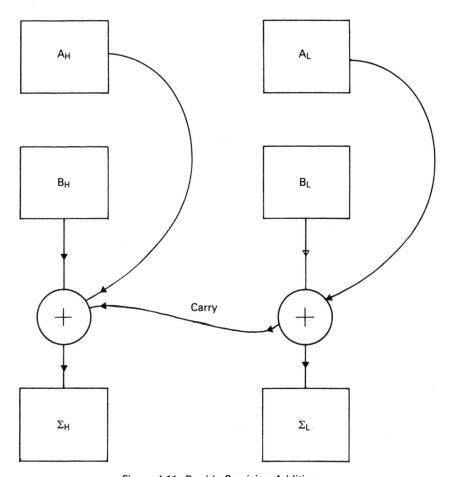

Figure 4.11: Double-Precision Addition

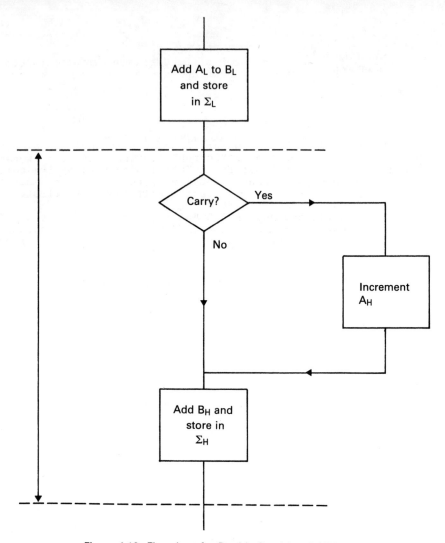

Figure 4.12: Flowchart for Double-Precision Addition

Clearly, however, the two stages cannot be entirely independent since there is always the possibility of a carry from Σ(L) to Σ(H).

Thus, the least significant words may be added in the usual way, but the most significant words must be added, and then incremented if the first addition produced a carry (as indicated by the carry flag). Since the addition of the most significant words will possibly alter the carry this incrementation must be carried out before the most significant words are added (see Figure 4.12).

The section between the dotted lines in Figure 4.12 must be repeated for each word in a multi-precision quantity, except for the least significant word. Some computers simplify the implementation of this section of the flowchart by providing an ADD-WITH-CARRY instruction which carries out the function

$$A(H) + B(H) + CARRY$$

all in one operation.

Subtraction follows a similar procedure to addition except that it is the presence of a "borrow" linking the two words which needs to be allowed for. This is achieved by the same flowchart as shown in Figure 4.12 except that

"ADD" becomes "SUBTRACT"
"CARRY" becomes "BORROW"
"INCREMENT" becomes "DECREMENT"

As with addition many computers provide a SUBTRACT-WITH-BORROW instruction to carry out the operations between the dotted lines in Figure 4.12, modified as above.

Thus to add a triple-precision number

Add	low-words
Add-with-carry	mid-words
Add-with-carry	high-words

and to subtract

Subtract	low-words
Subtract-with-borrow	mid-words
Subtract-with-borrow	high-words

In addition to the normal arithmetic operations, it is quite common to have to carry out shifting operations on multi-precision numbers. This is done with a combination of shift and of rotate type instructions acting on single words using the 'carry flag' to catch the bits which are shifted out of the word.

Illustrating this first with a logical right shift operation, it is necessary to start with the MOST significant word (see Figure 4.13).

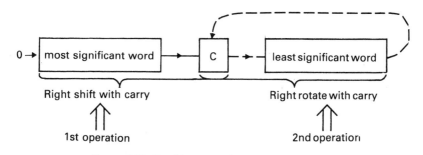

Figure 4.13: Double precision Logical Right Shift

Notice that the bit which "falls out" of the most significant word into the carry is subsequently rotated into the most significant place of the next word. A "rotate" is needed in the latter case since a straightforward "shift" would move zeros into the most significant place of the second word. The fact that the bit which leaves the least significant place of this word also goes into the carry does not matter since it will be overwritten by the next double-length shift operation.

The procedure may be extended to any number of words by simply using more 'right rotate' instructions.

i.e.

                logical right shift with carry   high-word
                right rotate with carry   middle-word
                right rotate with carry   low-word

Also, if arithmetic rather than logical shifting is needed, the first instruction is simply replaced by

                "Arithmetic right shift high-word".

Left shifts follow the same general procedure but start with the least significant word as in Figure 4.14.

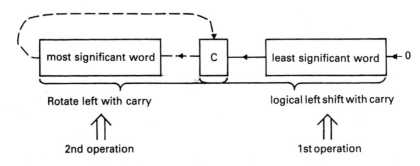

Figure 4.14: Double Precision Logical Left Shift

Again the procedure may be extended to any length with more rotate instructions and may be converted to an arithmetic operation by operating appropriately on the most significant word.

Both left and right shifts may be converted to long rotations with carry by using a rotate with carry for the first operation in each sequence instead of the shift operations shown above.

4.8 Floating point Arithmetic

Before considering exactly how floating point numbers may be processed, it is necessary to be familiar with the special case of multiplication and division by two in binary machines.

Consider the binary number 00110 (i.e. 6 denary)

if multiplied by two it must give the answer 12.

i.e. 01100

But this is simply the original number shifted left by one place. Thus we have the rules:-

To multiply a binary number by 2^n, shift left n times.

To divide a binary number by 2^n, shift right n times.

It must be emphasised that the shift operations involved are ARITHMETIC, that is, shifting operations which preserve the sign of the number. These are shown in Figure 4.15.

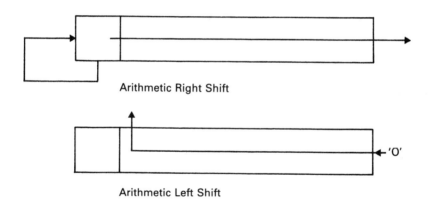

Arithmetic Right Shift

Arithmetic Left Shift

Figure 4.15: Arithmetic Shift Operations

In the right shift, the sign bit is shifted right and also replicates itself. In the left shift, the sign bit is undisturbed. If the two most significant bits are NOT the same before a left shift the left shift will result in an overflow. It is left as an exercise for the reader to demonstrate by example that these simple rules operate correctly.

Now a binary floating point number is written in the form:-

$$M*2^E$$

Thus the addition of two such numbers may be written:

$$(M1*2^{E1} + M1*2^{E2})$$

It is not correct to simply add the two mantissae together since they are raised to different powers of 2. To add them together they must be raised to the same power.

e.g.

$$\left[M1*2^{(E1-E2)} + M2\right] * 2^{E2} = \left[M1*2^{-(E2-E1)} + M2\right] * 2^{E2}$$

Now the term $M1*2\hat{\ }[-(E2-E1)]$ can be written as a simple binary fraction simply by shifting M1 right (E2-E1) times.

A right shift is required since left-shifting entails the danger of an overflow. If E2-E1 is negative then M2 should be shifted right (E1-E2) times. In this case the answer will have an exponent of E1.

i.e.

$$M1*2^{E1} + M2*2^{E2} = \left[M1 + M2*2^{-(E1-E2)}\right] * 2^{E1}$$

Thus the general rule is:

> shift right the mantissa corresponding to the lesser exponent and increase this exponent.

The procedure for addition is shown in Figure 4.16. Subtraction follows the same basic pattern except, of course, the final operation is subtraction.

This may be illustrated as follows:

	mantissa	exponent		
A)	0.1000	00010	$.5 \times 2^2$	$= 2$
B)	0.1000	11111	$.5 \times 2^{-1}$	$= 1/4$

To bring the two exponents into line, shift B right one place (dividing by 2) and increase the exponent by one to compensate. B now becomes

mantissa	exponent	
0.0100	00000	first shift
0.0010	00001	second shift
0.0001	00010	third shift

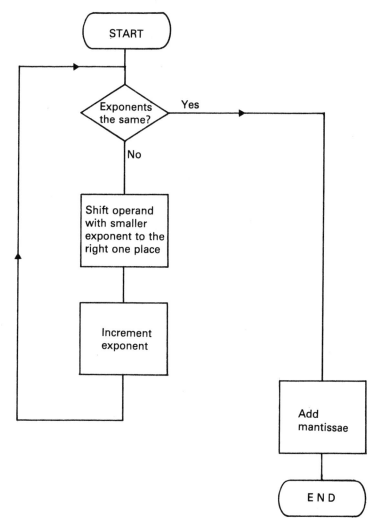

Figure 4.16: Floating point Addition

Thus the mantissa of the result is

```
0.1000        (A)
0.0001  +     (B)  shifted
_____
0.1001        .5625
======             10
```

and the exponent is, of course, 00010 = 2.
Thus the result is .5625 x 2^2 = 2.25

A number of problems may occur as a result of the above
operations.

(i) The addition of the mantissae may cause an overflow. In floating point arithmetic, this situation is recoverable. The true value of the mantissa is simply divided by two and the exponent of the result increased by one. This will only cause an irrecoverable error if the exponent overflows when it is incremented.

(ii) During right shifting, the mantissa could become zero. This implies that the significance of the smaller number is so low that it cannot be resolved when using the exponent of the larger number, and so it is treated as zero. This only happens if the ratio between the two numbers (dynamic range) is greater than $2^{(N-1)}$ where N is the number of bits used for the mantissa (including sign). The solution is clearly to use more bits for the mantissa.

By comparison, floating point multiplication is very simple:-

$$M1*2^{E1} \quad * \quad M2*2^{E2} \quad = \quad (M1 \, * \, M2) \, * \, 2^{(E1+E2)}$$

Thus multiplication is simply achieved by performing signed binary fraction multiplication on the mantissae and adding the exponents.

In the previous example:

```
E1      00010
E2      11111
        ─────
        00001    (=1)  by ordinary 2s complement addition
        ═════

M1      0.1000
M2      0.1000
        ──────
        0.0100   (=0.25) by ordinary 2s complement multiplication
        ══════
```

This gives an answer of $0.25 * 2^1 = 1/2$

which is clearly the correct answer (since 1/4 * 2 = 1/2).

It is worth noting that the result of this multiplication is in a non-standard form. In fact there is an infinite number of ways in which a floating point number can be stored:-

	mantissa	exponent
$1/2 * 2^0$	0.1000	00000
$1/4 * 2^1$	0.0100	00001
$1/8 * 2^2$	0.0010	00010

etc.

However, the normal form is the one which ensures that the mantissa is as large as possible within the computer word length limits. This is the first form shown above. It is usual to NORMALISE floating point numbers after operations and this ensures that there is always a 1 following the binary point, a situation which provides the maximum resolution for the mantissa.

Floating point division is also very simple:

$$M1*2^{E1} \quad / \quad M2*2^{E2} \quad = \quad (M1 \ / \ M2) * 2^{E1-E2}$$

The division is achieved by dividing the divisor mantissa into the dividend mantissa and subtracting the divisor exponent from the dividend exponent.

4.9 Binary Coded Decimal Arithmetic

Binary coded decimal numbers are added much like any other binary integers. There is, however, one difference which is best illustrated by two examples.

0010	0111	27		0010	0111	27
		10				10
0010	0001	21		0010	0110	26
		10				10
0100	1000			0100	1101	
4	8			4	D	

Both additions are correct if the operands are regarded as binary integers, but if they are regarded as BCD numbers the left hand example is correct but the right hand one is not. Indeed, hexadecimal notation has had to be used for the 'units' digit since it is out of the normal denary range.

If the right hand addition had been done in denary notation there would have been a carry from the "units" to the "tens". This did not occur in the straightforward addition because the radix base for a group of 4 bits is $2^4 = 16$, not 10. This could be detected and the carry generated artificially if a suitable program were written.

Secondly the "units" digit, "D", is not valid, (it represents 13 denary). It should be 3 which is the difference of the value of the carry (= 10 because the radix base is 10 for BCD) and the value actually obtained. Thus it is possible to correct the addition by generating a carry and subtracting 10 (denary) from the decade generating the carry if, but only if, the result of the addition in that decade is greater than 9.

In fact, both corrections can be achieved at once by the simple expedient of adding 16 - 10 = 6 to the erroneous decade.

Thus, in the example, the result should be modified thus:

```
0100  1101   =    4D
      0110   =     6
─────────────    ───
0101  0011        53
─────────────    ───
    1
```

The refined procedure is, therefore, shown in Figure 4.17.

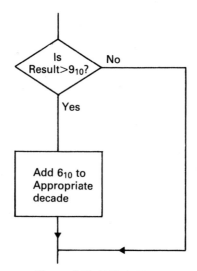

Figure 4.17: BCD Addition

The test for "result > 9" will involve checking if one of the codes A to F OR a carry has been generated in the decade. This operation is frequently available as a special instruction "Decimal Adjust", particularly in microprocessors where there is often a requirement to perform BCD arithmetic. In machines which can contain more than one decade of BCD per word (8-, 12-, 16-bits) the adjustment is usually carried out on all decades at once and the process of BCD addition is reduced to:

```
Add both operands
Decimal Adjust
```

In many machines the inter-decade carries (called half carries) are made available as status flags.

Subtraction is performed in an analogous way as is shown by
the following example.

```
0100  0010          42
0001  0101  -       15  -
────────────        ──
0010  1101          27
────────────        ──

111 ⌣1 1

    borrow
```

The result of a binary subtraction is clearly incorrect (20).
The reason for this is the inter-decade borrow that was
necessary. In binary terms this was worth 16 (denary) whereas
the decimal borrow is only worth 10. Thus the value in the
lower decade is 6 too large. Hence the adjustment rule for
subtraction is

> if a decade generates a borrow, subtract 6 from the
> answer in that decade.

In the example:

```
0010  1101
      0110  -
────────────
0010  0111
────────────
      11
```

which is the correct result.

4.10 Offset Binary Arithmetic

Arithmetic will not usually be carried out using the offset
binary format. Instead the offset binary will be converted to
2s complement binary before any significant calculations are
done. However, it is possible to carry out one addition or
subtraction between two offset binary quantities provided the
result is required in 2s complement notation.

This is particularly useful since the most usual source of
offset binary is an analogue-digital convertor. It is
frequently necessary to compare the output of such a convertor
(representing some measured value such as temperature) with a
specified set point. Thus provided the set point is specified
in offset binary format, the comparison and conversion may be
carried out in a single operation.

This may be verified by remembering that the n-bit offset binary representation of the number x is, in fact, the number

$$2^{n-1} + x = x_0$$

$$\text{and} \quad 2^{n-1} + y = y_0$$

offset binary

Hence

$$x_0 - y_0 = (2^{n-1} + x) - (2^{n-1} + y)$$

$$= x - y$$

Similarly for addition:

$$x_0 + y_0 = (2^{n-1} + x) + (2^{n-1} + y)$$

$$= 2^n + x + y$$

This appears as x+y since 2^n is in fact a carry out of the most significant place and does not appear in the answer.

5. Methods of Addressing

In order that a computer may function it is necessary to be able to specify the exact location of operands or instructions. Operands may reside in memory or in one of the registers of the computer while instructions will always be found in memory. Modern minicomputers and microprocessors are capable of accessing up to 8 megabytes of memory without making use of memory management techniques. Each memory location responds to a particular binary pattern on the address bus and the numerical equivalent of this binary pattern is termed the location's address.

Instructions may need to operate on either one or two operands and then store the result thus the most general instruction is of the form:

(source 1) . operation . (source 2) ⟶ (destination)

Thus, in principle, three addresses must be supplied by the instruction. However, the majority of minicomputers and microprocessors avoid this by requiring that the destination address is the same as that of the second source. In the majority of microprocessors and also in the simpler minicomputers, the situation is further simplified by assuming that both the second source and the destination is in the machine's principal register, the accumulator. This is the assumption that was made in Chapter 2.

Even with the most restrictive assumptions, however, the amount of space required within an instruction to specify the address can become detrimental to efficiency. For instance, consider an 8-bit microprocessor with a maximum address space of 2^16 = 64K. To specify just one memory location will require two bytes of memory and an addition byte will be required for the instruction code itself. Thus, to improve the situation, other methods of specifying the address to be accessed must be devised. These usually involve including only a limited amount of addressing information within the instruction. This information is combined with some additional information available within the machine to produce the required physical address. There exists a range of methods (addressing modes) which may be employed to calculate the physical address. The general approach is shown in Figure 5.1.

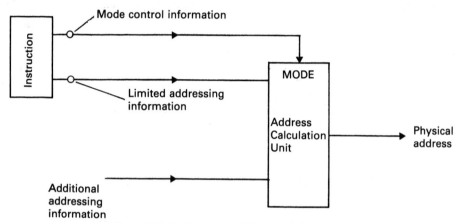

Figure 5.1: Calculation of Physical Addresses

While the various addressing modes may be used to minimise the amount of storage used by a program, they are also used to ensure that the computations required are carried out as effectively as possible (e.g. indexed addressing) or to give the finished program some desirable operational features such as relocatability (by using relative addressing, for instance).

The computational unit used for address calculation may be a separate, purpose-designed unit. However, in many simpler computers, the main arithmetic unit is used for this purpose, as required.

In the following sections some of the more common addressing methods will be discussed. Where examples are given it will be assumed that the example computer is of the simplest type. This will mean that only one operand address (the "source") is contained within the instruction, the remaining operand and destination being in the machine's principal register. Further, it will be assumed in the examples that the "limited addressing information" (Figure 5.1) occupies a separate word to the operation code. This is common in microprocessors but not always necessary in longer word-length machines.

88

5.1 Absolute Addressing

This is the most straightforward addressing method as it involves no computations whatsoever, the complete address of the operand being part of the instruction. Inevitably this leads to instructions which occupy a considerable amount of memory space. In a typical microprocessor with an 8-bit word and a maximum memory size of 64K, the address occupies two words (bytes) and the instruction code itself one. This leads to a 3-word instruction layout as shown in Figure 5.2. This is clearly rather inefficient in the use of memory space and, perhaps more important, it leads to a relatively slow execution speed since three accesses are required before any useful computational activity can take place.

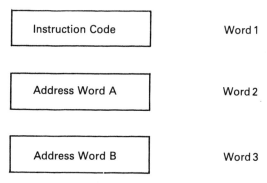

Figure 5.2: Absolute Addressing

In order to produce the 16-bit address necessary for a 64K memory, words 2 and 3 of the instruction are placed side-by-side. In most systems, address word A will contain the most significant 8 bits of the address while word B contains the least significant 8. This rule is not invariable, however, and the roles of words A and B may sometimes be reversed.

In order to improve efficiency, some systems permit a variation of absolute addressing in which the most significant address word is eliminated. This leads to a two-word instruction as shown in Figure 5.3.

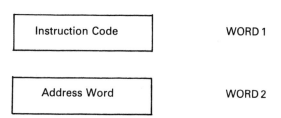

Figure 5.3: Modified Absolute Addressing Using 2 Words

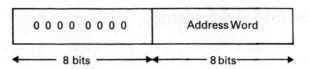

Figure 5.4: Calculation of Physical Address for Modified Form of Absolute Addressing

The full 16-bit address is formed by adding 8 zeros into the most significant places of the address space as shown in Figure 5.4.

This will only permit the first 256 memory locations to be accessed and, in the interests of efficiency, these are reserved for frequently accessed data items.

It will be appreciated that in a 16-bit machine with a 64K addressing space, the above problems do not exist 'and all absolute addressing instructions will employ one word for instruction code etc. and a second word for address information.

5.2 Paged Addressing

Paged addressing is a simple method of permitting the full memory space to be addressed while still retaining the economy of the two-word instruction outlined above.

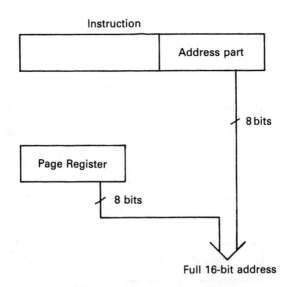

Figure 5.5: Paged Addressing

Instead of arbitrarily filling the most significant bits with zeros, these bits are filled with the contents of a special machine register called a PAGE REGISTER. As will be appreciated from Figure 5.5, this operation does not in fact involve any arithmetic and so it is very economical in hardware and does not impose any execution time overhead.

The layout of the instruction is as shown in Figure 5.3. If the address part of the instruction is given by

1010 0010 (A2)

and the page register is pre-loaded with

0001 0001 (11)

then the operand specified resides in memory address

0001 0001 1010 0010 (11A2)

Since the page register may be loaded under program control, this method of addressing permits the advantages of the shortened form of absolute addressing to be extended to the whole of memory. Paged addressing is at its most useful when blocks of data have to be accessed since then it is rarely necessary to change the page register contents.

The name, paged addressing, comes from the fact that the contents of the page register may be thought of as defining the lowest address on the "current page" of memory. The addressing information within the instruction is the offset of the addressed location from the page boundary (Figure 5.6).

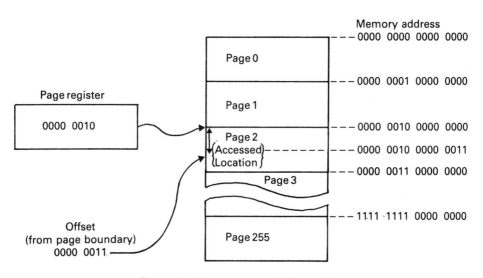

Figure 5.6: Arrangement of Memory 'Pages'

5.3 Relative Addressing

This is a modified form of the addressing method outlined above. Instead of a fixed page boundary being used as the datum to which the offset is added, the datum is chosen to be the current value of the sequence control register. Thus the offset is more-or-less relative to the location of the instruction. Furthermore the offset is interpreted as a 2s complement number so that the offset can be used to reference addresses occurring before, or after, the current instruction.

The value used as datum is the current value of the SCR which, of course, will be pointing to the next instruction, not the current instruction. In a typical minicomputer or microprocessor, the offset occupies the word following the instruction operation code. In some microprocessors the offset is increased to 16 bits and the total instruction occupies three words.

Memory Address

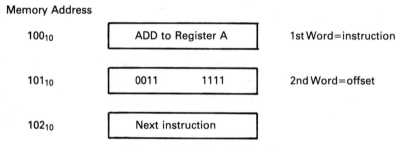

Figure 5.7: Relative Addressing

In Figure 5.7, the offset is 63; thus the reference operand is 102+63=165.

Had the offset been 1011 1111, this would have been interpreted as the 2s complement number -65 and the operand would have been fetched from location 102-65=37.

The philosophy behind this mode is that most references will be to addresses fairly close to the instruction. This is certainly true if a good programming style is developed and programs are constructed as fairly small and relatively self-contained modules.

The mode also has another advantage. The address specified by the instruction is not absolute, it is relative to the instruction, wherever that occurs in memory. So it is quite easy to relocate a whole block of code from one section of memory to another. This is done very frequently in multi-task disk-based systems.

5.4 Indirect Addressing

This mode of addressing does not specify the operand address directly, but it does indicate precisely where that address may be found.

The addressing information contained within the instruction is used to access a memory location. The contents of this location are then accessed and used as the actual address of the operands (Figure 5.8).

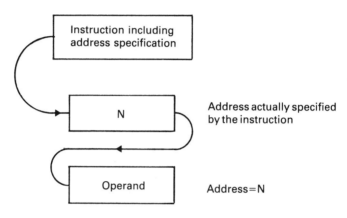

Figure 5.8: Indirect Addressing

The intermediate memory location is usually termed a "pointer" location. The instruction itself may specify which location is to be used as a pointer location using any of the available addressing methods. This has purposely been left vague in Figure 5.8.

Because one or more additional memory references are required, indirect addressing is relatively slow. However, it does permit the data accessed by a particular instruction to be changed during program execution. This is most helpful when accessing tables of data etc. Figure 5.9 is a flowchart of a program which finds the sum of a set of data items held in a table. Indirect addressing is used to access each operand in turn and the pointer location is incremented after each access.

In order to reduce the time penalty involved in indirect addressing, some machines permit one or more internal registers to be used as pointer locations. This is the so-called REGISTER INDIRECT addressing method.

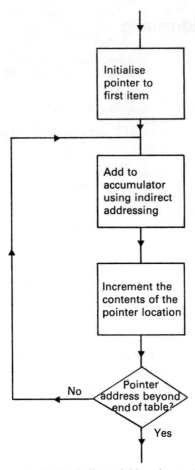

Figure 5.9: Using Indirect Addressing to Access a Table of Data

5.5 Indexed Addressing

This is somewhat similar to relative addressing except that
the datum for calculating the operand address is the contents
of a special register called the INDEX REGISTER. Because
machines which provide indexed addressing also provide a
number of very useful instructions to manipulate the contents
of this register, indexed addressing is a very powerful and
flexible method of referencing data. The totalisator example
above is an ideal application for index-mode addressing.

Typical instructions associated with index registers are:

        INX   increment the index register

        CPX   ALPHA   compare the contents of the index
                        register with ALPHA

Both of these are taken from the MC6800 instruction set. INX is used to step through tables etc, CPX is used, in connection with a suitable jump-type instruction, to cause an exit from a program loop when the end of a data table is reached.

Typically, an index addressing instruction will take the form shown in Figure 5.10.

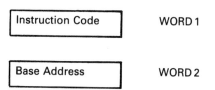

Figure 5.10: Index Addressing Instruction

The physical address of the operand is computed by adding the contents of the index register to the base address. In 8-bit computers, the base address will often be an 8-bit quantity while the index register will be the full width of the address bus (usually 16 bits). In such circumstances the base address specified in the instruction is assumed to have 8 '0's in the most significant places. Alternatively, in some machines, two words may be used to specify a full 16-bit base address.

In addition to simplifying the accessing of data in tables, indexed addressing is very useful for code-conversion exercises.

Consider a table, starting at memory location 1000, containing the ASCII codes for various symbols.

```
1000   00100101    %
       00100001    !
       00111111    ?
       00111101    =
         .
         .
         .
```

A second table is located at memory address 2000 and contains, in the same order, the corresponding EBCDIC codes.

```
2000   01101100    %
       01011010    !
       01101111    ?
       01111110    =
         .
         .
         .
```

The first table is searched until a match is found between the table entry and the character to be converted. The table is accessed using indexed addressing with 1000 as the base address. When a match is found the contents of the index register represents the distance into the table that the match was found. The corresponding EBCDIC character is, by definition, the same distance into the second table. Thus it may be retrieved by leaving the index register unchanged and using indexed addressing with A BASE ADDRESS OF 2000.

The whole process is shown in flowchart form in Figure 5.11.

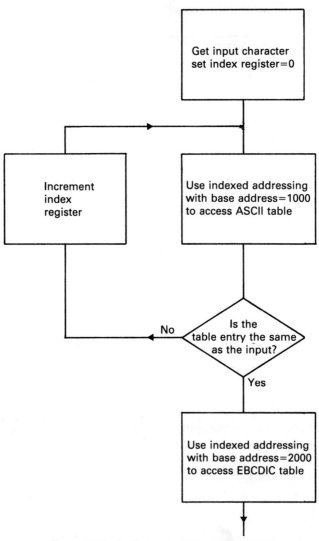

Figure 5.11: An Example Using Indexed Addressing

5.6 Auto-Increment Addressing

This is a special form of indirect addressing in which the contents of the pointer location are changed during the execution of the instruction. It will be appreciated from the totalisator example in Section 5.4 that it is frequently necessary to increment the pointer location in addition to using it to access operands. When simple indirect addressing is used a second access to the pointer is necessary to achieve this incrementation and this wastes time. Instead the incrementation can be combined with the use of the pointer for operand access and it is this combined operation which is known as auto-increment addressing. The actions taken by a typical auto-increment instruction are:

    1) fetch pointer
    2) use it to access operand
    3) increment pointer
    4) restore pointer to memory

The above sequence describes a post-incrementation auto-increment access. In some machines steps 2 and 3 are reversed to produce a pre-increment version.

As a complement to auto-increment addressing there is an auto-decrement addressing mode. Such a mode operates as described in Stages 1 - 4 above except that decrementation takes the place of incrementation. Again there exist both pre- and post-decrementation variants. To be most useful auto-increment and auto-decrement instructions should be paired as follows:

    (a) Pre auto-increment with post auto-decrement

    (b) Post auto-increment with pre auto-decrement

The pairing (a) implies that the pointer is incremented before being used to (say) store some data. Thus the pointer is left pointing to the last item of data. Clearly to recover this data the pointer must be first used then decremented to point to the previous data item (post decrementation).

The pairing (b) achieves the same objective except that the pointer always points to the next vacant location.

5.7 Immediate Mode Addressing

When using immediate mode addressing no operand address at all is given. Instead the operand itself forms part of the instruction as shown in Figure 5.12.

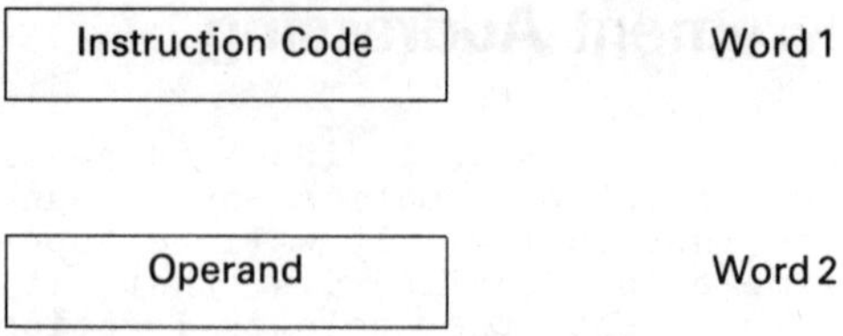

| Instruction Code | Word 1
|------------------|

| Operand | Word 2
|---------|

Figure 5.12: An Immediate Mode Instruction

This form of addressing is used where constant data has to be injected into the program. This occurs most commonly in the initialisation phases of a program.

5.8 Implicit Addressing

This is one of a number of names used to cover those instructions which, by their very nature, do not require any memory addressing information. Examples of such instructions include

    increment index register

    complement accumulator

    etc.

6. Memory Systems

There exists a wide variety of types of memory suitable for use in micro-processor based systems and the correct selection of memory type and organisation can play an important part in achieving the full potential of any particular system or product.

Memories may be required to perform a number of distinct functions:

- Workspace memory:

    required for the temporary storage of variables during a calculation. This would normally require fast access and the data stored would have a short useful life.

- Data memory:

    used to store constants, tables or results etc. Depending of the particular application, the requirements of this usage could be similar to workspace memory or might require a permanent storage medium.

- Program memory:

    used to store the instructions which control the operation of the processor. In very many applications, the requirement will be for a virtually permanent storage medium.

This Chapter will give details of the various memory types available for use with microprocessors and also will show how these memories may be chosen for any given application.

6.1 Terminology of Memory Systems

There are a number of specialised terms used to describe the various attributes of memory systems. It will be convenient for the ensuing discussion of memories if these terms are defined here.

Read-Only-Memory (ROM) -

A type of memory in which information is stored permanently. The information stored within the memory may be read by the processor but the 'write' operation has no meaning and any attempt to change the data stored by writing new data to the memory is totally ineffective. This type of memory is widely used for the storage of computer programs for systems with a dedicated function.

Read-Write-Memory (RWM) -

A form of memory in which it is possible to read data from memory or to write data into memory. Data written into memory will overwrite the previous contents. This type of memory is frequently (and incorrectly) referred to as Random-Access-Memory (RAM).

Volatile Memory -

A type of memory in which all data is lost if the power supply is removed. Clearly ROM cannot be volatile if it is to be of any use! All commonly used read-write memories are volatile and if non-volatility is required, a suitable battery back-up for the memory power supply is needed.

Serial Access Memory -

A memory device in which each item of data is made available for access in turn. Thus the time taken to read or write to such a memory is dependent on the actual address being written to. Typical serial access memories include shift-register-based systems and magnetic systems such as discs and tapes.

Random-Access-Memory (RAM) -

A memory device in which the actual address of data has no effect on the time taken to access the data. The term RAM is frequently mis-used when Read-Write memory is intended. All commonly used read-write and read-only memories exhibit this random access property.

100

Dynamic Memory -

> A type of memory in which data has a very short life
> (typically 1-2ms). In order to maintain data in such a
> memory, it has to be periodically refreshed using
> additional circuitry.

Static Memory -

> A type of memory which does not require refreshment.
> Data in such memories is permanent unless it is
> overwritten or destroyed by power supply failure.

6.2 General Arrangement of Random Access Memory Systems

Memory systems are capable of storing large numbers of data
items and it is necessary for such systems to have a
mechanism whereby a particular data item may be accessed. To
achieve this each memory location is labelled with its own
unique ADDRESS. Every memory has an address port and a data
port (Figure 6.1). To read data from memory the address at
which the data is stored is supplied to the address port and
a "read" operation is specified on the Read-Write line. The
requisite data is then made available at the data port. To
write data into memory, the same procedure is used except
that a "write" operation is specified on the control line and
the data to be written is supplied to the data port. Read-
only-memories do not have a read-write control line and only
the read operation is meaningful.

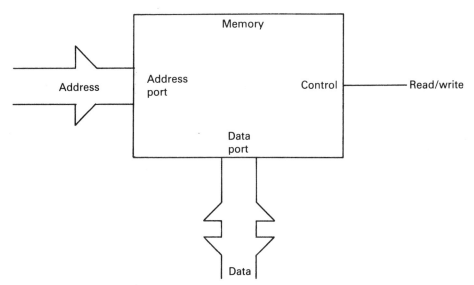

Figure 6.1: A Typical Memory System

The most usual way of organising the memory address system is the 2-dimensional array (Figure 6.2). This system operates as follows:-

The address of the data to be accessed is represented as an N-bit binary number thus allowing up to 2^N possible memory locations. To access a particular memory location, its binary address is split into two, one half being applied to the x-decoder and the other to the y-decoder. (For details of decoders, tri-state devices and other devices used in complete memory systems, see Appendix C). Each of these decoders is a 1-out-of-m type decoder and causes one of its output lines to be energised. The memory cell at the intersection of the two energised lines is the selected memory cell.

Example: Consider a 6-bit address word.
Each decoder is a 1-out-of-8 $(8=2^{(6\div2)})$
if the address is $\underline{101}$ $\underline{001}$ $=(41_{10})$

y decoder   x decoder
line 5   line 1
the cell shown shaded on Figure 6.2 is selected.

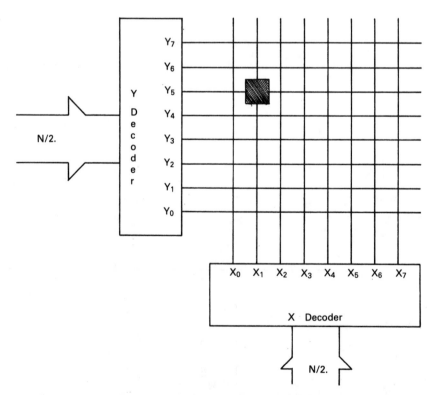

Figure 6.2: An Address Decoding Scheme

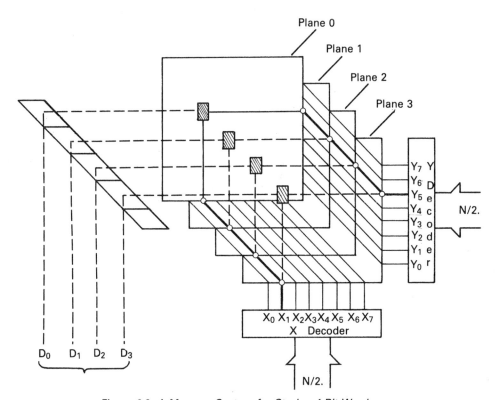

Figure 6.3: A Memory System for Storing 4-Bit Words

Each memory cell in one of these 2-dimensional arrays is capable of storing a single bit and the complete array of memory cells is termed a memory plane.

To be useful, however, a memory system must be capable of accessing complete words of information rather than just single bits. Thus a memory for a j-bit word-length computer will be made up of j 2-dimensional memory planes (Figure 6.3). To address a complete word, the same address is supplied to each memory plane and the individual bits of the word are extracted from the appropriate cell in each plane. The extracted bits are assembled into a complete word of data before being supplied to the processor.

6.3 Structure of a Static Read/Write Memory Cell

The most common form of static Read/Write memory cell is fabricated using MOS technology and it is this type of cell which is illustrated in Figure 6.4. The heart of the cell is the pair of transistors T1-T2 which are connected in the form

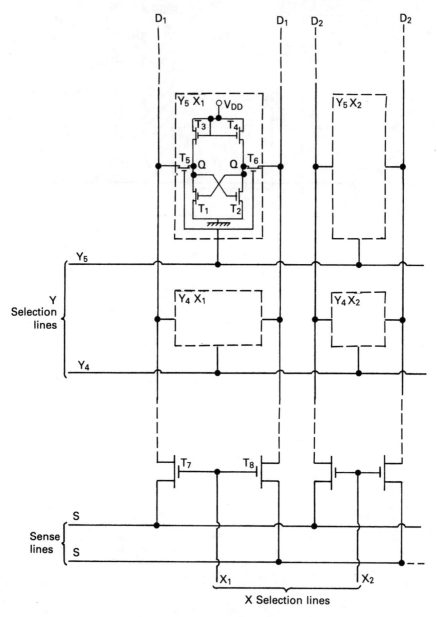

Figure 6.4: A Static Read-Write Memory Cell

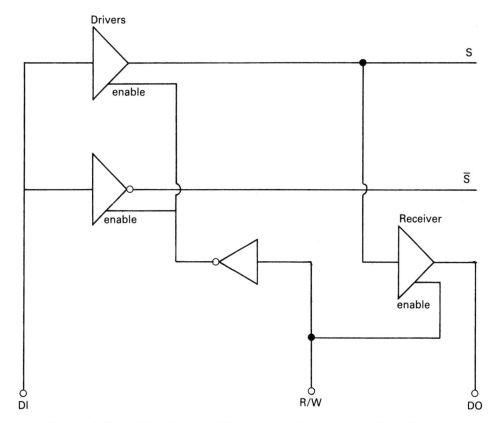

Figure 6.5: Sense Line Drivers and Receivers for the Static Read/Write Memory

of a bistable and which use T3-T4 as load resistors. If T2 is conducting and T1 is cut off (i.e. not conducting) the cell is storing a '1'.

Data is read from all the cells in the array via the two sense lines s and s̄ (inverse of s).

Selection is accomplished using the coincidence method outlined above using the x and y selection lines shown.

To select the cell located at the intersection of the X1 and Y5 selection lines, these two lines must be energised by the address decoders (Figure 6.2).

As will be seen from Figure 6.4, data from a memory cell can only reach the sense lines if T5, T6, T7 and T8 are all conducting.

T5 and T6 are caused to conduct by their respective row selection line y. While the data from each column of cells, controlled by T7 and T8 can only gain access to the sense lines if the appropriate column selection line x is energised. In this way, coincidence addressing is achieved.

In the example of Figure 6.2 all cells connected to the Y5 line will _apply their data to their respective column data lines (D, D̄) but only the data lines of column X1 will be connected to the sense lines, thus cell Y5,X1 is selected.

The data on the sense lines is buffered and made available to the system.

To write data to a cell, the addressing is as for a read operation but the sense lines are driven rather than acting as data receivers (Figure 6.5) and this forces the addressed cell to store a '1' or a '0' as determined by the incoming data.

Because static memory cells consist of a relatively large number of transistors (6) of which at least two are conducting at any one time they tend to consume relatively large amounts of power and each cell occupies a fairly large area on a silicon chip. These two factors tend to limit the size of memory which can be accommodated in a single package and also the viability of backing-up such memories for long periods using batteries.

6.4 Structure of a Dynamic Read/Write Memory

A dynamic read-write memory cell is illustrated in Figure 6.6. The storage element consists of the gate-to-substrate capacitance Cg. The addressing is again by the coincidence method but in this instance two row selection lines (for reading and writing) and two column selection lines (for reading and writing) are required. To select a particular cell for reading, the appropriate column and row lines must be energised. Likewise, for writing, the appropriate row and column write lines must be energised.

To write into a particular cell, the appropriate row write line is energised. This connects Cg to the column write line via T1. The input data is then directed to the appropriate column write line by the x address decoder. Thus the data is written into Cg via T1. T1 is fully charged for a logic '1' and discharged for a '0'.

To read data from the cell, the appropriate row read line is energised, thus connecting the cell to its column read line. The appropriate column read line is selected by the x address decoder and the data is routed to the output of the memory.

If Cg is charged (logic '1'), T2 is 'on' and hence the column read line is connected to ground and a logic '0' is read.

Thus the data output is the inverse of the stored data. This is easily corrected by inverters between the read lines and the data lines.

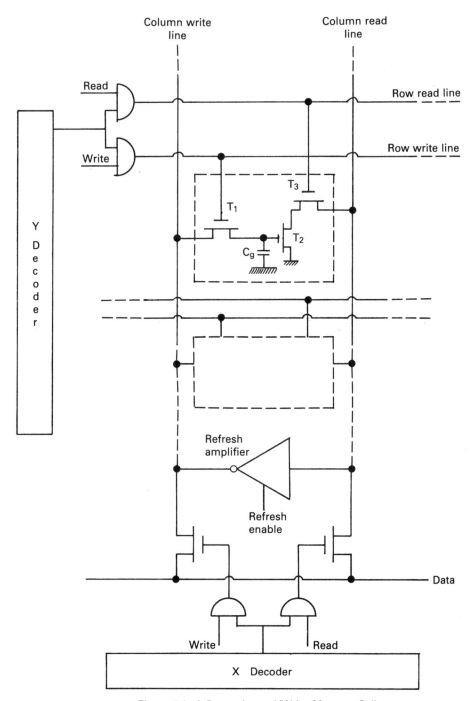

Figure 6.6: A Dynamic read/Write Memory Cell

Despite the fact that T2 has a very high input resistance the small value of Cg means that its stored charge is rapidly depleted and the data is lost. To avoid this, the data is refreshed every 1ms - 3ms. The refresh operation is achieved by applying both row read and row write signals and enabling the refresh amplifier. Thus the data is read from the cell before it decays, is amplified and inverted by the refresh amplifier and is then re-applied to Cg via T1.

Because each column of memory is independent and equipped with its own refresh amplifier, all of the cells in a particular row may be refreshed at the same time. This takes typically less than 400ns. Within the maximum period allowed for refreshment, each row in turn must be refreshed. This is achieved by having external control circuitry including a timer and counter to carry out this function. Currently, however, the tendency is to integrate more and more of this circuitry onto the memory chips themselves.

Some dynamic memory systems cause every cell in a particular row to be refreshed each time a cell in that row is accessed. This requires a slightly different arrangement to that shown in Figure 6.6. However, it does not remove the necessity to refresh every row systematically as outlined above.

The refresh process is typically carried out by providing the memory system with a counter which is incremented by a suitable timer. The counter is used to specify which row is to be refreshed and the timer interval is determined by dividing the maximum refresh period by the number of rows in the memory array. Thus a typical 16K dynamic Read-Write memory would be organised as 128 rows x 128 columns (since 128 x 128 = 16K). This requires a timer interval of 2ms / 128 = 15.6 usec if every cell is to be refreshed once in every 2msec.

Each refresh operation takes approximately one memory cycle time and if it is assumed that this is about 400ns the memory availability may be calculated as

$$\frac{15.6 - 0.4}{15.6} = 97.5\%$$

Clearly any attempted memory access during a refresh cycle cannot be honoured. The access will be delayed until the refresh is complete and so the processor will experience an excessively long access time. This could result, as explained later, in the data being mis-read or mis-written. To avoid this the refresh circuits will generate a NOT READY signal to warn the processor. The block diagram of a typical dynamic memory system is shown in Figure 6.7.

The operation of this circuit (which does not represent an actual product) may be briefly explained as follows.

During normal accesses the address bus lines A0-A13 (for a 16K memory) are divided into row and column addresses (7 bits

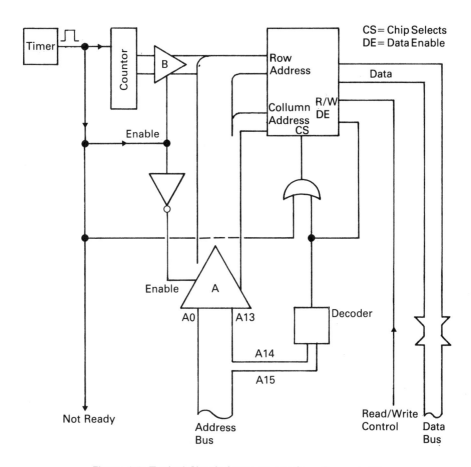

Figure 6.7: Typical Circuit Arrangement for a Dynamic Memory

each). The remaining two address lines are decoded and used to operate the chip select input (CS) and also the Data enable (DE). The function of 'CS' is to activate the memory while 'DE' is used solely to enable the connection of the data bus to the memory.

During a refresh operation, the timer increments the counter and disables the address bus receiver (A) while enabling the output of the counter (B). In this way a conflict on the row address lines is avoided. The timer also enables the 'CS' thus activating the memory. The DE pin is not used and no data reaches the bus.

In practice, additional circuitry would be needed to co-ordinate the refresh operations with normal memory accesses otherwise there is a danger of one activity breaking into the other.

A further complication is the fact that most manufacturers use the same pins for both row and column addressing differentiating between the uses by appropriate multiplexing signals. This enables a 64K x 1 bit memory to be housed in a 16-pin package. As can be seen from Figure 6.6, a dynamic memory cell consists of three transistors only and it is therefore possible to put more dynamic cells in a package than is possible with static cells. Further, when no read/write operations are in progress, the power consumption is very low since T1 and T2 are off. This feature makes dynamic memories very suitable for large memories or where long-term battery back-up is required. The need for refresh circuitry is becoming less of a problem with the passing of time, but dynamic memory is still contra-indicated for very small memory systems.

An example of the incorporation of refresh circuitry on the same chip as the memory cells is provided by the MOSTEK MK4164 (a 64K x 1 bit memory) which only requires its refresh pin to be taken to logic '0' for a fully syncronised refresh cycle and counter update to take place. (The chip also incorporates a timer for use during emergency battery back-up situations).

6.5 Read-Only Memories

These devices have information stored in them at the time of manufacture or shortly afterwards. Once stored, the data in memory is unalterable and any changes to the data require a new memory to be fitted. ROMs are widely used for program storage in microprocessor systems; by their very nature they are non-volatile.

A typical ROM memory cell is very simple (Figure 6.8) consisting of one transistor only. This is a MASK PROGRAMMED ROM - a device which is programmed during manufacture. Coincident addressing is again used, the cell at the junction of the selected row and column being accessed.

A particular transistor can only turn on if its source (lower terminal) is grounded (via the column select transistor) and its gate is driven (via the row select line). All non-selected transistors permit the data line to 'float'. If a selected transistor turns on, a logic '0' is forced onto the data line. Whether or not a selected transistor turns on may be determined in either of two ways.

(i)   If the stored bit pattern is determined by the mask used to lay down the metallisation pattern, then some of the links, L, will be present and others missing. Only if the link is present on the selected transistor will it turn on ('0' stored).

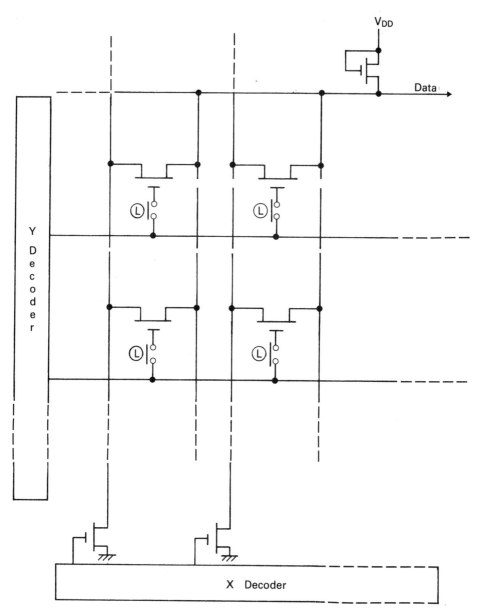

Figure 6.8: Mask-Programmed ROM

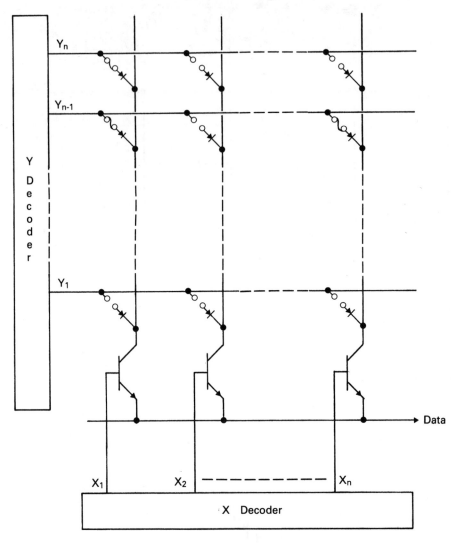

Figure 6.9: Fusible-Link PROM

(ii)   Alternatively, the bit pattern may be determined by the mask used to control the growth of silicon oxide in the gate region of each transistor. If a thick oxide layer has been permitted to grow at the gate of the selected transistor, then it will not turn on. A thin oxide layer will permit it to turn on ('0' stored).

Thus mask programmed ROMs have their contents determined by the manufacturing process. This is relatively easily achieved and results in a very low-cost device provided that the cost of producing the customising mask ($ 1000 - $ 2000) for the process can be spread over a large enough number of units. It may take several weeks (typically 6) from the time of ordering before production units are available. Mask production is a computerised operation and the user merely sends the manufacturer the specification for the device (usually on floppy discs, punched cards or paper tape) and the bulk of the processing is then carried out automatically.

Where the production run is too short to justify the use of mask-programmed ROMs, ultra-violet-light eraseable PROMs are frequently used. These may be readily programmed by the user and are more fully decribed in the next section.

Where a short access time is required, a fusible-link PROM may be used (Figure 6.9).

Fusible-link PROMs are fabricated using bipolar technology and are consequently faster than MOS memories. The device is read by pulsing the appropriate row select line and by connecting the appropriate column select line to the sense line (coincidence addressing). The absence of a fusible-link results in a '0' being detected while the presence of a link results in a '1' being seen. To program the device, the fusible links are "blown" selectively using relatively high current pulses. The diodes are required in the memory structure to avoid establishing current paths from one row line to another, thus presenting false data to the output.

For instance, if Y(n) and X(n) are selected, a '0' should be read (no fuse at the intersection) but without the diodes the voltage on the Y(n) line would be connected to the Y(n-1) line via the Y(n-1),X1 fuse and thus through the fuse at Y(n-1),X(n) to the data line.

6.6 Reusable PROMs

User-programmed PROMs of the fusible-link variety are not really suitable for development work since the frequency of changes required at this stage of a design can result in excessive wastage of memory devices. Fortunately, there exist two types of PROM which are re-programmable.

The ultra-violet erasable PROM (UVPROM) has a structure similar to that shown in Figure 6.10. Each memory cell consists of a single MOS transistor with its gate connection left open. Under normal circumstances, this transistor will not conduct. However, if a very high voltage is applied between source and drain avalanche conduction occurs across the gate insulation thus charging the gate and allowing the transistor to conduct. The charge thus stored leaks away very slowly (10 years at 125°C) and can, for all practical purposes, be regarded as permanent.

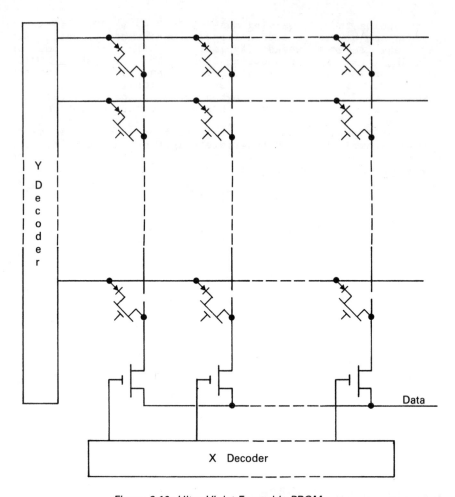

Figure 6.10: Ultra-Violet Eraseable PROM

The memory is addressed using the coincidence method. A pulse is placed on the row lines and is conducted through to the column lines only where the transistor gates have been charged. The appropriate column is selected by the x-decoder and the data, from this column only, is transferred to the data line.

Programming a UVPROM is achieved relatively slowly because the high voltages required can only be applied for short periods. The high programming voltage (typically +25v) is applied to a special pin on the memory package (this pin being kept at +5v for normal memory access purposes) and the address is presented at the appropriate pins. The data is then presented at the data pins of the device and a pulse applied to the 'program' pin of the memory. New address and

114

data signals are then presented to the device and the procedure repeated until the whole memory is programmed. Older designs can only stand a 1ms programming pulse due to overheating and so the complete cycle of addressing must be repeated as many as 100 times before the chip is fully programmed. The latest devices, however, can withstand a full 50ms programming pulse and so each location may be programmed by a single pulse and only one cycle round the addresses is necessary.

The stored data must be completely erased before the device is re-programmed. This erasure is achieved by exposing the device to ultra-violet light for about 10-30 minutes. The light penetrates the device via a quartz window and dissipates the charges accumulated in the gate regions.

Less common than the ultra-violet erasable PROM (UVPROM) is the Electrically Alterable Read Only Memory (EAROM). This type of device may be read relatively rapidly. It has the property that it may be erased electrically in about 100ms and data can be written into it in about 15ms. This type of memory is particularly useful in equipment which has to be configured by the end-user. It would be inconvenient to use UVPROMs for this purpose (because of the special equipment required) and equally it would be very tedious to configure the system every time it was switched on. EAROMs provide the ideal answer since they may be permanently embedded in the system and still provide the necessary programming qualities. Since the system only accesses such memories to read the data (except during the very infrequent reconfiguration procedure) the slow write access is of no importance.

6.7 Timing and Control Signals for Memories

In order that a memory may function properly in a complete microprocessor system, it is necessary that it receives timing and control signals. Typically these consist of the following:

Address signals:

These serve to ensure that the correct memory cell(s) are accessed.

Read/Write:

This is used to control whether data is written into the memory or read from it.

Validity signals:

Frequently signals will appear on the address and read/write lines at times other than those when it is desired to access memory. To avoid any false accesses the processor provides a "valid" signal to indicate that the control signals are to be interpreted for memory access (e.g. Valid Memory Address, VMA, in the Motorola 6800 microprocessor). In some systems, it is necessary for the user to generate his own VALID signal (e.g. by the logical OR of $\overline{RD}$ and $\overline{WR}$ in the 8085 microprocessor; see Appendix A).

Chip Select:

To build up large memory systems it is necessary to use many memory ICs. All of these must be connected to the data bus but only one may have control at any given time; otherwise there would be ambiguity in the data transmitted and possible damage to the system. This is avoided by using the chip "select" inputs to ensure that only one device is enabled at any given time.

The bus structure to which the memory is connected will impose certain constraints on the system and these must be taken into account. Such constraints might typically include

(i)   The time after the start of the bus cycle when the address information is available T(AV) in Figure 6.11.

(ii)   The time after the start of the bus cycle when the various control signals are usable. T(VV) and T(RV) in Figure 6.11 (different controls may well have different timings).

(iii)   The delay from the start of the bus cycle until data is put on the bus by the processor (in the case of a write cycle).

(iv)   The time period immediately preceding the end of the bus cycle for which the data supplied by a memory must be stable - data setup time (in the case of a read cycle).

(v)   In some systems, there is also a requirement for the data (and sometimes other signals) to be held after the end of the cycle. This is termed the "data hold time". This requirement is not shown in Figure 6.11.

Likewise, a memory circuit will itself impose certain constraints on the system. The data presented to it must remain stable for a certain time before the memory is deselected. Likewise, there is a certain access time after the memory is selected before the data is made available to the bus.

Where a device has several enabling inputs, it should not be assumed that the access time for each is identical. For instance, the 2716 UVPROM requires a delay of 450ns after the address and chip select signals have been set before the data is valid, but only 120 nsec delay after the output enable has been set. Both the memory timing constraints and the bus timing constraints must be satisfied.

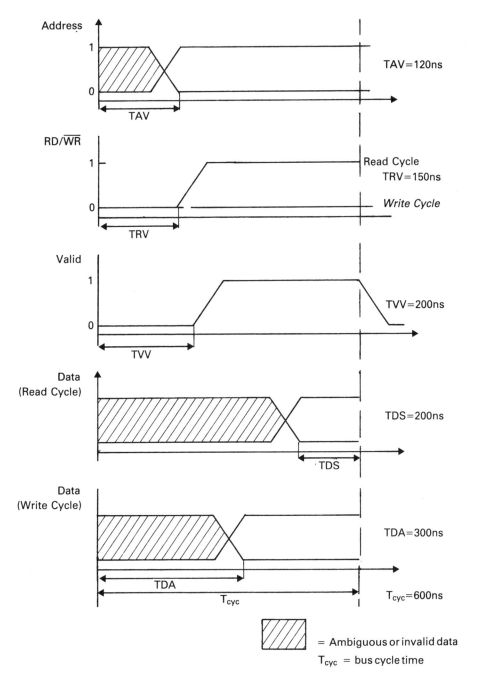

Figure 6.11: An Example of a Typical Bus Timing Situation

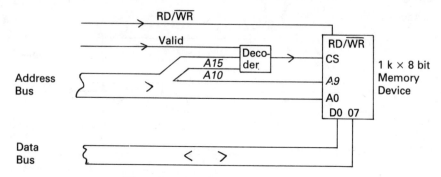

Figure 6.12: A simple memory system

Figure 6.11 shows a typical bus timing situation. As an example, consider the constraints put on the memory chip in Figure 6.12 by this bus timing. In particular, consider the memory access time and memory data set-up time requirements.

In Figure 6.12 the RD/$\overline{\text{WR}}$ line is taken directly to the corresponding pin on the memory chip. Because it is a 1K memory chip ten address lines (A0-A9) are taken directly to the chip (2^{10}=1K) while the remainder are applied to a decoder along with the "VALID" signal.

For the purposes of the example the decoder will be assumed to take 50ns to provide its output.

Memory Read:

The CS input will be active 50ns after the last input to the decoder is active. The last input is 'VALID' so CS becomes active 250ns into the bus cycle. Since the data must be valid 200ns before the end of the cycle this implies that, with a cycle time of 600ns, the data must be valid 400ns into the cycle.

Thus the maximum allowable access time from chip select becoming valid is

$$400\text{ns} - 250\text{ns} = 150\text{ns}$$

The address signals themselves are valid 120ns into the cycle so the maximum allowable access time from address valid is

$$400\text{ns} - 120\text{ns} = 280\text{ns}$$

An examination of the specification for the 2114-2 static read/write memory shows that the address access time (TA) is 200ns while the chip select access time (TCO) is 70ns and so this device will operate satisfactorily in the read mode. (The 2114-3 with TA=300ns and TCO=100ns will not, of course, operate properly.)

Memory Write:

The data from the processor is valid for (T(cyc)-T(DA)) = 300ns before the end of the bus cycle and so any memory which has a data set up time of less than this will function satisfactorily provided that the address and chip select signals are set up sufficiently rapidly.

As noted above, the address signals are valid for the last 480ns of the bus cycle and the chip select signal is valid for the last 350ns. The 2114-2 memory circuit referred to above has the following requirements

minimum time for which address lines are valid	200ns	(480ns)
minimum time for which CS is valid	120ns	(350ns)
minimum data set up time	120ns	(300ns)

The figures in brackets are those achieved by the example system, from which it will become apparent that the 2114-2 will also operate in write mode. (As indeed so will the 2114-3 and the 2114-4, although these will not work in the read mode!)

In order that slow memories may be used (and this normally includes dynamic memories since, during refresh anyway, they appear to the system to have an extended access time) special steps must be taken. One possibility is to increase T(cyc) by slowing down the system clock. There is usually a limit to this in microprocessor systems since some processors will cease to operate correctly with very slow clocks (the MC6800 has a maximum value of 10 usec for T(cyc)). The clock slowing method has the further disadvantage that all processor cycles are slowed, not just those where memory is being accessed, thus reducing the system throughput.

A more efficient method involves the introduction of a degree of asynchronism into the bus. Most systems permit the use of a "READY" line in the bus (this is part of the Intel 8085 system). When this ready line is left at logic '1', the bus operations proceed at full speed. When it is taken to logic '0', extra time slices are added to the current bus cycle (these are usually called 'wait states') until the ready line is again at logic '1'. Thus a slow memory system merely has to generate a logic '0' pulse of sufficient length and then apply this to the ready line or its equivalent.

6.8 Address Decoding

Those address lines which are not required for the on-chip decoding of memory addresses are usually applied to an external decoder which combines them in an appropriate fashion to operate the memory chip select pin(s).

The use of the chip select pin(s) is of interest. Consider the case of a 2K memory of 8-bit words made up of memory circuits each capable of storing 1/2K of 8-bit words, the system uses a 16-bit address bus. A possible arrangement is shown in Figure 6.13.

All of the data lines from each circuit are connected together; likewise all of the address lines A0-A8 are supplied to each memory circuit for use by the internal decode circuits.

Read/write is applied to all circuits. The chip select input for each circuit is separately processed so that only one is enabled at any given time. A memory circuit will only be enabled if:

(i)   "valid" is true indicating a valid access to memory.

(ii)   A11-A15 are all '0' since a 2K memory only consists of locations 0 to 2047 (or 0000 0000 0000 0000 to 0000 0111 1111 1111).

(iii)   its own "chip selector" is giving a '1' output. Thus

chip A responds only in the range

	00000	00	000000000
to	00000	00	111111111

chip B responds in the range

	00000	01	000000000
to	00000	01	111111111

chip C responds in the range

	00000	10	000000000
to	00000	10	111111111

chip D responds in the range

	00000	11	000000000
to	00000	11	111111111

Fixed by the use of A11-A15 to enable all of the individual decoders

Combination determined by the particular AND gate combining A9 and A10

Address lines supplied to the chip itself

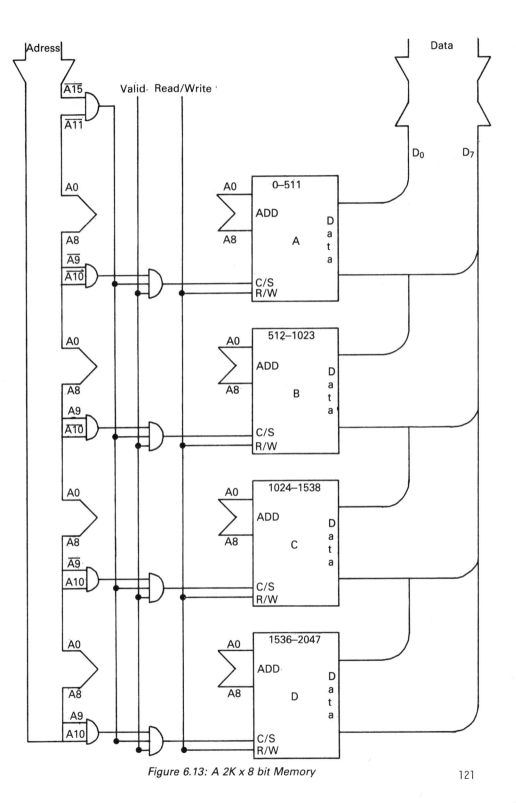

Figure 6.13: A 2K x 8 bit Memory

121

Omission of the decoder responding to A11-A15 would result in these bits being ignored. In these circumstances, issuing the address:-

    5004 (4096+8) = 00010 00 000001000

would cause the location

    8 = 00000 00 000001000

to be addressed since the most significant 5 bits are "don't cares" (see Appendix C).

This technique of "partial decoding" can be used to good effect in small systems to economise on hardware. However, it does limit expansion at a later date. This partial decoding technique may also be carried further. For instance, A10 could be applied to the chip select of memory A; A11 to memory B; A12 to memory C and A13 to memory D. The VALID signal would have to be incorporated in some other way, typically by using a second 'CS' pin which is often provided. This would separate accesses to the four memory chips but, of course, would set up a whole range of alternative addresses to which each chip could respond. Further the range of addresses to which A will respond overlaps that to which B will respond (e.g. 00000 11 000001000) and a reference to such overlapping addresses will probably cause one or both memory circuits to be destroyed. Thus while economies are introduced by this approach the programmer must be very sure that no such illegal accesses can be made, even by accident.

6.9 Selection of Memory Type

The factors governing the selection of memory type for a given application have already been presented and it is the purpose of this section to draw together these various factors.

For high-speed applications (access time of the order of 10ns - 40ns) bipolar technology devices must be used. If lower speed operation (40ns to 200ns) can be tolerated (as is usual) MOS technology devices with their higher storage capacity may be used. For read/write memory applications a wide variety of devices exist with capacities up to a typical maximum of 256K bits per chip.

As a rule, the larger capacity chips are of the dynamic type, static read/write memories having a typical upper limit of about 16K bits per chip.

Static memory has the advantage of design simplicity (no refresh circuits) but requires more power which may be a deciding factor in large systems. Where battery back-up of the memory is required dynamic memories are to be preferred because of their very low standby current. Currently the refresh circuitry is available in specially manufactured support chips and the tendency is for these to be incorporated onto the memory chip itself to form pseudo-static memory.

Where read-only memory is concerned, mask-programmed devices are most economical for long production runs but, where this is not the case, UVPROMs are indicated.

UVPROMs are also indicated for the storage of "Personality subroutines" which can vary from option-to-option in a given product and for the development phases of a project when frequent program changes are likely.

The technology used in MOS memories should also be given consideration:

P-MOS: Rather slow

N-MOS: Faster than P-MOS and may approach the speed of bipolar technology

C-MOS: Relatively fast and very low power consumption. High noise immunity. Technology is more complex than P- or N-MOS and hence the cost is higher.

All other considerations being equal, it is advantageous to select a memory which requires only a single +5V power supply rather than the triple power supplies (+5V, -5V, 12V for example) needed by some devices. It is also prudent to choose a device which can be obtained readily from several manufacturers.

Where the security of data during a power fail situation is required, low power dynamic and particularly C-MOS memories are to be recommended.

6.10 Selection of Memory Architecture

Once the selection of memory devices has been carried out according to the criteria discussed above it is likely that there will remain a certain amount of choice as to which particular device is to be used. One choice which could exist is that of whether to construct the memory from bit-organised or from word-organised chips.

For instance, the 2K-word memory shown in Figure 6.13 is constructed from four word-organised (1/2K x 8-bit) chips. It could equally well have been constructed from 8-bit-organised chips (2K x 1-bit) (Figure 6.14).

In the bit-organised memory, each chip has provision for 2K addresses and there is no need to provide external individual

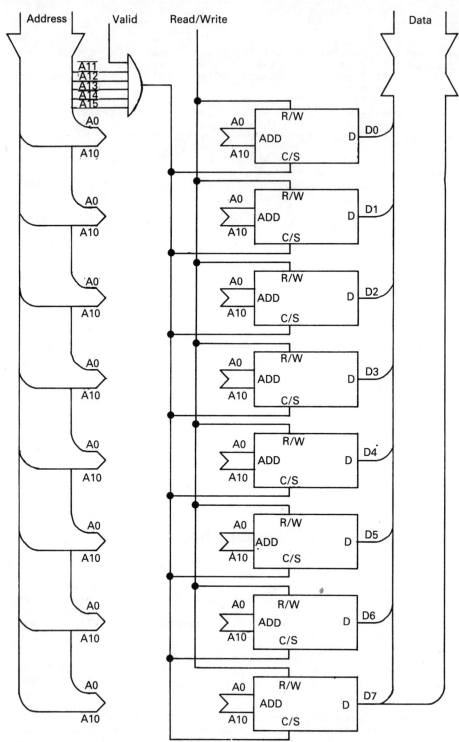

124 . Figure 6.14: A 2K x 8 bit Memory Using Bit-Organised Memory Chips

address decoding as was the case for Figure 6.13. Only one external gate is needed to operate the chip select pin with CS=$\overline{A15}.\overline{A14}.\overline{A13}.\overline{A12}.\overline{A11}.\overline{VMA}$. Even this could be eliminated if partial decoding were permissible in the application in which case the 2K memory would have no other components than the memory chips themselves.

The bit-organised memory would also be smaller since each of the individual circuits would only require 16 pins (data, R/W, CS, OV, +5V, 11 address). Thus the 2K memory, including full decoding, would have 142 soldered joints and occupy an area of about 30 sq cm.

The word-organised memory would involve larger circuits each with 24 pins (8 data, 9 address, CS, R/W, OV, +5V = 21 + 3 spare). Thus the 2K memory, with full decoding, would occupy an area of about 46 sq cm with 124 soldered joints.

The balance between the two methods of construction will vary depending upon the available memory devices and the overall size of the memory.

The spare pins in the 24-pin package noted above are frequently used to provide additional "chip-select" inputs. These can be used as part of the addressing mechanism to reduce or eliminate the need for external decoders. This effectively amounts to integrating the pair of "AND" gates associated with each memory chip in Figure 6.13 onto the chip itself.

7. Input-Output Operations – I

The input of information to a computer and the output of information from a computer are two of the most important functions which have to be considered. Without efficient I/O provision the power of a computer is completely trapped.

In order to establish a link between a computer and its peripherals, an appropriate interface must be built. This is done at two levels. At the hardware level, the necessary control and data signals must pass between the two ends of the I/O link and they must be made compatible in both the time and the electrical senses. At the software level, the necessary steps must be taken to issue the appropriate commands, to check whether data is ready and to read it into or write it out of) the computer.

The hardware section is usually referred to as 'the interface' and the software package as a 'device handler' or a 'device driver'.

There are two rather different ways in which the connection of peripherals to a CPU may be organised. In the first instance, one may take the view that input-output operations are a distinctive part of a computer's functionality. This leads naturally to the provision of a set of signals designed specifically for I/O operations - the SEPARATE I/O BUS. As an alternative to the process of transferring data to and from peripherals may be regarded as being little different from the exchange of data between the CPU and memory and the same set of control signals used for both purposes - the INTEGRATED I/O BUS.

The separate I/O bus approach usually offers the user a simpler set of signals for the control of peripherals. It also provides a useful degree of isolation between the machine and the outside world since a certain amount of electronics is usually required to convert the internal (memory) bus signals into the simplified I/O bus signals. Many minicomputers use this scheme for I/O transactions (for example, the Digital Equipment Corporation PDP-8 and the Data General Nova).

The provision of a separate I/O is not practicable for a microprocessor since there are insufficient pins available to permit the designers to provide two bus structures. Thus the user is forced to utilise the memory-bus signals for peripheral control. This is, in practice, not too much of a problem since the manufacturers also provide a wide selection of peripheral controllers in which all of the necessary logic is included (see Chapter 14). There is, of course, nothing to stop the user designing his own set of I/O bus signals and providing the necessary logic to convert the microprocessor signals to this standard. However, there is rarely any advantage in taking this course unless one is intending to convert to one of the 'standard' bus systems such as the IEEE GPIB (see Chapter 12).

When an integrated I/O bus structure is used the peripheral may simply be regarded as one (or more) memory locations which may be written to or read from using the normal 'Read' and 'Write' instructions. Thus there are no special I/O instructions. This has certain advantages if the CPU is capable of carrying out operations on memory as well as accumulators since there is then no need to waste time transferring data from the peripheral into an accumulator before processing it (the MC6800 is an example of this approach - see Chapter 9).

Other examples of the integrated I/O bus approach do distinguish between memory and peripheral_ accesses. This is achieved by a single control line (IO/$\overline{M}$ in the Intel 8085 - see Appendix A). The distinction between memory and peripherals results in the provision of two special I/O instructions, 'IN' which replaces the memory read operation, and 'OUT' to replace the memory write. If this approach is adopted, then the advantages of being able to operate on peripherals in the same way as memory is lost; however, certain advantages are obtained. The address space used for peripherals is different from that provided for memory and need not be as extensive. A 64K memory space, requiring 16 address bits is typical but the peripheral address space is frequently restricted to 256 locations which require only 8 address lines. Thus, whereas a typical read instruction in a microprocessor will be followed by two bytes to express the address, an IN instruction need only be followed by a single address byte, saving both time and program space. It is, of course, possible for the user to choose to ignore the IO/$\overline{M}$ control line and to design his interfaces as memory mapped (as opposed to I/O mapped) systems if, in the context of a particular application, the advantages of so doing outweigh the other considerations.

Most peripherals have a number of distinct functions associated with them. When such peripherals are connected to a separate I/O bus structure, there exists a particular I/O instruction association with each possible action. The peripheral is commanded to carry out the particular function in question by the pattern of signals presented to it on the function lines of the bus (see below). These function lines reflect the particular I/O instruction being obeyed.

When the integrated I/O bus structure is being used (whether memory-mapped or I/O mapped) the possibility of distinguishing between various actions via function lines does not exist since they are not present in the bus structure. Instead each peripheral has a COMMAND REGISTER built into it. This serves in a manner very similar to that of the instruction register of a CPU. The command register has its own address and by writing to this address a suitable pattern of ones and zeros may be placed in the command register. The hardware of the peripheral interface interprets this pattern and initiates the appropriate actions. Usually each bit of the command register is associated with a particular action, thus making the system very easy to use. Most integrated I/O bus peripherals will have several registers (e.g. command, status, data) associated with them, each occupying its own address.

7.1 Hardware Components of Interfaces

Within an interface, there are four important pieces of hardware which must be understood before the function of the whole system can be appreciated. These are Decoders, Buffer Registers and Flags and Tri-state bus drivers. Further details may be found in Appendix C.

(i)   Decoders

A decoder is used to monitor a set of signals and to indicate when these signals assume a specified combination of values. For instance, the address lines of the I/O bus are used to determine which peripheral is to be used in a given transfer. Thus every peripheral has in its interface a decoder. When the particular combination of ones and zeros for which a decoder is designed appears on the address lines of the bus this decoder, AND NO OTHER, produces a logic 1 at its output. This output is used to enable the peripheral. All other decoders will produce 0 at their outputs and hence all other peripherals are disabled. Similarly, decoders are used to determine which of the possible functions is actually being requested (some decoders produce logic 0 when selected and 1 otherwise, but the principle remains the same).

(ii)   Buffer Registers

These are similar in form to the registers of the computer. Their purpose is to store temporarily the data passing to and from the computer so that it is available at the correct times. They therefore help to resolve the differences of speed between the computer operations and peripheral operations. An input strobe control causes the data present on the input lines to be latched into the buffer.

(iii)   Flags

It is frequently necessary to signal the status of the peripheral to the computer. For instance, is the peripheral busy? ; is data available? etc. These pieces of binary status information are stored in single-bit registers which can be interrogated by the computer when it requires the information. As a rule, they can be SET (to logic '1') or RESET (CLEARED) (to logic '0') by the operation of the peripheral. As a rule, the computer can also clear the flag. The following symbol will be used for a flag:

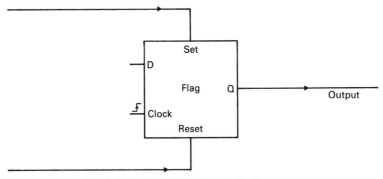

A logic '1' on the set line will set the flag.
A logic '1' on the reset line will clear it.
Q=D after being clocked.

Figure 7.1: Hardware Flag

(iv)   Tri-state Bus Drivers

In a multi-peripheral system, many devices will be capable of driving any one of the lines making up the bus. Clearly only one should have control of the bus at any given time. This is achieved by tri-state drivers which are placed between the source of the data and the bus. When the enable input is logic 0, no information is transmitted by the driver and it imposes a negligible load on the bus. When the enable input is logic 1, the data at the input to the driver is transmitted to the bus.

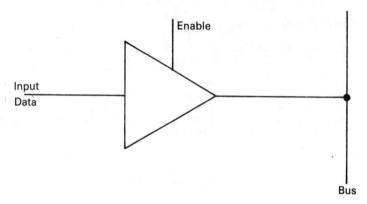

Figure 7.2: Tri-State Driver

7.2 Two Example Bus Structures

In the next section, the methods used to connect a typical peripheral (a paper-tape reader) to a computer will be described. The methods appropriate to a separate I/O bus are illustrated in Section 7.3.3. First, however, the structures of the two buses must be defined.

It is a common practice to have a single Input-Output bus to which all devices are connected. All of the peripheral devices will monitor the information which is passed along this bus but it is obviously essential that only one device at a time responds. As with all bussed systems only one transaction at a time is permissible. It is, therefore, necessary to include among the variety of signal lines ADDRESS SIGNALS. These are monitored by each device and enable it to determine whether it is being accessed by an I/O transaction.

As a rule, peripherals are relatively slow devices and it is, therefore, important to reconcile the high speed and relatively precise requirements of the computer with those of the peripheral. Thus the I/O bus provides CONTROL SIGNALS which pass from the peripheral to the computer and vice-versa. These may also be used, in the case of a separate I/O bus, to control the program execution conditional on some facet of the peripheral status (e.g. the skip line in Section 7.2.1). DATA SIGNALS are provided to permit the passage of data between the computer and the peripheral.

Finally, most devices are capable of more than one elementary operation and so it is necessary to signal which particular operation is required. This is achieved via function signals when a separate I/O bus architecture is in use. For integrated I/O bus architectures, the result is achieved by writing the appropriate pattern to the peripheral's command register.

7.2.1 A SEPARATE I/O BUS STRUCTURE

Illustrated below is the structure of a typical separate I/O bus. This example is modelled on the PDP-8/e but is considerably simplified to aid the discussion. As indicated above, a separate I/O bus implies a complete range of I/O instructions, one for each function or test possible on each peripheral. In this example, the instruction consists of 12 bits: three for the operation code and nine for other purposes. In the case of the I/O instructions, the operation code is always 6. The middle six bits express the peripheral address, thus permitting $2^6=64$ different peripherals. The final three bits enable any one of eight possible functions to be specified.

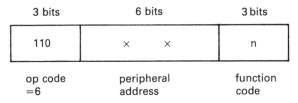

3 bits	6 bits	3 bits
110	× ×	n
op code =6	peripheral address	function code

Figure 7.3: I/O Instruction Format

The complete I/O bus structure may be thought of as being made up of four sub-buses.

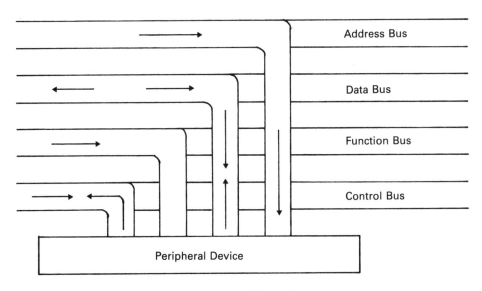

Figure 7.4: A Separate I/O Bus Structure

Address Bus:

This is effectively six lines carrying the signals generated by the six address bits, xx, in the I/O instruction. They are monitored by the address decoders in each peripheral. Only one peripheral is able to respond to any particular address.

Function Bus:

This is effectively three lines carrying the signal generated by the three function bits in the I/O instruction. All peripherals have function decoders which monitor these lines and initiate the appropriate actions provided the device itself has been addressed.

Data Bus:

A bi-directional bus of twelve lines which carries 12 bit data words to and from the accumulator.

Control Bus:

This consists of a number of lines carrying information to and from the computer. Amongst these are

   C0: This is effectively an "accumulator clear" control. If C0 is logic 0 during a data transfer, the accumulator is cleared before data is written into it.

   C1: Is used to determine the direction of data transfer. It is 1 for transfer out of the computer and 0 for transfer into the computer.

   Skip: Is used to provide the facility of testing the peripheral status. If skip = 0, the next instruction in the program is omitted.

   I/O Pause: Is used to indicate (by going to logic 0) that an I/O transfer is taking place. It represents the result of decoding the op-code '6' and is necessary because the I/O bus may contain "garbage" at other times and could accidentally cause a data transfer when none is intended.

Apart from "I/O pause", all of the above control signals are generated by the interface and would, in practice, have a resistor connecting each to logic 1 so that they are only asserted when driven to logic 0 (wired-or).

One of the functions of an interface is to make sure data is available at exactly the correct time during the "execute" cycle of the computer. For instance, the "skip" line is interrogated by the computer for a short time (0.1 usec) towards the end of the execute cycle. To help the interface synchronise with these requirements, special timing signals are sent along the I/O bus. In our simple example, we will not need to worry about these.

7.2.2 AN INTEGRATED I/O BUS STRUCTURE

An integrated I/O bus may be thought of as consisting of several sub-buses as illustrated above. However, the function bus will be missing. For the purposes of the example, a memory-mapped structure will be assumed and the basis of the bus structure is the MC6800 system. As described here, the structure is somewhat simplified (see Chapter 9 for more complete details). An integrated I/O bus structure using the alternative I/O-mapped technique would, usually, have less address lines used and all actions would be made dependent on an additional control line (IO/$\overline{\text{M}}$) being at logic 1 (see Appendix A for details of the Intel 8085 which uses such a system).

The signals present in the integrated bus structures are:-

Address Bus:

Sixteen address lines which are set up by the processor to indicate which memory address is being accessed. Peripheral registers are assigned addresses just as if they were ordinary memory locations.

Data Bus:

Eight bi-directional lines. Data will be put on these lines by the processor during a "write" instruction. During a "read" instruction, the processor will assume that a peripheral is placing data on these lines and will duly latch this data into one of its internal registers.

Control Bus:

This consists of a number of lines which give peripherals information about what the processor is doing and likewise enables the memory/peripherals to influence the actions of the processor. Among these signals are:

R/$\overline{\text{W}}$: This is logic '1' during a read operation and logic '0' during a write operation.

VMA: This signal is logic '1' when the address lines contain a valid memory address. At other times, when the address lines have other miscellaneous data on them, it has logic '0'.

7.3 Interface Design for a Paper-Tape Reader

A paper-tape reader contains a lamp which illuminates photocells via holes in the paper tape. There are nine photocells altogether corresponding to the eight channels of information on a typical paper tape. The ninth channel is used to read the sprocket holes. The output of the photocells

is amplified so that, at the output of the reader a logic 1
signal is available when a photocell is illuminated through a
hole in the tape, while a logic 0 is present when the
photocell is obscured by the paper (i.e. no hole). There is a
single input to the tape reader, when a logic 1 is present at
this input the motor clutch is engaged and the paper tape is
driven through the reading head. A logic output signals if
there is no tape loaded in the reader.

The objective of the exercise is to control the reader in
such a way that the paper tape is moved forward by ONE
character and the data carried by the newly positioned
character (an 8 bit word corresponding to the eight possible
positions for data holes on the tape) read into the computer.

If a typical paper tape reader is observed in operation, the
tape seems to move continuously through the reading head.
This is because the computer can absorb data at a very high
speed and the tape only has to pause for a few microseconds.
When 8 bit characters are read into a computer with a word
length greater than 8 bits, it is usual to read the character
into the least significant 8 bits of the accumulator.

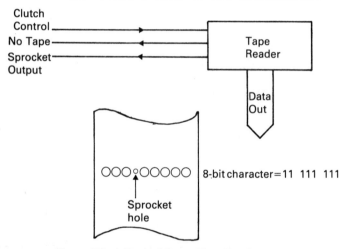

Figure 7.5: A Typical Paper-Tape Reader

7.3.1 PAPER TAPE READER INTERFACE FOR A SEPARATE I/O BUS STRUCTURE

The example tape reader will have peripheral address 111 000
(70 octal). In practice, four I/O instructions are required
in order to drive the reader. These will be labelled F0, F1,
F2, F3.

F0: Fetch a new character

F1: Test the flag to see if it has been SET (indicating a new
character is ready). Skip the next sequential instruction if
the flag IS set.

F2: Read the new character into the accumulator and clear the flag to indicate that this has been done.

F3: Test the reader to see if there is tape in it. Skip the next sequential instruction if there IS TAPE in the reader.

The necessary interface structure to implement these instructions is shown below.

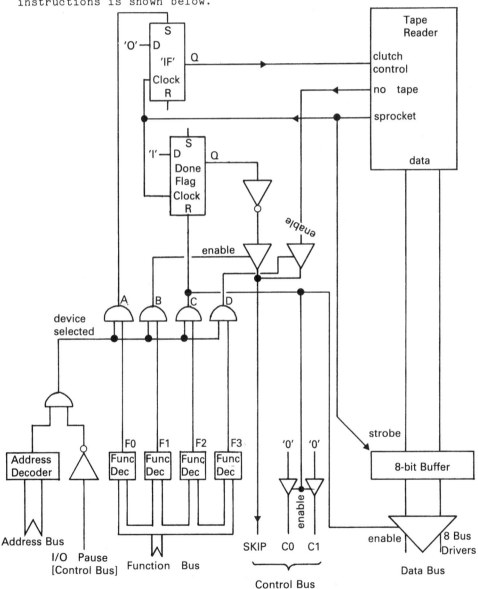

Figure 7.6: Pape-reader Interface for a Separate I/O Bus

135

The operation of each of the functions is as follows:

F0: The paper tape reader address 70 is decoded by the address decoder and the I/O pause goes to logic 0 to indicate a valid I/O instruction. This is inverted to logic 1 and applied with the address decoder output to an 'AND' gate. The output from this gate is a logic 1 indicating that the paper tape reader has been selected. Function decoder F0 has a 1 on its output but all the other function decoders have 0 on their output. Thus only 'AND' gate A has a 1 on its output and this sets the internal flag, 'IF'. Thus the clutch is energised and the paper tape moves forward. After a short while the sprocket hole of the next character is over the photocells and so the character is ready to be placed in the buffer. As the sprocket output goes from 0 (no hole) to 1 (hole), it resets the "internal flag" and strobes the data into the 8 bit buffer. Also the "DONE" flag is set.

F1: The device select signal is generated as described above. However, in this case the function decoder F1 has a logic 1 at its output. These two signals combine to produce a logic 1 at the output of the 'AND' gate B which enables the flag onto the skip line. This is applied to the SKIP control line via the inverter shown. If the flag was set, the skip line goes to logic 0 and the next instruction in the program is skipped. If the flag is not set (data not ready) then the next instruction is obeyed,

F2: The device select signal is generated as for F0 but in this case F2 function decoder has a logic 1 at its output thus placing a logic 1 at the output of "AND" gate C. This causes several actions.

   (i)   C0 is forced to logic 0, thus clearing the accumulator.

   (ii)   C1 is forced to logic 0 indicating an input of data to the accumulator.

   (iii)   The eight data bus drivers are enabled thus putting the data onto the data bus.

   (iv)   The 'DONE' flag is reset.

F3: The device select signal is generated as for F0 but in this case the F3 function decoder has a logic 1 at its output, thus placing a logic 1 at the output of "AND" gate D. This enables the "NO TAPE" signal onto the skip line thus causing the next sequential instruction to be skipped if the "NO TAPE" signal is logic 0. If the 'NO TAPE' signal is logic 1 (indicating that there is no paper tape in the reader) the next instruction will be executed.

7.3.2 THE DEVICE HANDLER FOR THE SEPARATE I/O BUS INTERFACE

In order to read a single character into the accumulator the actions specified in the following flowchart must be completed.

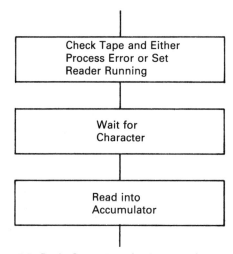

Figure 7.7: Basic Operations for Reading One Character

The first and last actions are quite straightforward but the middle one requires a little explanation.

The program cannot simply wait for a specified length of time because, peripherals being electro-mechanical devices, their speed of response can vary with circumstances. However, the availability of data is signalled by the flag going from logic 0 to logic 1. Thus, if the program tests the flag repeatedly it will be notified immediately the flag is set.

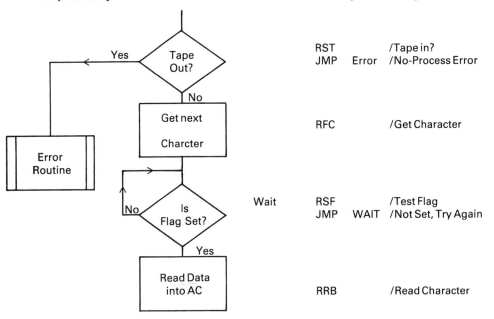

Figure 7.8: Device Driver for Paper Tape Reader on Separate I/O Bus

This is most conveniently carried out by a looped program with the skip function (F1) causing an exit from the loop as soon as the flag is set. For the purposes of the example, the following mnemonics may be defined and related to the interface functions.

Mnemonic	Function	Octal Code	Comment
RFC	F0	6700	Reader. Fetch Character.
RSF	F1	6701	Reader. Skip on Flag.
RRB	F2	6702	Reader. Read Buffer.
RST	F3	6703	Reader. Skip if tape NOT OUT.

7.3.3 PAPER TAPE READER INTERFACE FOR A MEMORY-MAPPED I/O BUS STRUCTURE

The tape reader will require three registers associated with it. A data register to hold the character just read off the tape; a status register which may be interrogated to determine whether the character is ready, or the paper tape has run out; and a command register to which the appropriate bit pattern may be written in order to start the reader. The addresses and (arbitrary) layout of these registers is shown below.

Writing the pattern 0000 0001 to the command register will cause the reader to start.

When the status register is read a '1' in the most significant place indicates that the character is ready for input. This condition is most easily detected by testing the contents of the status register for MINUS (MSB set equals a negative number). A '1' in the least significant place indicates NO TAPE.

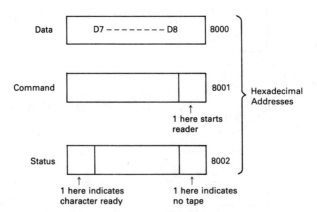

Figure 7:9: Layout of Registers in a Paper Tape Reader Interface for an Integrated I/O Bus

Reading the data register brings the character into the accumulator.

The circuit of the interface is shown below (Figure 7.10).

The address decoding is achieved by the 'AND' gates D, E, F and G. It will be noted that the address 8000 corresponds to the most significant address line, A15, being 1 with all others 0. Address 8001 corresponds to A15 and A0 being 1 while 8002 corresponds to A15 and A1 being 1.

'AND' gate D decodes the condition A15 = 1

$$A14 \longrightarrow A2 = 0$$

and in addition includes the valid memory address signal VMA. Thus gate D has an output of '1' only if a valid memory reference to an address in the range 8000 to 8003 is on the address bus. Gates E, F and G further refine this to produce the three select signals AS0, AS1 and AS2 corresponding to 8000, 8001 and 8002 respectively.

The operation of the circuit as a whole may now be described. To start the reader, a logic 1 must be written to the command register at location 8001. Thus the output of gate F (AS1) will become logic 1 and R/$\overline{W}$ will go to logic 0 (write). Thus 'AND' gate A will be enabled and the contents of the data bus line D0 (least significant bit) will be passed to the 'set' input of the internal flag. Line D0 will of course be at logic 1 since this is the data being written out. The internal flag will therefore set and the tape will advance until the next sprocket hole is sensed. This will cause a $0 \longrightarrow 1$ transition on the 'sprocket' line, thus resetting the internal flag, stopping the reader, setting the DONE flag and strobing the data from the reader into the data register.

To detect the status of the interface a read of the status register, at location 8002, will be carried out. While this is in progress the output of gate G (AS2) will go to logic 1 as will the R/$\overline{W}$ line (Read). Consequently the output of gate C will go to logic 1 enabling the two tri-state drivers. One of these drivers places the contents of the 'DONE' flag on data line D7 while the other places the output of the 'NO TAPE' sensor on data line D0. Thus the status of the reader is made available to the data bus and hence read into the CPU.

Finally the character itself may be read by reading the data register at location 8000. In this instance the output of gate E goes to logic 1 (AS0) as does the R/$\overline{W}$ (Read) hence the output of gate B goes to logic 1. This enables the eight tri-state drivers at the output of the data register thus placing the character onto the data bus, enabling it to be read into the CPU. Additionally the 'DONE' flag is cleared to indicate that the data has been read.

It will be noted that, although the interface nominally has three registers, only one exists as such. The remainder are simply a collection of flags and other signals that happen to be connected to particular lines in the data bus.

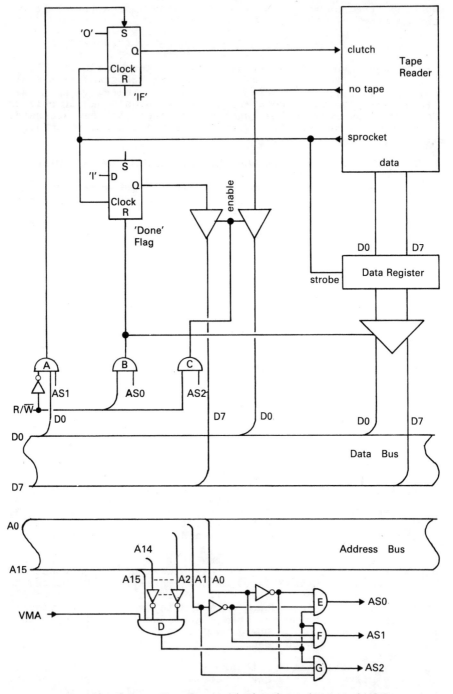

Figure 7.10: Paper Tape Reader Interface for an Integrated I/O Bus

In the example the process of writing to the status register has no meaning, the status register being a source of data. Likewise reading from the command register is meaningless. Both these facts are reflected in the way R/$\overline{W}$ is used to enable gates C and A respectively. There is, therefore, no reason why both should not occupy the same address, 8001. This simply means that gate G is removed and AS1 is used to enable gate C as well as gate A. Thus writing to 8001 would cause the command register to be written to while reading from 8001 would cause the status register to be accessed. This is a common technique with integrated I/O bus interfaces.

7.3.4 THE DEVICE HANDLER FOR THE INTEGRATED I/O BUS INTERFACE

The basic tasks required of the program are the same as those described in Section 7.3.2 but clearly the means of achieving them will be somewhat different. The flowchart shown below illustrates the process. The phrases in quotation marks would be replaced by the appropriate mnemonics in a particular system and it is left as an exercise for the reader to do this after studying Chapter 9 (or Appendix A as appropriate).

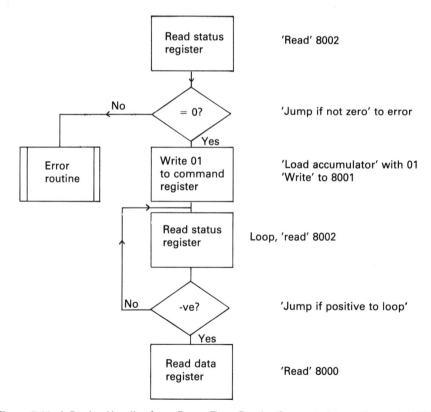

Figure 7.11: A Device Handler for a Paper Tape Reader Connected to an Integrated I/O Bus

7.4 Analysis of Wasted Time

High-speed paper tape readers can read about 200 characters per second (this corresponds to 100 feet/minute tape speed). Thus it takes about 5ms for the character to be fetched. The computer, therefore, spends 5ms in the 'wait loop' of the program above. This is very wasteful since, in this time, over 1000 average instructions could be obeyed. This waste of time is usually unacceptable and a more efficient method of data transfer must be devised.

The method of data transfer described so far is called PROGRAMMED DATA TRANSFER since the computer program is dedicated to the I/O function throughout the operation.

7.5 Interfacing Using LSI Devices

The interface designs presented in this and the next Chapter have been achieved by assembling relatively simple modules (decoders, tri-state drivers, etc.). Designs for other types of interface may be developed along broadly similar lines and will have generally similar circuit diagrams, differing only in respect of such details as the number of status flags, the operations implemented and, of course, the direction of data transfer. Nevertheless, the costs of designing such special-purpose interfaces is quite high because each has to be considered individually. This leads to high circuit design costs, high costs for small production runs of circuit boards and high assembly costs because of the large number of small, general-purpose, integrated circuits used in the design.

With the currently available techniques for large scale integration (LSI) of circuits, it is perfectly practicable to assemble all of the required hardware for an interface on a single integrated circuit. This is not, of course, economically viable unless the circuit can be sold in sufficiently large quantities to recover the high initial design costs. This situation prevents special-purpose interfaces being produced in this way. However, the similarities between specially designed interfaces are so great that it is possible to design circuits which will cope with most commonly-occurring situations. This is achieved by providing more hardware in the circuit than would be necessary for a simple special-purpose interface and then allowing the end user to select the required items from this 'tool kit'. The additional cost of the redundant hardware is measured in pence and is insignificant when compared with the design costs of a special-purpose interface.

Of course, the selection and interconnection of the required components within this 'super interface' cannot be carried out in a conventional way with a soldering iron and wire since the components are all integrated into a tiny sliver of

silicon. Instead the connections are made electronically by
writing particular patterns of 1s and 0s into special
configuration registers within the device. This is carried
out under software control each time the system is switched
on.

These INTERFACE ADAPTORS are available for a wide range of
applications such as serial and parallel data transfer,
control of disk systems, control of cathode-ray-tube (CRT)
displays, etc. They are designed to operate with the kind of
integrated bus structure common in microprocessor systems and
each microprocessor manufacturer usually provides a number of
these interface adaptors to suit the bus structure of his own
product.

A representative selection of these cost-saving interface
adaptors will be described later in Chapter 14 and also in
Appendix B.

8. Input-Output Operations – II

The situation outlined in Section 7.4 may be likened to a senior businessman trying to contact a customer by telephone. The customer is out, but the businessman keeps the telephone ringing so as to contact his customer at the earliest possible opportunity. As a result much of his very valuable time is wasted.

A much more sensible approach would have been to ask the telephone operator to dial the call and to put it through to the businessman when his customer is available. In this way our businessman could have made use of the wasted time.

The same approach can be used for organising peripherals. The peripheral is asked to perform a particular function and, when it is complete, to interrupt the operation of the computer. In order to make this possible, some additional hardware is required, and the appropriate software must be written to respond to the interrupt.

8.1 A Simple Interrupt System

Consider a computer with a single control line in the I/O bus which is used to permit interrupt operation of peripherals.

The interrupt system as a whole can be turned on or turned off using special instructions. Assuming that the interrupt system is on, the machine obeys the main program until a peripheral asserts the interrupt line by pulling it down to logic 0. Once this has happened, the following is a typical sequence of events which might occur:-

(i)   The current instruction is completed in the normal way.

(ii)   Once the instruction is finished, the interrupt system is turned off.

(iii) The current value of the sequence control register is stored in a reserved location.

(iv)   The SCR is set to a particular address (perhaps 0000) and the instructions found in this and the following locations obeyed.

It will be seen that an interrupt effectively causes a jump to a routine which commences at 0000. The actions which must be taken by this routine will be discussed a little later.

Notice also that the interrupt system is turned off once an interrupt has occurred. This is very necessary since any further interrupts would force a second jump to location 0 and would overwrite the previous value of the SCR stored in the reserved location. This would make it impossible to return from the first interrupt. This simple interrupt routine is, therefore, not RE-ENTRANT.

8.1.1 AN INTERRUPT INTERFACE FOR A SEPARATE I/O BUS

In order to connect the paper tape reader discussed in Section 7.3 to the separate I/O bus structure described in that section, certain modifications must be made. First, it must be assumed that an interrupt line (asserted at logic 0) is added to the bus. Secondly, the tape reader must be connected to this additional line in such a way that it is possible, under software control, to enable or disable interrupts from the tape reader (as distinct from enabling or disabling the interrupt system as a whole). Figure 8.1 shows how the interface structure of Figure 7.6 may be modified to accommodate these new requirements.

Two new operations, designated F4 to enable reader interrupts and F5 to disable them, are required. The design shown permits the tape reader to interrupt every time it has a new character ready.

As will be seen from the diagram, very little additional hardware is needed. When the flag sets, due to a new character being read, a logic 0 is applied to the interrupt bus via an open-collector NAND gate (see Appendix C-2). If the gate is enabled (by the interrupt control flag being already set) then the interrupt line is pulled down to logic 0 and an interrupt occurs. No other circuitry has been changed so the

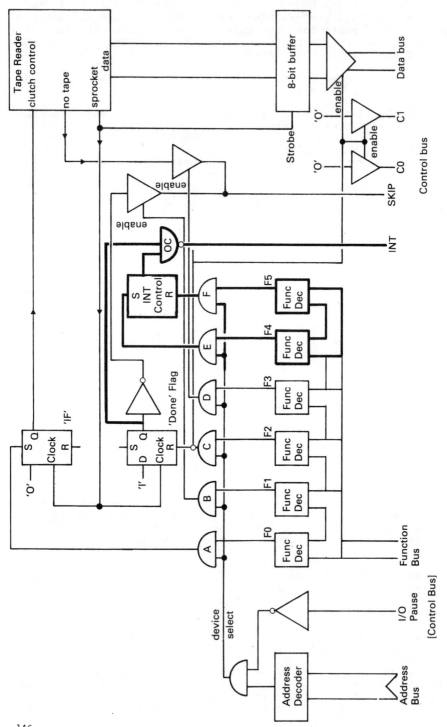

Figure 8.1: Modifications to Figure 7.6 to Permit Interrupt Operation

146

status of every peripheral flag, including that of the tape reader, can be examined using instructions which assert the skip line, as outlined in 7.3.1.

The operation of the two new instructions which control the interrupt mechanism is as follows:

F4: The device select signal is generated by the address decoder and I/O pause signals. The function decoder sees the code '4' on the function bus and puts a logic 1 on its output. Thus AND gate E has a 1 on its output and this is applied to the "set" input of the interrupt control flag. Thus its output is set to logic 1 until another I/O instruction resets it. In this way interrupts are enabled.

F5: This operates identically to F4 except that the code '5' must exist on the function bus. Thus AND gate F has a logic 1 on its output and this resets the interrupt control flag, thus disabling interrupts.

8.1.2 THE INTERRUPT HANDLING ROUTINE

The servicing of an interrupt requires three distinct tasks to be completed.

(i)   The "status" of the machine must be saved.

(ii)   The operations required by the peripheral must be carried out.

(iii)   The "status" of the machine must be restored.

Since an interrupt may occur at any time, it is impossible to make any generalisations about what use is being made of specific registers and condition-code flags within the processor. Thus any registers etc. which can be altered during the servicing of an interrupt must be stored away until the job is complete. Following the servicing of the peripheral, these registers etc. must be restored.

Included in the status of the machine is the contents of the program counter. However, in the structure described above, this is automatically saved in a hardware-determined memory location.

A simple approach to status saving would be to allocate a specific memory location for the storage of each register. An alternative in a processor which supports a stack is to place all of the items on this stack (see 8.6).

The operations required to service the peripheral are, in the case of the tape reader, quite simple. It is merely necessary to read the character, store it and then to set the reader running again.

147

Following this the registers of the machine must be reloaded with their original contents, the interrupt system turned back on and the interrupted program restarted at the address specified (in the hardware determined location in the example above).

A typical interrupt routine to handle a tape reader will occupy about 24 usec. Of these only three instructions, occupying 5 usec, are actually controlling the tape reader. The remaining time of 19 usec is the overhead imposed by having to use interrupts. So far as tape reader operations are concerned, this is quite efficient since by "investing" 19 usec, (5,000 - 19) usec of time that would otherwise have been wasted is recovered (since otherwise 5ms would be spent in a wait loop). On the other hand it would be questionable whether it would be worthwhile going to all this trouble for a very fast peripheral which could respond in, say, 40 usec as this would only gain 21 usec of usable time.

8.1.3 AN INTERRUPT INTERFACE FOR AN INTEGRATED BUS STRUCTURE

In Figure 7.10, the hardware for a programmed I/O interface between a paper tape reader and an integrated (and memory-mapped) system bus was shown.

The modification of this system to operate with interrupts is straightforward. One bit of the command register must be allocated to enable/disable interrupts. With this modification the command register looks like:

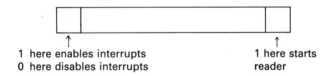

1 here enables interrupts
0 here disables interrupts

1 here starts
reader

The bus will also require an interrupt line; this may be assumed to be asserted at logic 0.

With this type of interface it is common to permit the status of the interrupt enable flag to be read back as one bit of the status register. This feature is not strictly necessary but will be included in this example. The layout of the status register will then be:

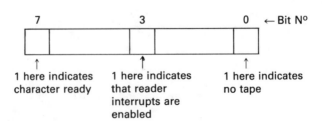

7   3   0   ← Bit Nº

1 here indicates
character ready

1 here indicates
that reader
interrupts are
enabled

1 here indicates
no tape

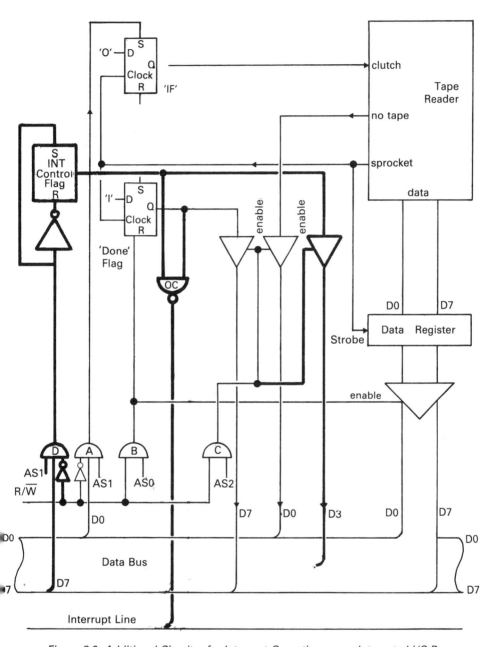

Figure 8.2: Additional Circuitry for Interrupt Operation on an Integrated I/O Bus

Figure 8.2 shows the modifications required to convert the interface shown in Figure 7.10 to interrupt operation. The new gate, gate D, is enabled under the same circumstances as gate A, i.e. a write to the command register. When this occurs, bit 7 of the data bus is connected to the interrupt control flag and either sets it or resets it, depending on the logic level of bit 7.

When the interrupt control flag is set, its output enables the open-collector NAND gate (see Appendix C-2) which then places the output of the "done" flag on the interrupt line. As soon as the "done" flag sets an interrupt will occur.

The status of the interrupt control flag is admitted to line D3 of the data bus when the status register is read.

8.2 Interrupt Handlers for Multi-Device Systems

The interrupt handling routine outlined in 8.1.2 above will only work with one device since after the initial housekeeping the program reads in data, assuming that the tape reader has caused the interrupt. If there is more than one device connected to the interrupt line this assumption cannot be made and steps must be taken to identify the source of interrupt and then to select the appropriate device-handling subroutine.

The interrupting device is identified by examining the flags of all devices connected to the interrupt bus. Any device with a flag set is assumed to have caused the interrupt. This process of interrogation is called "POLLING" and it is done using the various device "skip on flag" instructions in a separate I/O bus structure (or their equivalents in an integrated I/O bus structure). This is illustrated below for the case of a system with four devices attached, a keyboard, a printer, a tape reader and a tape punch.

The mnemonics used in the example program for the device "skip on flag" instructions are:-

keyboard:-	KSF	(keyboard, skip on flag set)
printer:-	TSF	(typewriter, skip on flag set)
reader:-	RSF	(reader, skip on flag set)
punch:-	PSF	(punch, skip on flag set)

8.2.1 THE POLLING ROUTINE

The polling routine is entered immediately after the initial housekeeping routine. In the example each flag is tested in turn. When a flag which is set is found, control is passed immediately to the device handling routine which can be located anywhere in memory.

Once this routine has been completed, control can be passed back to the next instruction in the polling routine, or it can be passed directly to the status restoring routine and the remainder of the polling routine bypassed.

The latter method is used in the example since this saves time. It is quite unlikely that other devices will have set their flags at about the same time as the device which has received service. Thus checking the rest of the skip chain is probably a waste of time. If, by some coincidence, another flag has been set it will cause an interrupt as soon as the interrupt system is turned back on and thus cause a second entry to the polling routine. Thus no device is overlooked.

The polling routine flowchart is shown below.

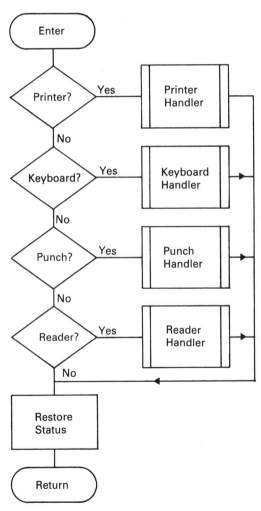

Figure 8.3: Polling to Determine the Source of an Interrupt

The polling routine consists of a large number of "test-then-jump" type instructions. These are often included in the processor's instruction set as "skip if" instructions and so the polling routine is often referred to as a SKIP CHAIN (Figure 8.4).

```
⎧ SKIP    if printer flag set    ⎫
⎨ SKIP                           ⎬
⎩ JUMP    to printer handler     ⎭
⎧ SKIP    if keyboard flag set   ⎫
⎨ SKIP                           ⎬
⎩ JUMP    to keyboard handler    ⎭
⎧ SKIP    if punch flag set      ⎫
⎨ SKIP                           ⎬
⎩ JUMP    to punch handler       ⎭
⎧ SKIP    if reader flag set     ⎫
⎨ SKIP                           ⎬
⎩ JUMP    to reader handler      ⎭

⎧ Restore                        ⎫
⎨ Status                         ⎬
```

Figure 8.4: A Skip Chain

In Figure 8.4 the SKIP instruction causes the next sequential instruction to be omitted while the SKIP IF instruction does the same conditional upon some event. The brackets in Figure 8.4 indicate the group of instructions which must be inserted into the skip chain for each distinct device being tested.

Because the skip chain and device handlers clearly involve considerable overheads care must be taken to reduce these as much as possible. This can be achieved by ensuring that the average number of instructions executed in the skip chain is minimised.

Although the ACTUAL NUMBER of instructions is fixed by the number of devices, the number of INSTRUCTIONS EXECUTED ON AVERAGE may be reduced by putting those devices which cause the most frequent interrupts near to the top of the skip chain. In this way, it is only on rare occasions that the full length of the chain is traversed.

EXAMPLE:

In the above skip chain, assume that a "SKIP" and a "SKIP IF" instruction both execute in 2 usec, and that a jump instruction executes in 4 usec.

Thus for every device which is tested, but which has not caused an interrupt 4 usec (2 skips) are required. Finally, when the interrupting device is interrogated it takes 6 usec (skip + jump) to reach the service routine.

Assume that out of every ten interrupt requests:

    the printer causes   4
    the keyboard causes   3
    the punch causes   2
    the reader causes   1

Then the average time to reach the service routine if the skip chain is arranged as shown in Figure 8.3 and 8.4 is:

0.1[4(6us) + 3(4us+6us) + 2(2x4us+6us) + 1(3x4us+6us)] = 10us
   ↑   ↑   ↑   ↑
   Printer   keyboard   punch service   reader service
   service   service time   time   time
   time

If the skip chain had been arranged in precisely the wrong order, the calculation would have been:

0.1[1(6us) + 2(4us+6us) + 3(2x4us+6us) + 4(3x4us+6us)] = 14us
   ↑   ↑   ↑   ↑
   Reader   punch   keyboard   printer

Thus it may be seen that devices should be arranged in order of decreasing frequency of interrupt, starting with the most frequent interrupter at the head of the skip chain.

8.3 Randomly Occurring Events

In real-time systems it is the rule rather than the exception that events (such as fire alarms, switch closures, etc.) occur at unpredictable time intervals. Additionally some of these conditions will require very rapid response. One way of satisfying the demand is to look at the device flags of these devices at frequent intervals.

However, this is highly inefficient since if there were 100 possible events and they needed scanning every 0.1 sec the 100-device skip chain would have to be executed once every 0.1 sec.

Although this approach was adopted for a few early experiments in real-time control systems, it is not particularly satisfactory and a much better way of dealing with unpredictable events is to arrange for each possible event to cause an interrupt when it occurs.

8.4 Other Mechanisms for Reacting to Interrupts

The mechanism so far outlined is appropriate for very simple machines. To recap, the machine performs an elementary jump to a processor-specified location and all other housekeeping is left to the programmer. In particular, the return address was stored in a fixed location and this made the interrupt routine non-reentrant. Thus other interrupts, no matter how urgent, must be locked out while the current one is dealt with. It is open to the programmer to get around this by recovering the return address and storing it elsewhere, but this is time consuming.

Most modern microprocessors, however, support stack handling and make use of this facility in the operation both of subroutines and interrupts. This process was illustrated in Chapter 2 for the case of subroutines.

When a stack is used for interrupt linkage the contents of the program counter are pushed onto the stack before the program counter is loaded with the address of the interrupt handler. To return from the interrupt the old program counter contents are popped off the stack and into the program counter (just like a return from subroutine).

An example of a machine which treats interrupts and subroutines in just this way is the Intel 8085.

Some processors elaborate on this procedure because it is realised that, in most cases, the complete status of the machine will have to be saved. In these cases, an interrupt causes not just the program counter to be stacked, but all of the other registers and flags too, thus saving the programmer the effort of writing the necessary code and also speeding up execution. The Motorola 6800 is an example of a machine which uses this approach.

In these cases, returning from an interrupt routine (with all the machine status stacked) is different from returning from a subroutine (with only the program counter stacked). Thus two different instructions are needed (typically RTI - return from interrupt and RTS - return from subroutine).

8.5 Locating the Source of an Interrupt Rapidly

The simple computer system so far discussed has only one interrupt line and so, of necessity, all devices make use of this line and the programmer has to determine the source of interrupt by "polling". This can prove very time consuming.

One method of avoiding this problem is to use a computer with many independent interrupt lines (perhaps 16). Each line will have associated with it an address to which control is transferred when an interrupt is received. The memory address to which control is transferred may be fixed by the processor hardware (e.g. 8085) or may be determined by the programmer (e.g. MC6800 in which the programmer loads the desired address into a particular memory location specified by the designers). Thus if fewer devices are in use then the number of interrupt lines, it is possible to return to the simple situation of placing the appropriate device handler at each of the interrupt addresses. If there are more than this number of peripherals then it will be necessary to include a skip chain at each of the interrupt addresses. However, the speed of execution should be much greater since there will be fewer devices on each interrupt line than is the case for a single interrupt line and thus there will be fewer device flags to poll.

An alternative approach which is usable even when the number of devices far exceeds the number of available interrupt lines is to use the interrupt vectoring technique.

For the purposes of explanation assume that there are many peripheral devices connected to the I/O bus and that the contents of memory are as shown in the diagram below. There is only a single interrupt line.

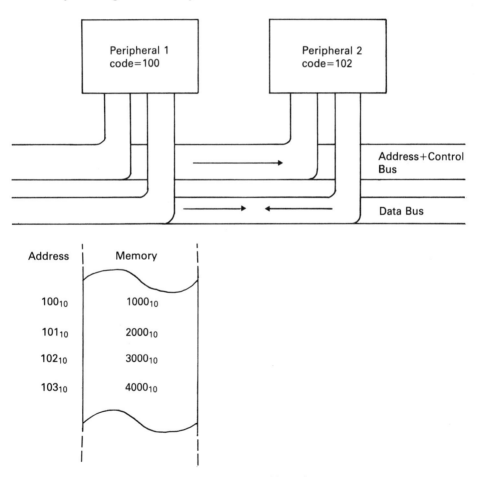

Figure 8.5: Interrupt Vectoring

If peripheral number 2, for instance, requires service it will assert the interrupt line; on completion of the current instruction the computer will jump to the interrupt handler subroutine. The machine status is then saved in the usual way (unless this has already been done automatically). Thus far the system has behaved in an identical way to the simplest of systems. However, from this point onwards, the handling of the interrupt is very different.

The computer issues a special I/O instruction which interrogates all of the peripherals in the system. However, only the peripheral which has asserted the interrupt line is able to respond (due to the hardware design of the peripheral interfaces). This it does by placing a unique identification code onto the data lines of the I/O bus. This code is, in fact, a pointer address which can be used in an indirect jump instruction to transfer control to the specific device handler for the peripheral in question. In the example, peripheral 2 would place the code 102 on the data lines. The computer then extracts the contents of location 102 in memory and uses them as the address to which control should be transferred. In practice, the interrogation of the peripherals is usually an automatic part of the interrupt handling hardware in the processor and requires no explicit programming steps.

A variation of the above procedure is that, instead of reading an identification code, the code put onto the bus by the peripheral is a simple instruction code. The computer reads this from the data bus into the instruction register and then obeys it. The instruction would normally be a "jump".

The identification or instruction code associated with each peripheral is determined by some very simple wiring within the interface and could be changed at any time although this is rarely necessary. The address of the service routine in the example of Figure 8.5 is determined solely by the programmer's software. In the above example, if the programmer had loaded 6000 into location 102, then the device handler would have been located at 6000. Where the code produced by the peripheral is a "jump" instruction the programmer does not have this freedom.

There is only one slight complication. If two devices happen to set their interrupt flags within one or two microseconds of each other, both would try to respond with their own device codes. The result would be a nonsense. Fortunately it is quite easy to construct some hardware in the interfaces which will protect against this occurrence, the so-called "daisy chain" approach. This method effectively assigns a priority to each peripheral and arranges that only the highest priority interrupting device can respond (Section 8.6).

8.6 Priority of Service Routines

The urgency of service requests can vary immensely. At one extreme, an interrupt indicating "power failure" has got to be serviced within a few microseconds before the supply voltage drops below predetermined level. If this job is not executed rapidly enough, the status of the machine may be lost and physical damage could be done to devices such as disc drives. At the other extreme, it probably does not matter if a line of text is delayed by a few seconds.

In a practical system, there are many jobs to be done and since there is usually only one processor available to execute them, some means of arbitrating between jobs is required. The task of running the correct job is left to the operating system, which chooses between the various jobs ready for execution on the basis of priority associated with the job. (0 = high priority, larger numbers = lower priority.) The operation of a skip chain is rather more complex when the various jobs associated with different peripherals have different priorities. First, the interrupt system can no longer remain OFF while an interrupt is serviced because this could permit a low priority job to "lock out" a high priority job. This requirement means that the interrupt return address must be saved so that it cannot be overwritten (for example, on a stack).

Once the status of the machine has been saved, the source of the interrupt must be identified. This can be simply achieved using the methods previously described. As soon as the source of the interrupt is known, its priority is compared with that of the interrupted program. If the priority of the new interrupt is higher then the status of the previous job is "packed up" and stored temporarily until it can resume, the new job is started and the interrupt system is turned back on. However, if the reverse were true, the new source of interrupt would have been noted down in some internal data table, its hardware flag cleared (so that further interrupts will not be generated) the old job restarted and the interrupt system turned on again.

The list of jobs waiting to be started, or partially completed, is called the job queue. It is one of the main functions of an operating system to maintain such a queue. The basic logic of the priority decision process outlined above is shown in the flowchart below.

It can be seen from the above description and flowchart that, although the assignment of priorities is necessary, it adds considerably to the system overheads. It is, therefore, important to avoid unnecessary entries into the interrupt handler. Such entries may be defined as those which do not result in a change in the program running in the system. Thus interrupts originating from devices with lower priority than the current job should be inhibited. This is most easily done with external hardware and two possibilities will be outlined briefly.

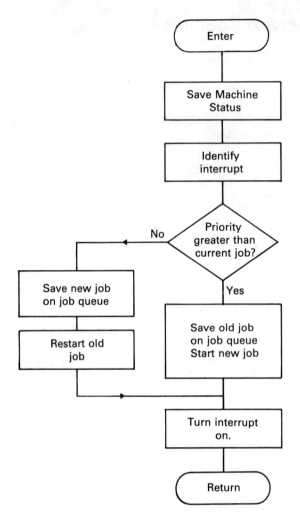

Figure 8.6: Flowchart for Determining Whether an Interrupting Task should be Allowed to Run.

If the machine has several interrupt lines, it is logical to associate a different priority with each one and to attach each device to the interrupt line of appropriate priority. Different levels of interrupt can then be disabled selectively by using a "lockout" register. This register is loaded under program control to inhibit all interrupts of the same, or lower, priority than that of the currently executing program (Figure 8.7).

An alternative method is to "Daisy Chain" the peripherals along a special "interrupt test" line. This method is illustrated below and is similar to that used by the Data General Nova minicomputers.

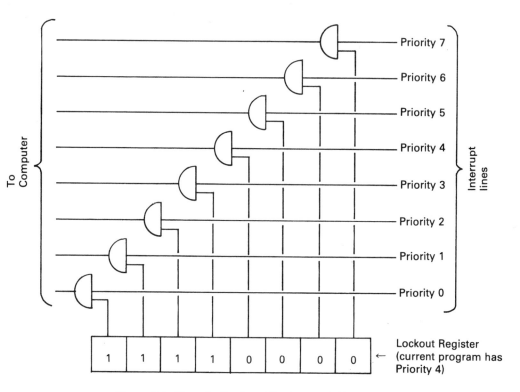

Figure 8.7: Use of a 'Lockout' Register to Inhibit Interrrupts

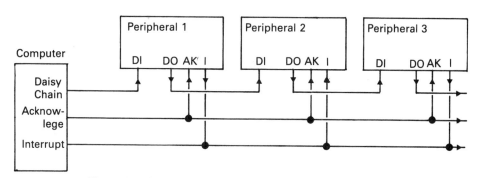

Figure 8.8: Connection of Peripherals to an Interrupt 'Daisy-Chain'

The computer issues two signals, a "daisy chain" signal and an "acknowledge" signal (for synchronisation). If both signals are received by a peripheral, and its interrupt flag is set, then its identification code is passed to the computer for servicing. However, not all of the peripherals will receive the daisy chain signal. If peripheral 2 is awaiting service then it will NOT pass on the signal to peripheral 3. Similarly, peripheral 1 will not pass on this

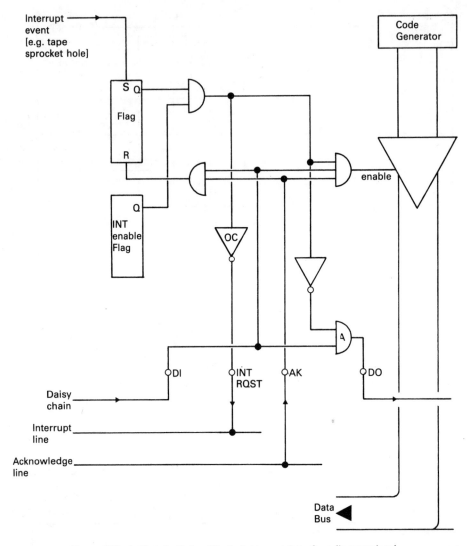

Figure 8.9: A Simple Daisy Chain Interrupt Interface (incomplete)

signal if it requires service. Thus the peripheral nearest to the computer has the highest priority, no other peripherals being able to request service until the latter's flag is cleared. In this system, this would be done at the end of the appropriate service routine.

The hardware which must reside in the peripheral to operate the daisy chain system is shown in Figure 8.9.

The operation is as follows. The device or devices force an interrupt by asserting the interrupt request line (provided

160

their flag(s) are set and they are interrupt enabled). The computer responds by sending a signal down the daisy chain (usually called a grant signal). Any non-interrupting interfaces simply pass the grant signal on. However, the first interrupting device inhibits the further propagation of grant since it will stop any signals passing through gate A.

Once a sufficient time has elapsed to allow the grant signal to propagate, the computer asserts the interrupt acknowledge line which has the effect of placing the device code on the data bus and clearing the device flag. Acknowledge is received by all interfaces but only the one which is interrupting AND which has received the grant signal can respond. After this procedure the computer uses the code to determine the appropriate interrupt service routine.

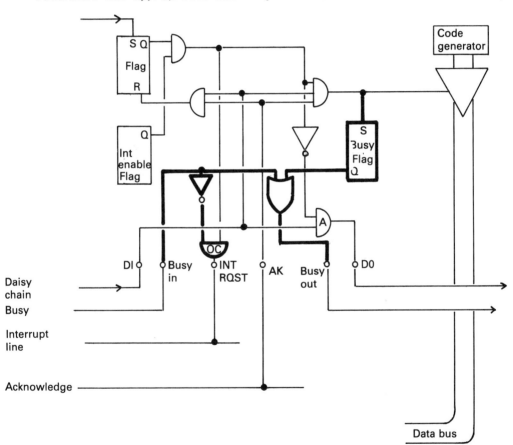

Figure 8.10: Modified Daisy-Chain Interface to Permit Use of a 'Busy' Signal (Incomplete)

If interrupts are now re-enabled, a second interrupting device could force a second entry to the interrupt arbitration system, and since the interrupt request flag of the first device has been cleared the second, lower priority, device will gain control. This may be avoided by leaving the interrupt system off but then high-priority devices would be locked out.

An alternative solution to this is to pass a "busy" signal down a second daisy chain. A high priority device will pass a busy signal down to a lower priority device either if it is itself being serviced or if it has received a busy signal from an even higher priority device. This implies an additional "busy" flag within each device, which is set when the interrupt is acknowledged and is reset by the interrupt handler once the service is complete.

The receipt of "busy" by a device implies that higher priority devices are being serviced by the processor and so the device receiving the "busy" must be inhibited from interrupting. Clearly the first device in the chain will receive a '0' on its busy input at all times. Figure 8.10 shows the modified interface (the interrupt enable flag controls and the busy flag reset have been omitted).

8.7 High-Speed Data Transfers – Direct Memory Access

So far, all data transfers which have been discussed have proceeded at a rate which is very much less than that at which the computer can obey instructions. However, cartridge type disks, for instance, can transmit data at over 100,000 bytes/sec and other types are even faster. It is clearly impossible, therefore, to read such data in under interrupt or program control - there simply is not sufficient time. This is especially critical since the magnetic medium has to move in order to transfer its information (you cannot read from a stationary disk) and if there is too much delay in reading a character, it will be lost.

High-speed data of this nature is usually transferred in blocks of about 128 bytes preceded by suitable block identification data. it is uneconomical to transfer single bytes or very small blocks because, in this situation, most of the storage medium would be occupied by the identification data.

The problem of transmitting high-speed data into the computer is solved by noting that the ultimate destination of such data is the computer memory. When the high-speed transfer is required, the data is not passed through the accumulator of the computer under software control but instead is sent directly to memory under the control of the peripheral controller. This peripheral controller is a piece of special purpose and fairly complex hardware which performs all the housekeeping functions normally undertaken by the software. This change of roles is possible because the task to be performed is well defined and unchanging.

The sequence of operations is roughly as follows:-

1) The computer decides that it requires more data from disk. It sends the following information to the disk controller in the ordinary programmed I/O mode:

   a) Address of block

   b) Number of bytes in block

   c) Address in memory to which first byte is to be loaded (subsequent bytes will be loaded into sequential locations).

2) The disk controller positions the reading heads of the disk and searches for the required data block (which could take as much as 200 milliseconds).

3) The first byte is extracted and checked for errors. Assuming it is acceptable, the computer is requested to halt on a special control line called "data break request" (DBR) or similar.

4) At the end of every memory cycle (not instruction) the DBR line is checked. If the disk is requesting service the computer issues an "ok" signal and HALTS.

5) On receiving the "ok" signal, the disk controller issues the first memory address to the memory and then places the first byte on the data bus and does a "write" in memory. As soon as this is complete the DBR line is released and the word count is updated as is the address counter.

6) The computer now continues its task, completely undisturbed except for a slight hesitation.

7) The disk controller checks the byte count against the required number of bytes in the transfer. If it is less than the requested number, the next byte is read from the disk and operations 3 to 7 are repeated.

8) If the byte count indicates that all the bytes in the block have been transferred, an interrupt is issued by the disk controller.

9) The computer receives and services the interrupt in the usual way, noting that transfer is now complete and generally doing any housekeeping that might be required.

Notice that, in the above description, none of the computer registers were used, the disk controller having (effectively) duplicate copies in its own hardware. Notice that the disk controller has access to the memory controls; during Direct Memory Access (DMA) the controller virtually takes over the computer. This direct memory access technique is termed "cycle stealing" and is shown diagramatically in Figure 8.11.

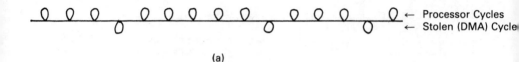

(a)

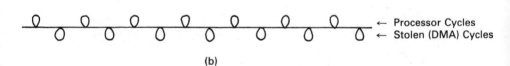

(b)

Figure 8.11: Cycle-Stealing DMA

a) shows a fairly normal case of cycle stealing while
b) shows the limiting condition for a very fast
   peripheral

The greatest time that a (cycle stealing) DMA controller will
have to wait for DBR to be recognised is one cycle of the
memory and the data will have to remain stable for a second
memory cycle while it is written to memory. Thus the time
between successive words being recovered from disk must be
greater than two memory cycles plus some housekeeping time.
This would typically be 300ns for fast semiconductor memory
or about 2 usec for slower core memory (corresponding to
transfer rates of 3M bytes/sec and 500K bytes/sec
respectively).

For very fast peripherals, this two-cycle delay may be too
long - in which case "burst mode" DMA must be used. In this
mode, the peripheral does not release the bus at the end of
step 5 above. Instead, it keeps the DBR line asserted until
the transfer is complete at step 8.

In this way, the transfer is completed at the maximum
possible rate and the processor goes into suspension while
this takes place. Burst-mode DMA is shown diagramatically in
Figure 8.12.

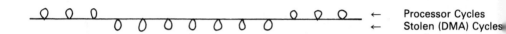

Figure 8.12: Burst-Mode DMA

In a system which uses DMA (for disk access or any other
purpose), the execution time of a program is unpredictable
and this must be taken account of when the system is
organised. In particular, timing must be accomplished with
hardware timers and not by software "delay loops".

A second source of high-speed data, and one of growing importance, is inter-processor communication. In principle it is possible to achieve this by using DMA techniques, having a separate communication channel between each and every processor in the system. This works well for systems with only a very small number of processors but it becomes increasingly expensive as the number of processors increases and it does not lend itself to ad hoc expansion.

A better solution is that adopted for internal communications within computers:- the Bus system. This is discussed in more detail in Chapter 12.

9 The Architecture and Instruction Set of the MC6800

The purpose of this Chapter is to show how the concepts which have been presented in earlier Chapters are, in practice, applied to a real device. This will be accomplished by studying in detail the Motorola 6800 microprocessor. Readers who would find a study of the Intel 8085/8080 processor more appropriate should substitute Appendix A for this Chapter.

The MC6800 was the first microprocessor produced by Motorola Semiconductors and it is contemporary with the Intel 8080. The architectural design of the MC6800, however, is very different from the 8080 and a comparative study of the two devices is quite interesting. These two devices between them have taken the majority of the market for mainstream 8-bit processors. The MC6800 is one of a family of processors which includes an enhanced 8-bit processor (the 6809) and a number of single-chip or two-chip processor sets. All of these processors are closely related to each other.

As with all significant microprocessors, the processor chip itself is one of a number of devices which make up the complete "family". These support devices along with the other processors related to the MC6800 will be discussed in Chapter 14 (or Appendix B in the case of devices related to the 8080/8085).

9.1 Programmer's Model of the MC6800

The architecture of a computer system is the way in which the fundamental functional units are arranged. Included under this heading must be the philosophy of the bus structure since this plays a very important role in determining the ease with which the various sub-units can communicate with each other and with the wider system.

The heart of the MC6800 microprocessor family is the MC6800 microprocessing unit which functions as the CPU. The microprocessing unit is supplied as a single package having forty connections through which all information and control signals are routed. Figure 9.1 is a simplified block diagram of the components which are incorporated within this package.

As may be seen from Figure 9.1, the microprocessing unit contains a central bus structure which is interfaced to the outside world either via the address output buffers or via the data buffer. Within the unit are contained the arithmetic-logic-unit, the control unit (called instruction decode and control in Figure 9.1) and ten registers. Each of these registers and the internal bus are 8 bits wide.

Two of these registers are designated as accumulators and may be used for general arithmetic and logical operations. One of the other registers functions as an instruction register and is loaded during the FETCH cycle of an instruction. There is a special "condition codes" register associated with the ALU, the function of which is to hold information about the results of operations on data held in the accumulators.

The remaining six registers are grouped in pairs, effectively forming a set of three 16-bit registers. One of these registers functions as program counter, one as stack pointer and one as an index register. Notice that, in each pair one register is labelled H for "high-order" and the other L for "low-order". In use the high-order register contains the most significant 8 bits of the 16-bit word while the low-order register contains the remainder.

Three items must be added to the MC6800 microprocessing unit before a central processor can be produced. A complete central processor based on the MC6800 is shown in Figure 9.2.

There are a number of important features which may be seen in Figure 9.2.

First, there is no distinction made between the connections made to a peripheral and those made to memory. In fact no distinction is made between memory locations and buffer registers in peripherals. Thus arithmetic may be performed directly on the contents of a register in a peripheral saving both time and storage space. The external bus illustrated in Figure 9.2 is an extension of the internal bus shown in Figure 9.1. The only differences between the two are that:

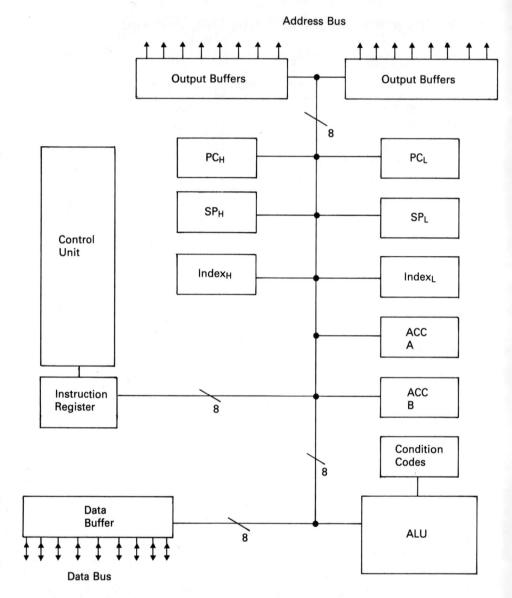

Figure 9.1: Block Diagram of MC6800 Microprocessing Unit

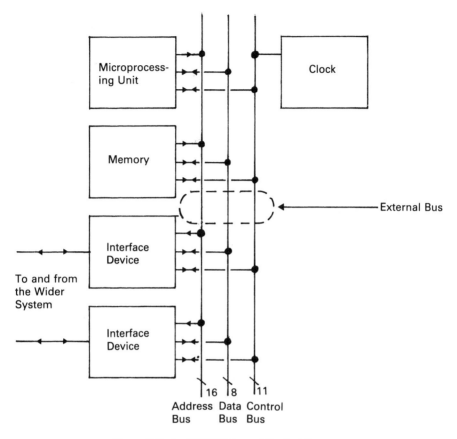

Figure 9.2: An MC6800-based Central Processor

(i)   control signals have been added to enable the external devices to be synchronised with the microprocessing unit.

(ii)   internally the 8-bit wide bus is used for both data and address information whereas externally the two functions are separated.

The second difference above has important consequences for the designer of microprocessor systems. Early microprocessors (not MC6800) had an external data/address bus which was an extension of the 8-bit internal bus and was used in turn for high- and low-order address information and for data. The designer had to ensure that the information on the bus was correctly routed, according to its nature, and this resulted in an increase in external circuit complexity. The reason for this procedure was to reduce the number of pins on the microprocessor package from 40 to 24 which was the maximum possible in the early '70s.

Some recent devices have returned to this practice in order to provide more advanced features without the necessity of using a 64-pin package.

Notice that an external clock has to be provided in order that the computation may step forward in an automatic and ordered fashion. The clock circuits are a source of control signals. The type of clock required by the MC6800 is termed a two-phase non-overlapping clock. The output signals of such a device are shown in Figure 9.3.

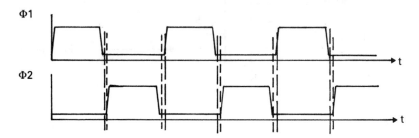

Figure 9.3 Clock Waveforms

During Phase 1 of the clock, the address of a new instruction is placed on the bus while during Phase 2 the instruction is loaded into the instruction register. If the instruction is one where no operand has to be extracted from memory then execution will take place during the next Phase 1 period and thus the minimum execution time is two clock cycles. More complex instructions may take several clock cycles and the longest instruction in the microprocessor's repertoire requires twelve clock cycles. The shortest clock cycle time is 1 usec, a limit imposed by the speed of the microprocessor's internal circuitry. The longest clock cycle time is 10 usec, a limit which is set by the need to regenerate at regular intervals the data within the internal registers of the microprocessor (dynamic storage cells are used).

9.1.1 PROGRAM COUNTER

So far as the user is concerned, the program counter appears as a single, 16-bit register. The contents of this register are automatically incremented during each instruction cycle so that it is always pointing to the next instruction to be executed. Note that a number of the MC6800 instructions are of two-word or three-word format so that during the execution of an instruction the program counter may be incremented two or three times.

The contents of the program counter may also be varied under program control by using instructions such as "jump to subroutine", "jump" and "branch".

It is possible for the MC6800 to support a maximum memory size of 2^16 locations, i.e. 64K of memory. This must, of course, include all peripherals etc. since these are addressed in the same way as memory.

9.1.2 STACK POINTER

The MC6800 has provision for a last-in-first-out stack. The stack consists of a number of consecutive locations in memory. The position and extent of the stack are determined by the programmer. There is no special area of memory designated for stack usage.

The stack in the MC6800 is organised so that it grows downwards in memory. When data is pushed onto the stack, it is written into the location in memory pointed to by the stack pointer. Following this the stack pointer is decremented.

The results of a push operation in MC6800 are illustrated in Figure 9.4.

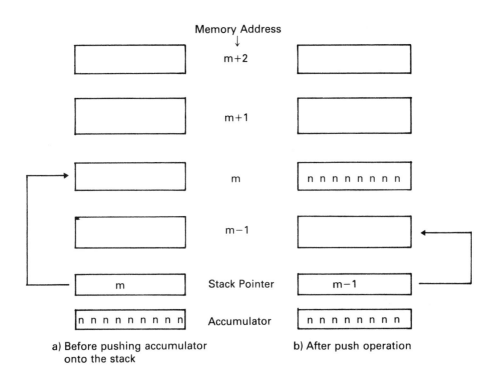

a) Before pushing accumulator onto the stack

b) After push operation

Figure 9.4: Operation of Stack in MC6800

171

The stack may be used under programmer control for a wide variety of purposes. In addition, it is used automatically during a jump to subroutine when the previous contents of the program counter are pushed onto the stack. Following an interrupt, the stack of the MC6800 will appear as shown in Figure 9.5, assuming that the stack pointer was pointing to location 'm' immediately prior to the occurrence of the interrupt.

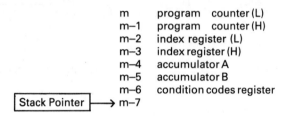

m	program counter (L)
m–1	program counter (H)
m–2	index register (L)
m–3	index register (H)
m–4	accumulator A
m–5	accumulator B
m–6	condition codes register
Stack Pointer ⟶ m–7	

Figure 9.5: Stack contents after an interrupt

This method of preserving machine status automatically saves a great deal of time since otherwise each individual item would have to be stored under program control.

9.1.3 INDEX REGISTER

The MC6800 makes use of a number of addressing modes which will be discussed fully in Section 9.2.

One of the most flexible of these addressing modes is indexed addressing. When this technique is used the offset specified in the instruction is added to the contents of the Index Register before being used to extract data. The contents of the Index Register can be varied under program control and thus indexed addressing provides a convenient means of accessing data in tables etc.

9.1.4 ACCUMULATORS

The MC6800 is equipped with two accumulators. Both accumulators may be used for the full range of arithmetic and logic operations performed by the processor. They may be used to hold intermediate results in a computation. This can result in a considerably reduced program length and improved execution time. The improved execution time results not only from the reduced number of instructions but because the operands do not have to be extracted from memory each time. This can be illustrated by using the example in Figure 9.6.

To perform the single accumulator program (a) using MC6800 would require the following resources:

Program storage	18 locations
Variable storage	3 locations
Execution time	27 usec

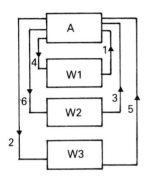

To interchange the position of
2 words in locations W1 and W2
in a processor with a single
register A, an intermediate
location W3 is needed.

(a)

To interchange the position of
2 words in locations W1 and W2
in a processor with 2 registers,
A and B, fewer processing steps
are needed.

(b)

Figure 9.6: Data Exchange Operation with (a) One Accumulator, and (b) Two Accumulators

using both accumulators (b):

```
    Program storage        12 locations
    Variable storage        2 locations
    Execution time         18 usec
```

In both cases, the execution time could be reduced by careful
selection of the positions in memory of the variables W1, W2
and W3 (so that "direct" rather than "extended" addressing
could be used (Section 9.2.1)).

9.1.5 CONDITION CODES REGISTER

All computers incorporate the facility to perform conditional
processing. That is they possess the ability to vary the
program steps which are executed depending upon the result of
some previous operation. For example, the processing may take
one route if the difference between two numbers is negative
and a different route if this difference is positive. In the
MC6800 microprocessing unit, this conditional processing
facility is associated with a special register called the
condition codes register. This is an 8-bit register of which
only 6 bits are used. Each of the 6 bits corresponds to a
particular condition (for example, accumulator = 0). When an
operation is carried out which affects the contents of an
accumulator then the condition codes register is set to
indicate the conditions relating to the result. The layout of
this register is shown in Figure 9.7.

| 1 | 1 | H | I | N | Z | V | C |

H = Half Carry   Z = Zero
I = Interrupt mask   V = Overflow
N = Negative   C = Carry

Figure 9.7: Condition Codes Register

By inspecting the appropriate bit of the condition codes register, the status of the result of an operation is readily detected. The individual bits of the condition codes register can be set and reset under program control and the whole contents of the register may be brought into accumulator A and vice versa. The significance of each of the condition codes bits is summarised below.

C: If an arithmetic operation results in a carry from the most significant bit of the accumulator, then this bit is set.

V: If an arithmetic operation causes a 2s complement overflow, this bit is set.

Z: This bit is set if the result of an arithmetic or logical operation is zero.

N: This bit is set if the result of an arithmetic or logical operation has a 1 in the most significant position (i.e. 2s complement negative).

I: When this bit is set to 1, it inhibits all interrupts except those designated as "Non-Maskable".

H: This is used for binary coded decimal arithmetic. Microprocessors find considerable application in accounting machines, cash registers etc. where the basic data is available in decimal format. Although it is not the most efficient method of processing, it is convenient in these situations to store data as BCD digits. Two such digits may be stored in an 8-bit word. When adding two such words, it is important to know when a carry has occurred from the least significant decade (stored in the right-hand 4 bits) into the most significant decade (left-hand 4 bits). The Half Carry gives this information.

Notice that I is not set as the result of an arithmetic or logical operation and that C, V and H are only affected by arithmetic operations as they have no meaning for logical operations.

9.2 Addressing Methods Used in the MC6800

The methods of addressing memory which are available to the programmer can greatly affect the efficiency with which programs are executed, both in terms of the amount of memory used and the speed of execution.

In this Section, those addressing methods which are available within the MC6800 will be summarised.

The following addressing methods are available in the MC6800:-

(i)   Absolute   (a) Direct
                        (b) Extended

(ii)   Immediate

(iii)   Implicit

(iv)   Indexed

(v)   Relative

9.2.1 ABSOLUTE ADDRESSING

Absolute addressing, as described in Chapter 5, is available in two forms in the MC6800. These are termed DIRECT and EXTENDED addressing.

Direct addressing occupies two bytes of storage. The first is used for the operation code and the second to store the address. Thus the address is only 8-bits long and these are assumed to be the least significant 8 bits of the full 16-bit address. The most significant 8 bits are set to zero and so this addressing method is restricted to the first 256 locations in memory.

Extended addressing by contrast occupies three bytes of storage and enables a full 16-bit address to be specified thus permitting access to all 64K memory locations. The first byte of the instruction specifies the operation code and the remaining two bytes, taken together, form a full 16-bit address. The layout of an extended addressing instruction is:

Operation code	byte 1
Hi-order address	byte 2
Lo-order address	byte 3

Because direct addressing involves the fetching of only two bytes, instructions using this method execute significantly faster than those using extended addressing. The first 256 memory locations are, therefore, usually reserved for frequently accessed items of data.

9.2.2 IMMEDIATE ADDRESSING

Immediate addressing follows exactly the pattern described in Chapter 5 and normally occupies two bytes of storage, the operation code occupying the first byte and the data the second. Three immediate mode instructions (CPX, LDX and LDS) occupy three bytes because they manipulate data held in the 16-bit index register or the stack pointer. In these cases the layout of the instructions is:

| Operation   Code | byte 1 |

| Hi-order   Data | byte 2 |

| Low-order   Data | byte 1 |

9.2.3 IMPLICIT ADDRESSING

In a number of MC6800 instructions, the operand(s) in question are implied in the actual description of the operation and so no further specification is needed. These instructions occupy one byte of storage and typically move data between the internal registers of the processor or cause simple operations to be carried out on the contents of these registers.

9.2.4 INDEXED ADDRESSING

The MC6800 employs a form of indexed addressing which results in instructions which occupy two bytes of storage. The first byte is used for the instruction code itself and the second byte contains an offset. The actual address referred to by the instruction is the sum of the contents of the index register (16 bits) and the offset (1 byte = 8 bits). The 8-bit offset is added in the least significant position as indicated below.

176

As described in Chapter 5, the "offset" which is carried in the second part of the instruction is frequently the base address of a table of data. The restricted 8-bit storage allocated to this offset clearly constrains the system so that such tables must be located in the first 256 memory locations.

9.2.5 RELATIVE ADDRESSING

The MC6800 incorporates the facility to use relative addressing but this facility is restricted to only one class of instruction, the BRANCH instructions. The format and operation of this addressing mode is exactly as described in Chapter 5, and the address specified will be in the range +129 to -126 locations of the current instruction.

9.2.6 OTHER ADDRESSING MODES

The preceding five sections have covered the main addressing modes provided by the MC6800. From the above it will be seen that indirect and auto-increment/autodecrement addressing is not generally provided. However, these modes can be achieved in certain restricted circumstances.

Indirect Addressing:

This mode, in the form of Register Indirect Addressing, is available using the index register to hold the pointer. When used for this purpose, the offset specified by the instruction must be zero.

Auto-increment/Auto-decrement:

Memory is addressed in an auto-decrement mode by all instructions which place data onto the stack. Auto-increment mode is used when data is popped from the stack. Thus auto-increment and auto-decrement addressing are restricted to those instructions which use the stack pointer.

9.3 The Instruction Set of the MC6800

All MC6800 instructions are accommodated in one to three bytes of storage and execute in between two and (exceptionally) twelve microseconds (assuming a 1 usec clock cycle).

9.3.1 DATA MOVEMENT INSTRUCTIONS

Data may be moved between any of the internal registers of
the processor provided that the sizes of the two registers
concerned are the same. The situation is shown in Figure 9.8a
below. From this it will be seen that the only path that is
missing is the one between accumulator B and the condition
codes register.

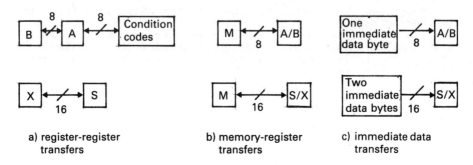

a) register-register   b) memory-register   c) immediate data
   transfers   transfers   transfers

Figure 9.8: Data paths in the MC6800

As shown in Figure 9.8b, each of the registers may be loaded
from data held in memory. The memory address may be specified
using either absolute or indexed addressing only. Where 16-
bits of data are to be transferred, these are located in
memory at the specified address (high-order data byte) and at
the next higher address (low-order data byte).

Each of the registers may be loaded with a constant using
immediate mode addressing. The constant (one or two bytes)
being located in memory immediately after the instruction
code.

In general, the data movement instructions affect the N, Z
and V bits of the condition codes register. There are,
however, exceptions to this and transfers between 16-bit
registers do not affect the condition codes register.
Obviously a transfer into the condition codes register will
affect all bits of it but a transfer from the condition codes
register does not change any bits in it.

9.3.2 ARITHMETIC AND LOGIC OPERATIONS

This class of instructions may conveniently be divided into
two, namely those that require two operands and those that
simply carry out operations on a single operand.

Two-operand instructions carry out manipulations of the form:

DATA   ●   (Register) ⟶ (Register)

Where the data item specified may be located in memory (using
absolute or indexed addressing) or may be immediate data.

178

The register involved may be either A or B and is the same on both sides of the above expression, (i.e. Data $\boxed{\cdot}$ (A)->(B) is NOT allowed).

The symbol $\boxed{\cdot}$ represents the actual two operand (dyadic) operation specified and may be chosen from the following repertoire:

> ADD
> ADD with carry
> SUBTRACT
> SUBTRACT with carry (borrow)
> AND
> OR
> EXCLUSIVE-OR

Notice that neither of the 16-bit registers may take part in the operations and the MC6800 does not support any 16-bit operations.

There are two dyadic operations in which the result does not replace the register operand. They take the form:

> Data $\boxed{\cdot}$ (Register)

and serve simply to set the condition codes register according to the result of the operation. The two instructions are:

> COMPARE - this is identical to SUBTRACT except that the result is not stored.

> BIT - this is identical to AND except that the result is not stored.

The usual purpose of COMPARE is to check when a variable reaches some limiting value and so the immediate-data form of this instruction is very common. Likewise the BIT instruction is used to select one or more bits from the 8-bit register contents.

In addition to the above repertoire of instructions, there are four which do not fit directly into the pattern. It is possible to add, subtract or compare register A with register B, leaving the result, where appropriate, in register A. Additionally, the index register may be compared with a 16-bit data item.

Single operand instructions carry out manipulations of the form:

$$(SOURCE) \xrightarrow{\text{operation}} SOURCE$$

where "SOURCE" is the location of the data item to be manipulated. This may be a memory location (specified by indexed or extended absolute addressing only) or either of the two general purpose registers (A/B).

The operations which may be carried out on the data are:

    TEST
    COMPLEMENT
    NEGATE
    INCREMENT
    DECREMENT
    CLEAR
    LOGICAL SHIFT LEFT/RIGHT
    ROTATE LEFT/RIGHT THROUGH CARRY
    ARITHMETIC SHIFT RIGHT

The first instruction, TEST, does not change the data but merely sets the condition codes register Z and N bits according to the value of the data.

The increment and decrement operations are also applicable to data held in the index register and stack pointer register.

The shift operations all involve the carry bit and may be represented as shown in Figure 9.9.

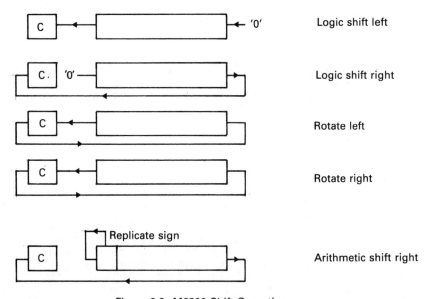

Figure 9.9: M6800 Shift Operations

It is possible to produce a "long-shift" involving both accumulators and memory by combining two or more shift instructions as outlined in Chapter 4.

9.3.3 STACK OPERATIONS

The MC6800 makes provision for stack handling by incorporating a stack pointer in the processor. The stack

180

itself is located in memory and grows downwards. The stack
pointer always points to the next vacant location on the
stack.

Instructions exist to transfer data from either register onto
the stack and vice versa. The stack is used automatically
during subroutine linkage, and also saves the machine status
during interrupts.

The condition codes register can only be transferred to the
stack by first bringing it into register A.

9.3.4 PROGRAM CONTROL

Control may be passed from one point in a program to another
by means of either a JUMP instruction or a BRANCH instruction.

There is only one Jump instruction and this is executed
unconditionally, the destination of the jump being specified
using either indexed or extended absolute addressing. Using
this instruction any location within memory may be reached.

The BRANCH group of instructions also cause a transfer of
control to another point in the program, but because relative
addressing is used for branch instructions, control may only
be passed to a location that is within the range +129 to -126
locations of the branch instruction itself.

Branching may take place unconditionally or, alternatively,
conditionally on one of the following events in the condition
codes register

Simple conditions:

Carry is set	C=1
Carry is reset	C=0
Overflow is set	V=1
Overflow is reset	V=0
Zero is set	Z=1
Zero is reset	Z=0
Minus is set	N=1
Minus is reset	N=0

Complex conditions: The following complex properties of the
result of some previous operation may be tested.

Result ≥ 0	$N \oplus V = 0$
Result > 0	$(N \oplus V) + Z = 0$
Result < 0	$N \oplus V = 1$
Result ≤ 0	$(N \oplus V) + Z = 1$
Neither carry nor zero are set	$C + Z = 0$
Either carry or zero or both are set	$C + Z = 1$

9.3.5   SUBROUTINE LINKAGE

A subroutine may be invoked using either the 2-byte BRANCH   TO
SUBROUTINE   or   the   3-byte   JUMP   TO SUBROUTINE instructions.
There are no conditional subroutine calls.

The branch instruction uses relative   addressing   and   so   the
entry   address of the subroutine must be within the range +129
to -126 locations   of   calling   instruction.   If   a   "Jump   to
subroutine"   is   used,   the   subroutine may be located anywhere
since   this   instruction   used   either   extended   absolute   or
indexed addressing.

When   a   subroutine is entered the return address is placed on
the stack automatically so that, on entry to the routine,   the
stack appears thus:

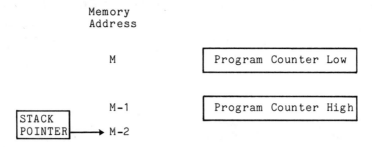

Irrespective   of   which   instruction   is   used   to   enter   the
subroutine,   the same RETURN FROM   SUBROUTINE   instruction   is
executed   in   order   to   resume   the   main   program.   This
instruction simply unstacks the return address and   places   it
in the program counter.

The   main   program   may   pass   parameters   to   a subroutine in
registers A or B,   via a known "communications area" in memory
or   on   the   stack.   Indexed   addressing   may   then be used to
access the parameters on   the   stack   without   disturbing   the
stack pointer.   Consider a situation when four parameters (P1-
P4) must be passed.   On entry to the subroutine the stack will
appear as:

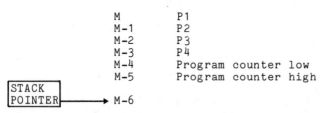

The   subroutine   then   executes   the   instruction which transfers
the contents of the stack pointer to the index register.   This
instruction   in   fact   loads   the   contents   of   the   stack pointer
plus one into the index register.   In the above   example,   M-5
will appear in the index register.

182

The parameters on the stack now become immediately available using indexed addressing, without any change in the stack pointer being required.

9.3.6 INTERRUPTS

The MC6800 provides two interrupt levels. Interrupts are generated when either of the interrupt lines are taken to logic 0.

Interrupts from the $\overline{IRQ}$ line may be turned on and off with the I bit in the condition codes register and instructions exist to permit this bit to be changed without altering any of the other bits in the condition codes register. Interrupts which occur on the $\overline{NMI}$ line (non-maskable interrupt line) are always honoured and cannot be inhibited. All devices required to cause an interrupt on one particular level are connected onto the $\overline{IRQ}$ (or $\overline{NMI}$) line in a 'wired-OR' fashion. The interrupt service routine then has to determine which particular device caused the interrupt.

When an interrupt occurs on the $\overline{IRQ}$ line the sequence of events shown in Figure 9.10 occurs. The current instruction is completed and then the interrupt mask bit (I) is checked. If interrupts are enabled (I=0) then the hardware causes the complete machine status to be placed on the stack as shown in Figure 9.5. The hardware then jumps to the interrupt service routine.

The location of the service routine is entirely at the discretion of the programmer. However, the hardware will assume that the programmer has stored the address of the first instruction of the routine in locations FFF8 and FFF9. These two locations contain the interrupt request vector. (The high-byte of the vector is in FFF8 and the low-byte in FFF9).

The last instruction in the service routine must be a "return from interrupt" which has the effect of restoring the machine status.

An interrupt on the NMI line is handled in a generally similar fashion except that

    (i)   the interrupt is serviced irrespective of the I bit.

    (ii)   the interrupt vector is located at FFFC and FFFD.

Thus the programmer may specify two separate service routines, one for interrupt requests (IRQ) and one for non-maskable interrupts (NMI). Generally, the non-maskable interrupt line is reserved for critical situations such as power failure.

In addition to hardware-generated interrupts the MC6800 provides a facility for software-generated interrupts. By

183

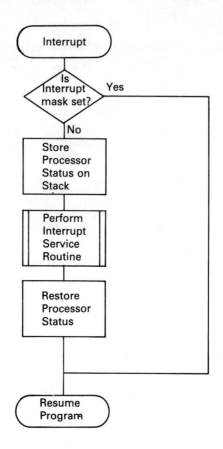

Figure 9.10: Servicing an Interrupt Request

executing a "SWI" instruction an interrupt service sequence is initiated. This functions in the same way as a non-maskable interrupt except that a different service routine vector is used. This vector is located at addresses FFFA and FFFB.

Where several interrupts occur at the same time they are dealt with in order of priority namely:

Decreasing
Priority

Non-maskable interrupt

Software interrupt

Interrupt request

It takes about 12 usec after the completion of an interrupted instruction before the processor begins execution of the service routine (assuming a 1 usec clock period). Much of this time delay is taken up with saving the machine status and may be avoided in some circumstances:-

184

If the processor has no further work to do and is simply waiting for an interrupt to occur, it can save the machine status before the interrupt occurs by executing a "WAI" (wait for interrupt) instruction. This causes the status to be stacked and then puts the machine into suspension. When the machine is "woken up" from a wait state by an interrupt, execution is immediately transferred to the appropriate service routine (5 usec with a 1 usec clock).

9.3.7 MISCELLANEOUS INSTRUCTIONS

In addition to the instructions reviewed above, there are four others which manipulate the contents of the condition codes register, and one which does nothing.

The no operation (NOP) merely causes a delay of two clock cycles in the execution of a program. In addition it is possible to individually set or to individually clear the carry bit (C) and the overflow bit (V) of the condition codes register.

9.4 The Bus Signals and Input-Output Operations

It has already been pointed out that the MC6800 microprocessing unit does not distinguish between memory and peripherals (integrated, memory-mapped I/O). In this section, the signals which are required to control information transfer along the bus will be examined.

Figure 9.2 shows a number of devices connected to the bus. Of these the memory, peripherals and microprocessor are all capable of putting information on the data bus. This situation requires that all bus connections should be of the "wired-OR" or "tri-state" configuration. Simple wired-OR arrangements suffer from the defect that they do not switch from a '0' state to a '1' state as rapidly as normal logic gates (which have a feature known as active pull-up). To overcome this, the data buffers of the microprocessing unit, the memory and the peripherals (Figure 9.2) are tri-state devices. When the enable control is not active, there is no passage for information from the microprocessor to the bus. The buffers appear to the bus as a high impedance (hi-Z) and do not interfere with any signals which may be placed on the bus by other devices. When the enable control is active then the information in the buffers is transferred to the bus via circuits which have the high speed characteristics of ordinary logic devices. Thus the buffers are capable of assuming one of three states: ACTIVE '1', ACTIVE '0' and Hi-Z. The designer must ensure that only one enabling control is active at any one time.

It would appear from Figure 9.2 that only one device, the microprocessing unit, is capable of originating address information and so there is no need for the address buffers to be tri-state. However, if Direct Memory Access is to be attempted, or if two microprocessors are to share the same bus system, there will be at least two sources of address information. For this reason, the microprocessing unit is equipped with tri-state address buffers too.

In addition to the eight data lines and sixteen address lines the bus has a number of other signals for control of information transfer, power supplies etc. These will be discussed below.

9.4.1 SYNCHRONOUS BUS TRANSFER SYSTEM

The bus structure associated with MC6800 is termed a synchronous structure. This means that events are assumed to take place within a certain time period during the machine instruction cycle. If, for any reason, these events do not occur during the appropriate time periods the instruction will not be properly executed and data transfer will not take place.

The advantages of a synchronous bus system are primarily that it is simple to use and that it requires the minimum of supervisory control signals to ensure proper data transfer. The disadvantages are that data can be lost if the timing arrangements are violated and it takes just as long to transfer data from a (relatively) fast device as it does from a slow device.

This is explained as follows. A slow device may make data available to the microprocessor just in time for that data to be read. However, a fast device may have the data available in (say) a quarter of this time and have to wait for the remainder of the cycle, idly keeping its data available. In an asynchronous bus system, the source of data advises the receiver as soon as the data is available, thus shortening the time for which the bus is being used.

The timing of a simple data transfer on the bus is shown in Figure 9.11.

The system is organised so that address information is available on the address bus not more than 270ns after clock Phase 1 is high. At this point, the decoders in the memory (or peripheral) can commence operations to extract the desired item of data. This data must be made available on the data bus at least 100ns before Phase 2 of the clock starts to fall away.

The time available between the address becoming valid and the data having to be present is the maximum access time which any memory (or peripheral) may display.

186

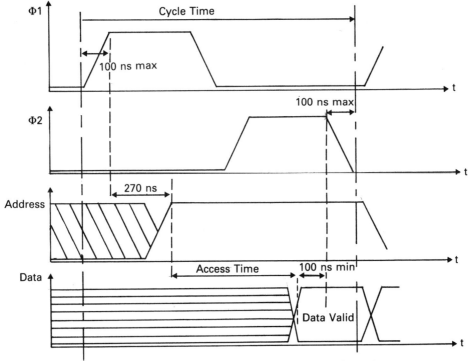

Figure 9.11: Timing of a Read-from-Memory Operation

The maximum access time is calculated thus:

```
Max access time  = Cycle time - address delay time - data
                   set up time - rise time - fall time

Address delay    = 270 nsec

Data set up      = 100 nsec

Rise time    ⎫
             ⎬  =  50 nsec
Fall time    ⎭

Cycle time       > 1 usec
                 < 10 usec
```

Thus memories and peripherals with an access time of less than 530ns may be used with the microprocessor when the latter is running at its maximum speed. If slower devices are to be used, then the clock must be slowed down. Using this technique, devices with an access time of up to 9.5 usec may be employed. However, a considerable penalty is paid for this facility since slowing down the clock increases the time taken for all instructions to be executed. This is one of the disadvantages of a synchronous bus system.

An alternative is to "stretch" Phase 2 of the clock waveform during accesses to slow memory. The clock generators which are supplied for use with the MC6800 (MC6871A, MC6871B and MC6875) permit this function to be achieved by providing a control signal input "memory-ready". When this signal is held low, Phase 2 of the clock is stretched. Details of these clock generators will be given in Chapter 14. It should be noted that Phase 2 of the clock should never be longer than 9.5 usec.

The address lines will select a particular location when both a read and a write operation is executed. The difference is signalled by one of the control lines from the microprocessing unit, a read/write line. When a read is signalled, the memory (or peripheral) is conditioned to provide data and the data buffers of the microprocessor and memory are organised so that data may flow from the bus into the processor.

During normal operations the address lines and the read/write control line may enter the high impedance state since they are tri-state devices. Once in this state, the data on the lines is indeterminate and may cause false reads or writes in the memory and peripherals. This is prevented by a second I/O control line called Valid Memory Address. This is not a tri-state signal and it is used to indicate to the memory and peripherals that the data on the address bus is indeed to be interpreted as an address.

9.4.2 INTERRUPT HANDLING

In order to provide efficient processing while handling slow peripherals, it is essential that a processor be equipped with an interrupt capability. Two interrupt request lines have been provided on the microprocessing unit. All devices which are required to cause an interrupt are connected to one or other of these lines in a wired-OR fashion.

One of the interrupt lines is called 'Interrupt Request'. When this line is asserted, the microprocessor completes its current instruction and then checks to see whether the mask bit, I, in the condition codes register is set. If it is not, then interrupts are allowed and the processor proceeds with the interrupt service routine as shown previously in Figure 9.10.

The mask bit in the condition codes register permits the user to ignore interrupts during particularly critical operations. However, there are some eventualities which are so important that they must not be inhibited by the mask, for instance, power failure. For such eventualities a special Non-Maskable interrupt input is provided. The servicing of a non-maskable interrupt is exactly as shown in Figure 9.10 except that the mask test is omitted. The service routine for non-maskable interrupts may be separate from that for other interrupts.

9.4.3 OTHER BUS CONTROL SIGNALS

It was mentioned in an earlier section that it is not unusual to find microprocessors used in systems where there are several devices which may take charge of the bus. This situation exists in any system employing Direct Memory Access or several microprocessors. It is for this reason that the MC6800 is equipped with tri-state address and data buffers. In order that the removal of a microprocessor from the bus is properly controlled four special control and status signals are provided.

(i)   Tri-state Control: operation of this control line forces the address and read/write lines into a high impedance state. By doing so, the microprocessor is effectively removed from the bus which may then be controlled by another device. During this process the clock must be stopped with Phase 1 = '1' and Phase 2 = '0'. Notice that the data buffers are NOT driven into a high impedance state by this signal and so the processor is not completely removed from the bus. This complete removal can be affected by a second control:-

(ii)   Data Bus Enable: operation of this control drives the data buffers into a high impedance state.

The two signals discussed above may be used together to achieve Direct Memory Access by the cycle stealing technique. It is only possible to use 'cycle stealing' since the operation of the Tri-state control also requires that the clock be stopped. This can only happen for a maximum of 9.5 usec for the same reason as the clock has a maximum period, namely data stored within the microprocessor will be lost if longer periods of operation without the clock are permitted.

In many MC6800 applications, but not all, "Data bus enable" is derived directly from Phase 2 of the clock. Since Phase 2 is held at logic 0 when the tri-state control is in use this single tri-state control effectively removes both the data and address buffers from the bus when this connection is employed.

If more than a few data items are to be transferred while the microprocessor is off the bus, then the burst mode (Data-Break) technique is used. Since this will require the microprocessor to be off the bus for longer than 9.5 usec, it is not practicable to stop the clock and use the tri-state control. Instead a different technique which does not require the clock to be stopped is employed. The control signals used are:

(i)   Halt: operation of this control causes the microprocessor to cease all activity and to place its data, address and read/write lines in a high impedance state. There is no need to stop the clock and so the processor may remain halted for as long as required. Once processing is halted another control line, Bus Available, signals this fact.

(ii)   Bus Available: once the microprocessor is removed from the bus this signal goes into a '1' state and signals to any device requesting the use of the bus that it may now commence operations.

In addition to its use as a data-break control, the halt line may be used as a means of stepping the processor through a program for debugging purposes. Note, however, that this procedure will not be as straightforward as stepping a minicomputer through a program since the user has no direct access to the accumulators, index register etc.

The state of the MC6800 when the Halt line is operated is broadly equivalent to the "Hold" state defined for many other types of microprocessor.

9.4.4 GETTING THE PROCESSOR STARTED

The last paragraph of the previous section will have served as a reminder that many of the facilities expected of a minicomputer are not readily available with a microprocessor. It is not possible to use a switch bank to toggle in a program, nor is it possible, having loaded a program, to set the program counter to the start address and switch to run.

To get round this difficulty, the MC6800 processor is fitted with a RESET input. When this signal is asserted the processor reloads the program counter with the contents of the two highest locations in memory. Having done this the instructions located at the locations specified by the new program counter contents are obeyed. These instructions will comprise an initialisation program plus perhaps some sort of loader which will permit other programs to be loaded from paper tape or some other convenient medium. In larger systems the initialisation program might well load a complete suite of programs from a small disc or a cassette backing store, and then proceed to execute these programs.

The question arises, however, as to how the two locations at the top of the memory and the initialisation program are placed in memory in the absence of a means for toggling them in. The instructions etc. must be permanently written into memory, that is they must form the contents of a read-only memory. Such a memory could be constructed from an array of resistors and diodes. In other words, a soldering iron takes the place of a set of switches! However, it is more likely that semiconductor ROM would be used.

The reset input may be regarded as a special sort of interrupt which is only used during power on situations. The "restart vector" being stored in locations FFFE and FFFF. The internal routine during restart is, however, slightly different from that employed by the normal interrupt response since there is little point in stacking the status of a machine which has previously been doing nothing!

In summary, therefore, the MC6800 bus consists of the following signals:

Address lines	16
Data lines	8
Read/write	1
Valid memory address	1
Tri-state control	1
Data bus enable	1
Halt	1
Bus available	1
Non-maskable interrupt	1
Interrupt request	1
Reset	1
Clock Phase 1	1
Clock Phase 2	1
Power (VCC)	1
Ground (0 volts)	2
Spare pins	2
Total	40 pins

10. Techniques for Communications

In order that a computer may be useful to man, it must communicate with the outside world. This communication may take place between the computer and the human operator or, equally usefully, the communication may be established between the computer and some other machinery. In Chapters 7 and 8, the problems of input-output communication were dealt with from the viewpoint of the central processor and attention was focussed on the way in which information could be passed from the computer to interface devices. This interface unit was assumed to absorb data as parallel words which somehow caused appropriate actions in the devices connected to the "real-world" side of the interface. It was mentioned that the interface could be made up of a number of standard logic circuit building blocks or alternatively that complete "interface adaptors" could be purchased to suit the microprocessor in use. The examples given were of the former approach and some examples of typical integrated circuit interface adaptors will be given in Chapter 14.

In this Chapter, attention will be focused on the kinds of devices that could be attached to the real-world side of the interface. These include devices for man-machine communication (such as lights, keyboards, visual display units, etc.) and also devices for machine-machine communications. This latter category includes a vast range of measurement transducers and actuation devices which would require a whole book to describe adequately. For this reason, none of these latter devices will be discussed and only those devices and techniques concerned with man-machine communications will be covered. One exception to this will be allowed, however, in the case of serial communication techniques since these are widely used both for the connection of visual display units, printers, etc. to computers and also for inter-computer communications over relatively large distances.

10.1 Simple Output Techniques

Probably the most frequently used output device is the simple indicator lamp. Filament lamps are not much used these days because of their relatively poor reliability and have been replaced by light emitting diodes (LEDs). These are small semiconductor devices which have the property of emitting light (usually red, but orange and green-emitting devices are also available) when a current is passed through them (Figure 10.1).

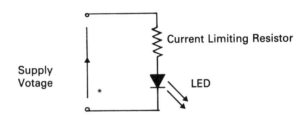

Figure 10.1: LED Indicator Circuit

The resistor is chosen to limit the current passing through the device to a safe level, usually in the order of 20mA. This current is drawn from the supply voltage controlling the LED and is a much higher value than can be provided by ordinary logic gates or by the outputs of typical interface adaptors. To provide this current, it is necessary to provide high-power buffers (see Appendix C) either in the form of transistors or in the form of a logic driver circuit such as the SN 7416 device.

The amount of light emitted by an LED depends on the current flowing. However, there is a limit to the average current which may flow before the device overheats and is destroyed. A peculiarity of these devices is that they appear brighter if the current is supplied in large, short pulses.

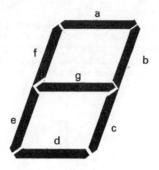

Figure 10.2: Arrangement of Segments in a 7-Segment Display

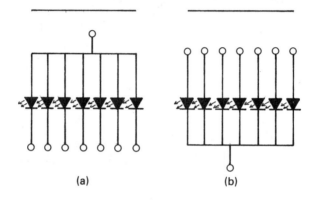

(a)　　　　　　　　　　(b)

Figure 10.3: Common Anode (a) and Common Cathode (b) Connections

Thus a 20mA average current could be supplied as

    (a)   20mA continuous, or

    (b)   100mA for 1ms in every 5ms

The latter arrangement would appear to be brighter.

10.1.1 ALPHA NUMERIC DISPLAYS

It is frequently necessary to display data which is more
complex than that possible with simple LED indicators. Where
the data is predominantly numerical, a 7-segment display is
frequently used. This consists of an assembly of bar-shaped
LEDs arranged as shown in Figure 10.2. These LEDs are
connected together with either all of their anodes (10.3a) or
all of their cathodes (10.3b) connected together. By

Segments							Display
a	b	c	d	e	f	g	
1	1	1	1	1	1	0	0
0	1	1	0	0	0	0	1
1	1	0	1	1	0	1	2
1	1	1	1	0	0	1	3
0	1	1	0	0	1	1	4
1	0	1	1	0	1	1	5
1	0	1	1	1	1	1	6
1	1	1	0	0	0	0	7
1	1	1	1	1	1	1	8
1	1	1	0	0	1	1	9
1	1	1	0	1	1	1	A
1	0	0	1	1	1	0	C
1	0	0	1	1	1	1	E
1	0	0	0	1	1	1	F
0	1	1	0	1	1	1	H
1	1	1	1	0	0	0	J
0	0	0	1	1	1	0	L
1	1	0	0	1	1	1	P
0	1	1	1	1	1	0	U
0	0	1	1	1	1	1	b
0	0	0	1	1	0	1	c
0	1	1	1	1	0	1	d
1	1	0	1	1	1	1	e
0	0	1	0	1	1	1	h
0	0	1	0	1	0	1	n
0	0	1	1	1	0	1	o
0	0	0	0	1	0	1	r
0	0	0	1	1	1	1	t

1=ON
0=OFF

Table 10.1: 7-segment Display Codes

selecting the bars which are illuminated it is possible to represent a fair number of different characters as summarised in Table 10.1.

In addition to the seven segments, there is frequently a decimal point provided positioned at the bottom right or left of the display.

Clearly it is necessary to select the correct code specifying the segments to be illuminated.

This may be carried out by software or hardware depending on the particular circumstances of the application.

To carry out the encoding by software, the contents of Table 10.1 would have to be stored in memory starting at a known location, (say location 1000). Indexed addressing (see

195

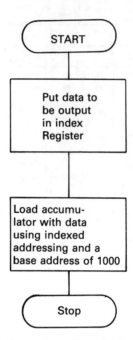

Figure 10.4: Software Encoding of 7-Segment Display

Section 5.5) could then be used to extract the desired code as shown in Figure 10.4.

The required 8-bit code (7 segment bits from Table 10.1 plus the decimal point bit) would then be in the accumulator and available for output via a suitable parallel I/O device (such as the PIA described in 14.1.1 or the 8255A described in B.2.2). As a rule, the output of the parallel I/O device will have to be buffered to provide sufficient current for the display.

Since external devices have to be connected to the output channel, it is often convenient to include the decoding logic in this hardware. In fact, the necessary drive and decoding logic can be obtained as a single integrated circuit such as the SN7447. This approach is illustrated in Figure 10.5 where it will be observed that this approach also economises on output lines since only one half of a standard output port is required. Since the SN7447 device outputs are active low, the circuit requires a common anode 7-segment display. Using the SN7447 BCD ⟶ 7-segment decoder involves a small penalty in that the non-numeric characters are no longer available. The seven resistors required by the circuit of Figure 10.5 may be obtained in a single 14-pin package, thus simplifying assembly.

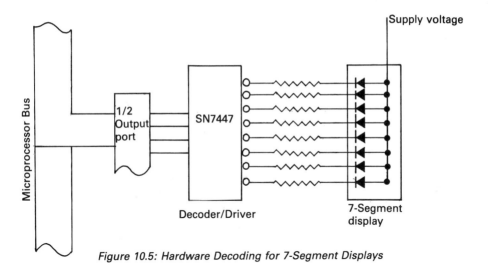

Figure 10.5: Hardware Decoding for 7-Segment Displays

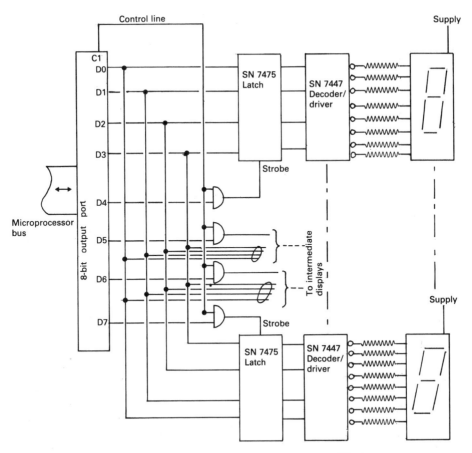

Figure 10.6: Multiplexed 4-digit 7-segment Display

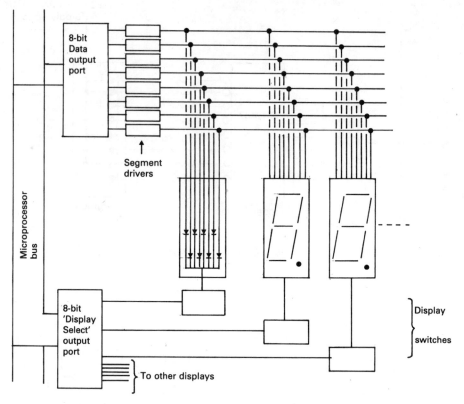

Figure 10.7: Pulse-Multiplexed 7-segment Displays

Where large displays are involved, the cost of the output ports in terms of money and board space could become excessive and it may be preferable to add latches to the circuit in Figure 10.5. In this way the output port may be used to load each of the display latches in turn. One half of the output port is used to supply the digit to the latch and the other being used to specify which latch is to be used. Figure 10.6 shows this approach which enables four displays to be driven from a single 8-bit port. The "strobe" is provided by one of the control lines usually associated with the port (for instance, CB2 of the 6820 PIA described in 14.1.1 and used as shown in Figure 14.7).

If more than four displays are required, this single output port could serve up to sixteen by using a 4- to 16-line decoder (e.g. 74159) to provide the strobe enable signals instead of using the four non-data output lines directly.

It is possible to purchase a single integrated circuit containing both the latches and the decoder and it is also possible to purchase a 7-segment display which incorporates its own decoder and latches.

One method of servicing multiple display units relies on the enhanced performance possible with pulsed operation of LEDs (Figure 10.7). Instead of using latches to permanently hold the displayed data, the latter is only provided for a short period of time. During this time, the current is pulsed in the display for which the data is destined by the strobe line for that display. The data is then changed to that destined for the next display unit and the current is pulsed in that one. This continues until all the displays have been serviced when the process repeats itself.

The segment drivers can be simple logic buffers or, as before, be replaced by a BCD -> 7-segment decoder-driver circuit. In this case, only four lines of the data output port will be required. The display switches are normally discrete transistors since, in the worst case, they have to carry the full current for all seven segments plus the decimal point.

It will be appreciated that in order to maintain a bright, flicker-free display the scanning operation must be continuous and will involve a significant overhead of processor time. In some applications, it may be best to delegate this task to a second processor so that the main processor can continue its task without the added complexity of continually having to update the display. There exist some single-chip microprocessors designed especailly to handle just this sort of I/O task. One example is the Intel UPI-41A discussed briefly in Chapter 17. This may be programmed by the end-user to suit his needs or, for a number of common tasks, may be obtained ready programmed. The 8278 is an example of this, being a UPI-41A ready programmed for LED display and keyboard scanning operations. In this case the end user simply treats the device as a kind of "intelligent peripheral" and does not become involved in the details of its operation.

Seven segment displays suffer from the disadvantage that they cannot represent all of the alpha-numeric characters and some of the characters that can be displayed are easily confused (for instance, 6 and b). This problem is overcome by dot matrix displays. Typically these displays consist of five columns each containing seven small LED "dots" (7 x 5 dot matrix) although other patterns are manufactured. These devices provide a far more refined display than is possible with the 7-segment variety but, of course, are more complex to control. Typically each row of the 7 x 5 matrix is scanned in turn and the appropriate 5-bit output used to define which LED dots in the current row are on. The required patterns are provided by a character generator such as the Signetics 2513. This is essentially a read-only memory which is capable of supporting up to 64 different characters each represented as seven 5-bit words (one per row) plus one spare row. Thus 512 5-bit words are stored as shown in Figure 10.8.

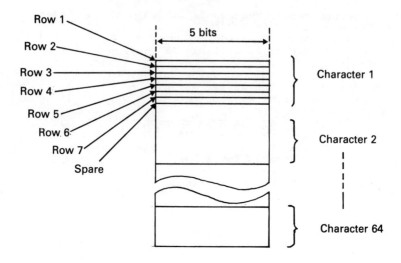

Figure 10.8: Arrangement of a 7×5 Dot Matrix Encoding ROM

The device has nine address lines, the most significant six specify which character is selected while the least significant three are used for row scanning.

The main problem with all LED-based displays is their low brightness. They are perfectly acceptable under normal indoor conditions but become almost invisible in bright daylight. A second disadvantage is the high current consumption of the devices which means that they are not very suitable for battery-powered equipment and also cannot be driven directly by normal integrated circuit devices.

These difficulties are overcome by the use of liquid crystal displays (LCDs) which consume as little as 1.5uA per 7-segment display and may be operated directly by a 5 volt supply. In addition to requiring very little power these displays are visible under any lighting condition from ordinary room illumination to bright sunlight. A typical LCD reflects light when de-energised but becomes transparent when an electric field is applied. If the LCD panel has a black background this then appears similar to black print on a light coloured paper. The displays are available in 7-segment format and as complete matrix display panels (e.g. Epson EA/EG series modules).

10.2 Simple Input Devices

The simplest input device available to designers is a switch and these are widely used both individually and in the form of keyboard assemblies. The most commonly used type of switch is mechanical involving either simple contact closure (Figure 10.9a) or changeover (Figure 10.9b). In order to be suitable for input to an interface adaptor, the change-of-state of a switch must be converted to a logic signal as shown in Figure 10.9c.

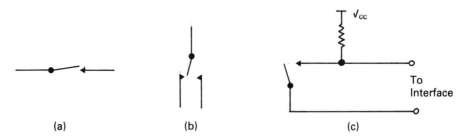

(a)   (b)   (c)

Figure 10.9: Switch Arrangements

The major problem with mechanical switches is that of contact bounce. When a switch is closed it behaves in a manner similar to a weight on a spring and oscillates for a short while before finally settling, as shown in Figure 10.10.

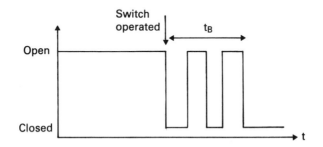

Figure 10.10: Contact Bounce

The period, t(B) is known as the bounce period, and is typically between 1ms and 5ms. Since computers operate much more rapidly than this it is possible for the bounce to be misinterpreted as several intentional switch closures. This may be overcome with either hardware or software debounce techniques. Figure 10.11 shows a typical hardware debounce circuit using 2 NAND gates to form a simple R-S latch.

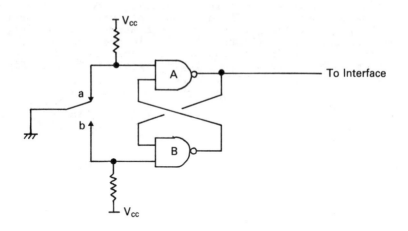

Figure 10.11: Hardware Debounce of a Switch

When the switch is in the position shown, gate A has a logic 0 on at least one input and this ensures that the output of gate A is logic 1. Thus gate B has a logic 1 on both its inputs and hence is providing a logic 0 output. Now, should the switch bounce so that the contact "a" is broken, this will result in a logic 1 being applied to one of gate A's inputs. However, since the other input is at logic 0 no change will occur at the output of gate A. In this way the bounce is not seen by the interface (unless the switch bounced right back to contact b, which is most unlikely). When the switch is moved back to position b the output of gate B will be forced from logic 0 to logic 1 thus forcing the output of gate A to logic 0. A little thought will show that this transition is also insensitive to bounce.

As an alternative, software may be used to debounce the switch as shown in Figure 10.12. The principle of operation of this is to recognise the first transition in the bounce sequence and then to ignore any subsequent transitions for a period in excess of the bounce period and then to read the final state of the switch and act accordingly. This is achieved by reading the switch at intervals in excess of the bounce period. When the switch changes state this is noted by setting 'SERVICE' to 1. Provided the switch is read less frequently than one bounce period, it can be guaranteed that, at the next reading, the switch will have settled and so it may be read and serviced. It may stay in this condition for a long time and so to avoid the service routine being executed many times, the flag 'SERVICE' is set to 0 as soon as the service routine has been executed.

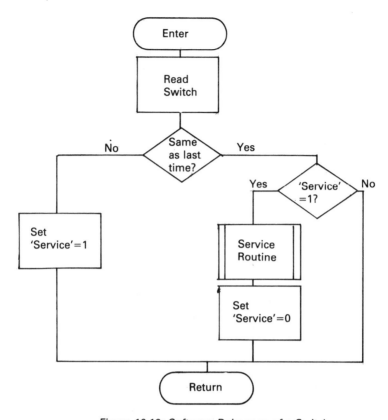

Figure 10.12: Software Debounce of a Switch

10.2.1 KEYBOARDS

One of the most common uses of swithces is assembled in the
form a keyboard. Keyboard input is a very flexible tool since
it enables data and instructions to be entered as a stream of
characters to be interpreted by software. In this way, one
can avoid covering the panel of an instrument with a large
number of selector switches and instead use a simple and
compact keyboard. Specific advantages of this approach are:

(i)   It is often less expensive

(ii)   It is neater, requires less hardware and is more
       reliable.

(iii) It is more flexible since new functions may be
       added by simply allowing new combinations of
       characters to be recognised. This merely involves
       a change of software and avoids any hardware
       modifications.

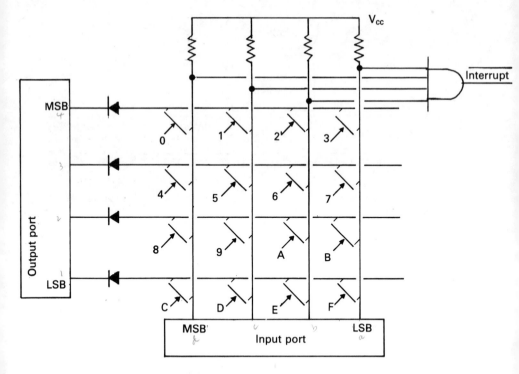

Figure 10.13: Keyboard Matrix

A keyboard consisting of, say, 64 keys would rarely be arranged so that each of the 64 keys could be interrogated individually since this would take too long and involve a great deal of wiring. Instead keyboards are normally arranged as a matrix as shown in Figure 10.13 and a scanning operation is carried out to identify the key which has been depressed.

The scanning operation is carried out as follows:

(i)   The output is set to drive every row line with a logic 0. Because of the "pull-up" resistors, the input port will receive all logic 1s unless one or more keys are pressed. When this occurs, there will be one or more zeros read in from the column(s) corresponding to the key closures.

(ii)   The fact that a key has closed is noted (e.g. 'SERVICE' = 1 in Figure 10.12) and the keyboard re-serviced after a delay greater than the contact bounce time.

(iii)   When the keyboard is again inspected after the delay the output port is re-configured so that the top row is driven with a logic 0 and all others with logic 1. The data at the input port

204

is read and will contain a logic 0 in the column position of any switch that is closed. If no switches are closed it will contain all logic 1s.

(iv)   This process is repeated until one of the input words does have a logic 0.

(v)   The data word output to the rows and the data word read in from the columns taken together as an 8-bit word form a unique code for each key (see Table 10.2). Once the code has been found, it can be converted into the required form (for instance, straight binary or ASCII) by a simple code conversion table-look-up routine.

(vi)   Once the key has been identified, the output port may be re-configured to all zeros and will be inspected at regular intervals. However, no notice will again be taken of the fact that the input data word contains a zero until the original key has been released as signalled by an all 1 data word being read in.

Figure 10.14 shows a flowchart for this procedure where 'SERVICE' = 1 indicates that they keyboard should be scanned (the same significance as in Figure 10.12) and 'RELEASE' = 0 indicates that the current key has not yet been released.

All of the above discussions have assumed that only one key has been pressed. If two keys are pressed, a number of consequences follow. First, when the rows are scanned, it is possible for an output at logic 1 to be connected to an output at logic 0. This would occur if keys 0 and 4 were

8-bit code

KEY	OUTPUT DATA				INPUT DATA			
0	0	1	1	1	0	1	1	1
1	0	1	1	1	1	0	1	1
2	0	1	1	1	1	1	0	1
3	0	1	1	1	1	1	1	0
4	1	0	1	1	0	1	1	1
5	1	0	1	1	1	0	1	1
6	1	0	1	1	1	1	0	1
7	1	0	1	1	1	1	1	0
8	1	1	0	1	0	1	1	1
9	1	1	0	1	1	0	1	1
A	1	1	0	1	1	1	0	1
B	1	1	0	1	1	1	1	0
C	1	1	1	0	0	1	1	1
D	1	1	1	0	1	0	1	1
E	1	1	1	0	1	1	0	1
F	1	1	1	0	1	1	1	0

Table 10.2 Keyboard Codes

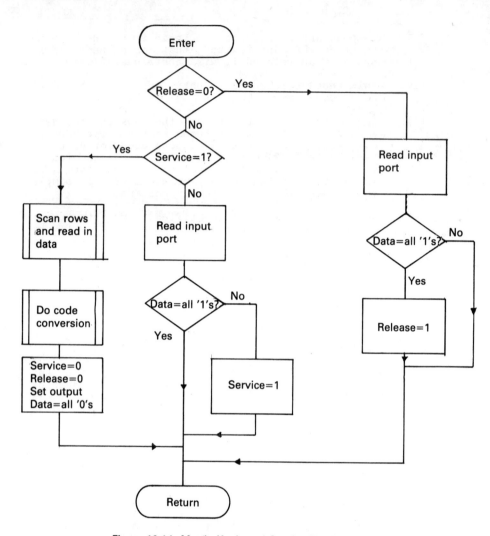

Figure 10.14: Matrix Keyboard Service Routine

pressed together. The electrical consequences of this happening are avoided by the presence of the diodes in the row lines.

The most usual reason for two keys being pressed is that the operator's fingers have not been accurately placed. Thus one key is usually closed in advance of the other, the pressure applied being different. The flowchart of Figure 10.14 will ensure that only the first depression is seen since this will be picked up by the first service scan after which the routine merely waits for the key (or in this case both keys) to be released before performing any further key scan operations. This is termed TWO-KEY ROLLOVER protection.

In the unlikely event of two keys being depressed simultaneously, the code read in would not be one of the valid codes. Depending on circumstances, the code could be ignored and an error signalled or the illegal code could be analysed to determine which keys have been pressed and one of these selected on some arbitrary basis.

10.3 Serial Data Systems

So far the communication techniques described have used parallel I/O ports for their operation. This means that relatively complex devices such as keyboards require many wires in order to connect them to the interface adaptor and processor since each bit of information that has to be communicated requires its own connection. However, this arrangement is economical in its hardware requirements since the data to be transmitted is naturally available in parallel form. It also permits very rapid transmission of data since only one time slot is needed for the total transfer of the data.

Unfortunately, as the separation between the peripheral device and the processor increases the amount of wire involved and its cost becomes excessive. Under these circumstances it becomes attractive to send information in serial format. To achieve this only one wire is required since only one bit of information is sent in each time slot. Thus to send an 8-bit data word would require eight time slots. This reduction in speed is usually acceptable since most peripherals communicate relatively small amounts of information.

Serial transmission has been widely used for many years for the communication of messages from one place to another. Thus typewriter-like equipment capable of electrical communication was readily available when the pioneering computer manufacturers were looking for a cheap and reliable terminal for their machines. As a result serial transmission was, and still is, widely used for quite short distance communications even in situations where it would be practical to utilise parallel techniques. To summarise, therefore, we may say that serial communications are widely used

(i)   Where the peripherals natural operation generates data in serial format.

(ii)   Where the distances involved are large, making parallel communication too costly. This even includes transmission from one computer to another in a network situation provided that the traffic density is not too high.

(iii)   Where the availability of equipment is such that it is more attractive to use standard serial data equipment rather than design special purpose parallel data equipment.

Transmission rates with serial systems can range from 10 bytes/second to as much as 18,000 bytes/second using commonly available hardware.

From the above it will be appreciated that serial communications techniques provide access to a vast range of peripheral equipment and for this reason alone, they need to be well understood. In addition, the techniques are the basis for a large number of modern applications of computers in which both mainframes and microprocessor-based equipment have a function.

A typical serial transmission situation is shown in Figure 10.15. If the link only permits transmission from A to B it is said to be a SIMPLEX link. If two-way transmission is possible but in only one direction at a time, the link is HALF DUPLEX. Where it is possible to transmit in both directions at once the link is FULL DUPLEX.

Figure 10.15: A Serial Link

In the case of a half duplex link, provision must be made for the current transmitter to tell the current receiver that the line is free. This is usually accomplished by the sending of a special control character and is termed "turning the line round". In a realistic system, there might be many control characters each with its own specific purpose. The complete set of such characters along with a description of their use is termed the transmission protocol.

The serial transmission of a data word is accomplished by transmitting each bit of the data word in turn, usually commencing with the least significant digit. This is shown diagramatically in Figure 10.16 for the data word 10010110.

A number of problems immediately come to mind in considering how the waveform in Figure 10.16 might be received and recovered. These may be summarised:

(i)   How are the logic levels '1' and '0' to be represented?

(ii) When there is no change between adjacent bits, how does the receiver know where the boundary is and how does it distinguish between, say, one long '1' or two adjacent, short '1's?

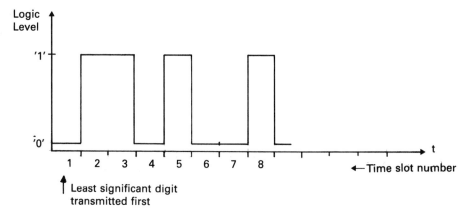

Figure 10.16: Serially Transmitted Data '10010110'

(iii) How does the receiver know where one character starts and the other finishes? There are a number of solutions to the first problem. The most straightforward answer is to allocate two voltage levels to correspond to the two logic levels, for instance,

+6 volts = '0'   (RS-232C typical levels)
-6 volts = '1'

or

+80 volts = '0' (Telegraphic systems)
-80 volts = '1'

As an alternative, current levels may be used in place of voltage levels and a very common standard for this technique is

+20 mA = '1'
 0 mA = '0'

It is frequently required that equipment should use the public telephone (as opposed to telegraph) system for communication and the regulations governing the use of this network preclude the sending of direct voltages or currents. In these circumstances, tones are used to indicate the two logic levels, typical choices being

2100 Hz = '0'
1300 Hz = '1'

This system is known as "Frequency Shift Keying" - FSK.

In order to transmit these two tones, equipment has to be placed between the data generating/data receiving equipment at either end of the link and the transmission medium (the telephone circuit). This equipment is called a MODEM (see Figure 10.17).

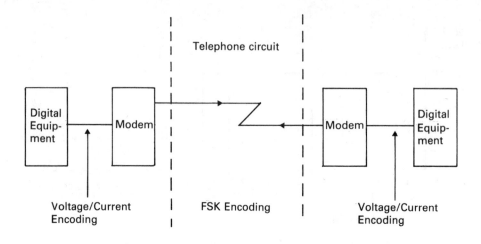

Figure 10.17: FSK Signalling over a Telephone Network

Problems (ii) and (iii) mentioned above are related since the determination of the first digit in a sequence is a prerequisite for finding the remainder. These are problems of TIMING and SYNCHRONISATION. The equipment sending the data will do so at a regular rate determined by some internal clock. All that the receiving equipment has to do is to interrogate the incoming data with the same regularity. In theory, this can be achieved by providing the receiver with a similar clock running at the same speed. However, in practice, it is never possible to ensure that two isolated clocks will run at the same speed and even the very best timing circuits, accurate to one part in a million, would drift sufficiently far apart to cause unreliable communications within 1 to 25 minutes (depending on transmission speed). Thus some provision must be made to pull the two clocks back into step at regular intervals.

It is thus accepted that both the transmitter and receiver are equipped with clocks which run at virtually the same speed and that these can be pulled into step at regular intervals (synchronised). Figure 10.18 shows three clock waveforms (a) and (b) are in synchronism but (c) is out of synchronisation with the other two even though it is virtually the same frequency.

It will be seen that at Ts the waveform (c) is pulled back into synchronism and continues thereon in step with (a) and (b) until the slight inaccuracies in timing again build up and cause them to drift out of synchronisation.

The necessary information to enable the receiving equipment to achieve synchronism with the transmitter is sent down the communications link. There are two basic methods of achieving this. Some systems send synchronising information along with every character sent (a character is typically between 5 and 8 bits), this is the START-STOP or ASYNCHRONOUS method. Other

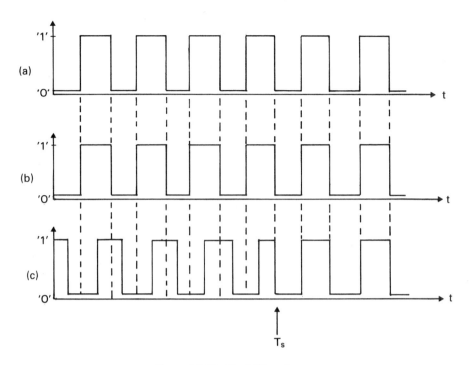

Figure 10.18: Clock Waveforms

systems send a special synchronisation pattern which is detected by the receiver and used by it to maintain synchronism for relatively long sequences of data. Both of these methods will be described in later sections.

If the receiver is able to reconstruct a timing waveform which is of the same frequency and in synchronism with that used to generate the transmitted data the problem of determining the boundaries between characters is virtually non-existent. None of this synchronisation would be necessary if it was possible for both the transmitter and receiver to utilise the same clock. This is rarely possible since the transmission of clock information would occupy a second transmission channel which is very inefficient.

10.3.1 ASYNCHRONOUS TRANSMISSION SYSTEMS

In asynchronous systems (sometimes called start-stop), each data character is sent individually and synchronisation between transmitter and receiver is established for each character. No attempt is made to maintain synchronism beyond this limit. Since characters contain at most 11 bits, the tolerance on the frequency of the clocks is quite wide.

When no data is being sent, the transmitter sends a continuous '1' level down the data link. This is the so-called IDLE condition. When data is to be sent the transmitter changes the level to '0' thus warning the receiver that information is about to be sent and providing a reference edge ('a' in Figure 10.19) so that the receiver's clock may be pulled into synchronism with that at the transmitter. This is the so-called START BIT.

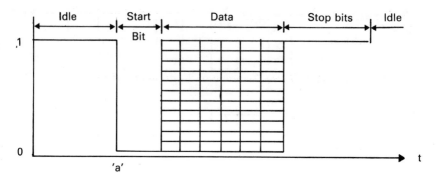

Figure 10.19: Typical Start-Stop Transmission Character

Following the start bit, a data character is sent. This typically consists of between 5 and 9 bits. Following this, the STOP BIT(S) are transmitted. This is done by transmitting a '1' over the link for 1, 1.5 or 2 bit times. The purpose of this is to enable the receiver to confirm that it has not lost synchronism during the character (it should be expecting the stop bits). Also, by making the stop bits = '1', a new start bit may follow immediately and provide the necessary transition to re-synchronise.

Both the transmitter and receiver must utilise the same technique for formatting data. This includes

(i)   nominal bit rate
(ii) number of bits in character
(iii) number of stop bits used

Many asynchronous transceivers actually use an internal clock rate that is higher than that of the nominal bit rate (usually by a factor of 4, 8 or 16). This is done so that the incoming data may be more reliably received. When data is transmitted it becomes distorted (Figure 10.20) so that the most reliable time to sample a bit to see whether it is '1' or '0' is usually half way through a bit time.

This is easily achieved with a fast clock. For instance, if the internal clock runs at four times the nominal frequency mid-bit sampling may be achieved by feeding this clock to a 2-bit counter which is reset as soon as the start bit transition is seen. If the input waveform is then sampled every time the count reaches 2, mid-bit sampling is achieved (see Figure 10.21).

212

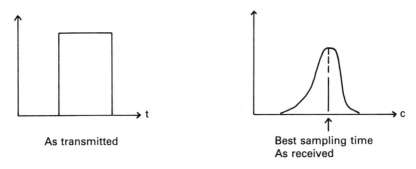

As transmitted

Best sampling time
As received

Figure 10.20: Pulse Distortion by Transmission Medium

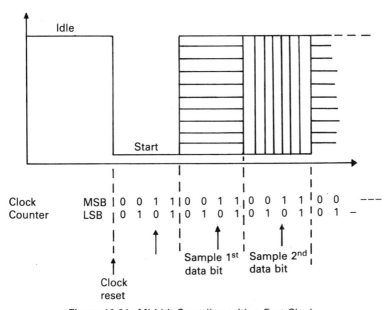

Figure 10.21: Mid-bit Sampling with a Fast Clock

A number of errors are possible with asynchronous transmission. First, the expected stop bits may not be seen by the receiver, either because they have become corrupted during transmission or because synchronism has been lost. This is termed a FRAMING ERROR. Secondly, characters may arrive too rapidly for the hardware or software of the receiver to cope. This is an OVERRUN ERROR and is a function of the receiver hardware and software rather than the transmission channel. Finally the data bits forming the character itself could become corrupted. This error would be detected either by hardware or software depending on the type of error protection which has been built into the system. For 8-bit data characters sent via asynchronous links, the most

213

usual form of error protection is provided by a parity bit. Parity error checking is usually built into the receiver hardware.

10.3.2 SYNCHRONOUS TRANSMISSION SYSTEMS

Synchronous transmission systems do not re-establish synchronism for each and every character transmitted. Instead data is sent in a continuous stream and any tendency for the receiver to drift out of synchronism is corrected periodically by the transmission of a special synchronisation character (SYN in Figure 10.22). The period between synchronisation characters could be anything between 100 and 1000 data characters depending on the circumstances (Figure 10.22a).

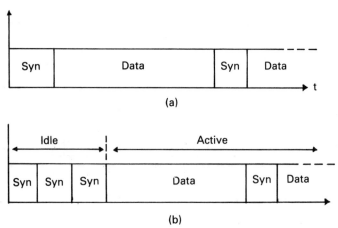

(a)

(b)

Figure 10.22: Synchronous Transmission

When the channel is idle, then continuous synchronisation characters are sent as shown in Figure 10.22b. These synchronisation characters are automatically inserted by the transmitting equipment and are automatically removed by the receiver. The user is totally unaware of the process. Should the transmitter ever run out of data to send then it will automatically insert synchronisation characters until the processor provides it with further data. In this way a continuous stream of characters is sent from transmitter to receiver.

Since synchronisation data is not sent with each character the efficiency of a synchronous system is potentially much higher than that of an asynchronous one. The receiver and transmitter must, of course, utilise the same data formatting rules. These include:

    (i)   transmission rate
    (ii)   synchronisation character(s)
    (iii) number of bits per character

There is a finite possibility of the transmitted data containing a pattern of bits which could be mistaken for the synchronisation character. This possibility is reduced if two or more synchronisation characters are used; the total synchronisation sequence then involves sending the complete set of synchronisation characters one after the other in the correct order.

The requirement that the transmitter and receiver agree over the length of each character assumes that the transmitted data is to be interpreted as a stream of characters. This is not always the case and some transmission systems do not restrict the data to be divided into (typically 8-bit) characters but rather assume it to be a continuous bit-stream. The interpretation of the received data is not really a problem concerning the method of transmission but rather of the PROTOCOL governing the conversation between transmitter and receiver. Such protocols include specifications as to how messages shall be recognised and routed, and also how errors shall be detected and corrected. It is sufficient here to remark that it is difficult to conceive how bit-stream data could be sent via a start-stop link.

An example of a character-oriented protocol for synchronous transmission is the IBM BISYNC. The format of a Bisync message is shown in Figure 10.23 where it is to be understood that the basic unit of transmission is an 8-bit character. The message starts with a pair of 8-bit synchronisation characters. Following this is the code for 'start of header' (SOH) which, in ASCII is "00000001". The next characters form the header section which carries various items of control information. The end of the header and the start of the text is indicated by the 'start of text' (SOT) character which, if ASCII is being used, will be the pattern "00000010". Following SOT is a stream of characters which represent the message to be sent. Finally the completion of the message is indicated by the 'END OF TEXT' (ETX) character which will be the bit pattern "00000011" if ASCII is being used. This is followed by a series of error control characters, the purpose of which is to verify the message sent. The header section and the 'SOH' character may be omitted.

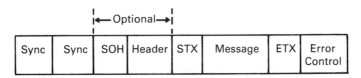

Figure 10.23: A Bisync Frame

By contrast, an example of a bit-oriented synchronous protocol is the Synchronous Data Link Control (SDLC) devised by IBM. Figure 10.24 shows a typical SDLC message frame which may be of any length and is not restricted to be multiples of a character length (bit-oriented). The frame starts with an 8-bit flag having the pattern '01111110' which serves as a synchronisation character. Following this are two 8-bit groups, the first providing address information (SDLC is designed to be used for sending messages between a number of stations in a network) and the second control information. After this comes an indefinitely long string of bits which constitute the body of the message. This is rounded off by a 16-bit error checking sequence and a repeat of the flag '01111110'.

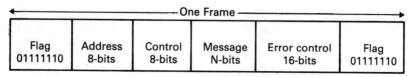

Figure 10.24: An SDLC Message Frame

The gap between frames is filled by repetitions of the flag pattern or the abort pattern ('1111 1111'). No "fill" characters are allowed in SDLC and if the data is not ready for sending when the transmitter requires it, the whole frame is aborted by sending the abort pattern.

One apparent problem for an SDLC system is the chance appearance of six consecutive '1's in the message. This will be interpreted as the flag pattern and cause premature closing of the frame. This is avoided by the transmission system which inserts a '0' after five consecutive '1's in the frame after the opening flag. This is termed 'zero bit insertion' and the inserted bit is automatically detected and removed by the receiver.

The preceding descriptions will serve to make the reader aware of the basic contrast between character-oriented protocols and bit-oriented protocols. The two examples discussed, · Bisync and SDLC, have far more detailed specifications than it is feasible to present in this section and the reader should consult the official specifications for a more complete description.

10.4 Error Control Techniques

In any data transmission operations, errors may occur. Ideally they should be detected and corrected but this is not always possible. At the very least, errors should be detected and an appropriate warning given. Errors can occur when data is transmitted from point to point whether by radio or wire systems. They can also occur when data is stored in a memory unit and subsequently recovered. The techniques used for the detection and possible correction of errors will depend very much on the nature of the transmitted data (is it a bit-stream or character-stream ?), on the transmission medium and on the nature of the phenomena which cause errors.

Two distinct classes of error may be identified as requiring different treatment, namely BURST ERRORS and SINGLE ERRORS. The former affect several adjacent bits in a transmitted message whereas the latter affect only one bit at a time with a relatively large number of uncorrupted bits separating them (Figure 10.25).

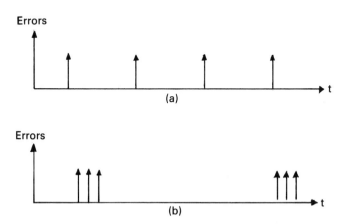

Figure 10.25: Single (a) and Burst (b) Errors in a System

It will be noted from Figure 10.25 that a system experiencing burst errors does not necessarily have a higher error rate on average. However, any error control system which operates on the assumption that errors will be isolated is bound to fail in a system which experiences burst errors.

In everyday situations, conversations are successfully carried out despite interfering noise sources such as automobiles etc. This is possible because language contains a large amount of redundancy. That is to say, the speech waveforms could be made to carry very much more information than is, in fact, transmitted during conversation. This situation arises from the operation of the various rules of grammar and pronunciation which enable the listener to 'fill in' any missed sounds with a fair degree of accuracy.

This same principle may be applied to digitally encoded information. By adding additional bits, according to some defined rule, to each character or message sent redundancy is built into the system. These redundant bits can be examined on reception and, using the same rules as were employed to generate them, they may be checked for correctness. If they appear to be incorrect, an error has occurred. There are a variety of different rules used to generate the error checking/correcting bits and some of these will be examined in the following Sections.

The sending of additional error control bits inevitably causes a loss of efficiency since they occupy valuable transmission capacity and yet do not themselves transmit useful information. They merely reduce the chance of useful information being lost. Any error control system can be characterised by:

    (i)   Its efficiency at detecting and/or correcting errors.

    (ii)   The amount of inefficiency it introduces into the system.

In this context, it should be noted that error correcting systems usually involve greater inefficiency than mere error checking systems. However, the latter introduce considerable additional inefficiency every time an error occurs since they cannot themselves correct the error, but have to request that the data be re-transmitted. The best solution in any given system depends on the size of the data blocks and the rate at which errors occur.

10.4.1 THE PARITY CHECKING SYSTEM

This is a very simple system in which one additional bit is added to each data string. The added PARITY BIT may be a '1' or a '0' depending on the characteristics of the data being protected and the type of parity system in use. The rules are as follows:

EVEN PARITY SYSTEM

    Count the number of '1's in the data being protected and set the parity bit to '1' if the count is odd or to '0' if it is even. Thus the protected character always has an even number of '1's in it.

ODD PARITY SYSTEM

    Count the number of '1's in the data being protected and set the parity bit to '1' if the count is even or to '0' if it is odd. Thus the protected character always has an odd number of '1's in it.

The operation of these rules for a 4-bit data string protected by a single parity bit is illustrated in Figure 10.26.

On reception, the data (including parity bit) is checked to see that it has an even number of '1's in an even parity system or an odd number of '1's in an odd parity system. If the received parity is satisfactory, the data is assumed to be uncorrupted and the parity bit is removed thus recovering the original data. If the received parity is wrong, an error has occurred. Unfortunately it is impossible to tell where the error is and thus correct it.

Protected by even parity	Data	Protected by odd parity
10010	0010	00010
01010	1010	11010
01111	1111	11111
10100	0100	00100
↑		↑
Parity bit		Parity bit

Figure 10.26: ODD and EVEN Parity Systems

For example

The character 0010 could be sent via an even parity system as 1 0010. A single error might cause this to be received as 10011 which, because it has odd parity, is detected as corrupt. Unfortunately, more than one legal character could give rise to this received character in the presence of a single error and so it is impossible to say what the original character was. The candidates are

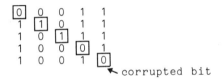

← corrupted bit

Further, it will be seen that a double error will result in a received character which has the correct parity and which, therefore, is assumed to be correct.

Thus a parity error control system can detect single errors (or triple errors) but cannot detect double (or quadruple) errors. It is, therefore, most useful in systems where burst errors are uncommon. It is, however, widely used since it involves the addition of relatively little redundant information. Parity checking is most commonly found in character-oriented transmission systems where a single parity bit is added to each character. Assuming, as is commonly the case, that each character is ASCII-encoded text, this will involve the addition of one parity bit to a 7-bit character resulting in an overall efficiency of 87%.

10.4.2 HAMMING ERROR CORRECTING CODES

The weakness of the parity check system is that it only requires two errors to transform one valid code into another. it is a "minimum distance two" code. Thus any single error generates a code word which is equidistant between a number of valid codes and there is no way in which it is possible to know which of the possibilities to accept.

In order to generate a more robust code, more redundancy (i.e. more check bits) must be added. This enables the code designer to chose his valid code words in such a way that more than two errors are required to re-create a valid code. As an example, consider the case of a code in which three errors must occur before a valid code can be re-created. If only one error occurs, the code so created will be one error away from the original valid code and two errors away from any other valid code, thus it is not difficult to deduce which is the correct original code (this assumes, of course, that single errors are more likely than double errors!). If two errors do occur then it will be possible to detect this fact but any attempt to correct it will yield a valid but erroneous code since the original code is now further away from the corrupt code than some other valid code. Thus an error control scheme based on this "minimum distance three" code could

(i)   Correct single errors, or

(ii)   Detect single and double errors

but it could not perform both functions.

An example of such a code is the Hamming Code which uses three parity check bits to protect a 4-bit data word, an overall efficiency of 57%. The code word is constructed as shown in Figure 10.27 where P is a parity bit, D is a data bit and the suffices indicate the position of the bit in the overall word.

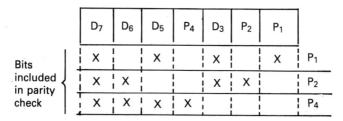

Data word = $D_7 D_6 D_5 D_3$
Parity word = $P_4 P_2 P_1$

Figure 10.27: Hamming Code

It will be seen in Figure 10.27 that each data bit is protected by two or more parity bits and that the way in which the parity bits cover the data bits follows a binary sequence. In fact, the rather odd arrangement of parity and data bits ensures that the parity word determined on checking the received character actually specifies the erroneous bit in a rather simple way.

The parity bits are inserted by applying an even parity criterion to the bits specified in Figure 10.27. This parity is checked on receipt an a '1' inserted in the parity word at the appropriate position if any of the parity checks fail.

The binary number so created actually specifies the bit position which is in error.

For Example

Data word = 1 1 0 1
D_7 D_6 D_5 D_3

Hence

$P_1 = 0$ checks D_7 D_5 D_3
$P_2 = 1$ checks D_7 D_6 D_3
$P_4 = 0$ checks D_7 D_6 D_5

Thus the transmitted word is:

1 1 0 0 1 1 0

If the received word is in error in one bit, we might receive:

1 0 0 0 1 1 0

Carrying out the parity checks yields
P_1 even, this is correct so $P_1 = 0$
P_2 odd, this is wrong so $P_2 = 1$
P_4 odd, this wrong so $P_4 = 1$.

Hence the parity word is 1 1 0 (binary 6) indicating that bit 6 of the received word (D_6) is in error and should be changed resulting in a received data word:

1 0 0 1

change D_6

1 1 0 1 = Corrected data

The same result could be achieved by applying simple logic to Figure 10.27. If both P2 and P4 fail then it is logical to assume that the fault was in a bit position covered by both of them, i.e. D6 or D7. However, D7 is also covered by P1 which is not in error so one must conclude that D6 is wrong.

The Hamming code principle may be extended for longer data words and in general, n check digits can protect [2^(n)-1-n] data bits.

Apart from their use in data transmission systems, Hamming codes have been used for memory systems in minicomputers. The 16-bit data word being protected by five check bits. This enables the machine to remain operational in the presence of a fault in a memory section and, further, provides diagnostic evidence on the frequency and position of occurrence of such errors thus simplifying maintenance, especially in the case of intermittent faults. The relatively high cost of this system, however, has meant that the simpler parity system remains the most popular for error control in memory systems.

10.4.3 BLOCK PARITY CHECKING

The parity checking of a single character may be extended to the checking of whole blocks of characters as shown in Figure 10.28 for a block consisting of five characters.

1	1	1	1	1	1
1	0	1	1	0	1
0	1	1	1	0	1
0	0	1	0	0	1
1	1	0	0	0	0
1	0	0	0	1	0
0	1	0	0	1	0
0	0	0	1	1	0

Character-level parity bits →

↑ Block-check character composed of row-parity bits

Figure 10.28: Block Parity Checking

The block check character is made up as shown with parity bits derived by considering the parity of the row. This character is then appended to the block. Using this technique it is possible to determine the position of a single error within the block as shown in Figure 10.29a. However, if two errors occur there are four possible sites for the erroneous bits and correction is not possible as shown in Figure 10.29b.

It will be seen from a comparison of Figure 10.28 with Figure 10.29b that the actual errors are in the positions indicated by the shaded boxes.

The block parity checking technique is appropriate in situations where information can naturally be divided into characters which are organised in blocks. Its error correcting possibilities may only be relied upon if the chances of two errors occurring in a whole block are small.

10.4.4 CHECKSUM TECHNIQUES

This is a very simple technique which is principally used when the information to be protected is in the form of characters. The significance of these characters is not important - they could be 8-bit data words, 16-bit data words, ASCII encoded text or any other form of data. When a string of such items are protected by a checksum, the data items are added together as if they were simply binary numbers. The result, if maintained to full precision, will usually exceed the length of the data characters and so must be shortened in some way until it only occupies the space of

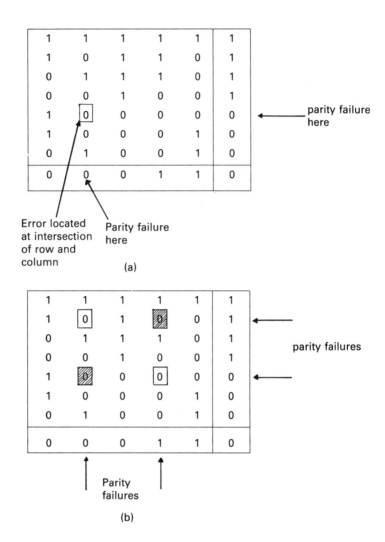

Figure 10.29: Error Detection with Block-Parity

one, or perhaps two, data characters. This truncation is achieved by simply ignoring the MOST SIGNIFICANT excess digits. Thus 8-bit characters are typically protected by a checksum of 8 or 16 bits length, any carry digits generated beyond this limit simply being ignored. The checksum so formed is then simply negated and appended to the data characters.

On recovery, a checksum is formed from the whole record and the result should, of course, be zero since the new checksum includes the old checksum and its negative.

For example, the following five 8-bit data characters are to be protected by an 8-bit checksum

```
0 0 1 1 1 1 1 1
1 0 1 1 1 1 1 1
1 0 0 0 0 0 0 0
1 1 0 0 0 0 0 0
1 1 1 0 0 0 0 0
```
$\overline{}$

1 1 0 0 0 1 1 1 1 0 = sum of characters

0 0 0 1 1 1 1 0 = truncated to 8 bits

1 1 1 0 0 0 1 0 = negated

Thus the protected data is

protected data $\begin{Bmatrix} 0 & 0 & 1 & 1 & 1 & 1 & 1 & 1 \\ 1 & 0 & 1 & 1 & 1 & 1 & 1 & 1 \\ 1 & 0 & 0 & 0 & 0 & 0 & 0 & 0 \\ 1 & 1 & 0 & 0 & 0 & 0 & 0 & 0 \\ 1 & 1 & 1 & 0 & 0 & 0 & 0 & 0 \end{Bmatrix}$ original data

$\phantom{protected data \{}$ 1 1 1 0 0 0 1 0 $\quad$ checksum

The checksum formed by the recovery equipment is the sum of all six digits, truncated to 8 bits by ignoring any digits which overflow the 8-bit limit

sum of characters = 1 0 0 0 0 0 0 0 0 0 0

truncated to 8 bits = 0 0 0 0 0 0 0 0

If an error had occurred, it is very unlikely that the new checksum would have been zero and so the presence of one or more errors would have been indicated, though not corrected.

10.4.5 CYCLIC REDUNDANCY CHECKING

In many ways this technique is similar to that of checksum generation as it produces a (typically) 16-bit check character which is appended to the data stream and subsequently checked when the data is recovered. The particular advantage of this scheme, however, is that it can be applied to bit streams, whether or not there are implied character boundaries, and furthermore it can be implemented by rather simple shift-register logic. This means that the generation of a cyclic redundancy check (CRC) character does not impose an overhead on the processor. Both these advantages mean that it is ideally suited to disk and tape storage systems in which context it is widely used. The arithmetic process involved in the generation of a CRC is that of division as distinct from the addition process used for checksum generation.

In CRC checking every binary number is thought of as defining a polynomial, for instance:

1 1 0 0 1

is thought of as

$$P(X) = 1*X^0 + 1*X^1 + 0*X^2 + 0*X^3 + 1*X^4 = 1 + X + X^4$$

Notice that the least significant bit of the number is associated with the highest power of $P(X)$.

In order to generate the CRC character, the polynomial represented by the data, $D(X)$ is divided by a CRC generating polynomial, $P(X)$ resulting in a quotient polynomial, $Q(X)$ and, in general, a remainder polynomial $R(X)$.

It is the binary number associated with this remainder polynomial which is added to the data stream as a CRC character.

Now $D(X) = P(X)Q(X)+R(X)$

or $D(X)-R(X) = P(X)Q(X)$ 10.1

Now if all the arithmetic is carried out "modulo 2", all "carries" and "borrows" will be ignored and so will not affect the calculation. This results in the strange situation of addition being the same as subtraction (see Appendix E). Using this fact, equation 10.1 can be rewritten as

$D(X)-R(X) = D(X)+R(X) = P(X)Q(X)$ 10.2

Now the data stream actually transmitted or recorded, $D'(X)$, is the original data stream with the remainder added.

i.e. $D'(X) = D(X)+R(X)$ 10.3

When the data stream is eventually recovered, the WHOLE of it is divided by $P(X)$ using modulo 2 arithmetic. This will, in general, form a new quotient $Q''(X)$ and a new remainder $R''(X)$. Denoting the received data, including errors as $D''(X)$, we have

$D''(X) = P(X)Q''(X)+R''(X)$ 10.4

However, if there have been no errors

$D''(X) = D'(X)$

which, from equations 10.2 and 10.3 is an exact multiple of $P(X)$ and so there will be no remainder $R''(X)$ and this constitutes the error check. It is very unlikely that a sequence of errors will provide a zero remainder on recovery if the polynomial, $P(X)$, is well chosen.

The final stage of the process of generating $D'(X)$ is one of addition, which can be relatively time consuming. However, if the addition can be arranged to be one in which R(X) is added to zeros only, the process becomes trivial. This is readily achieved by taking the actual data stream and appending M zeros to it to form the D(X) used in the calculations. The number M is chosen so that the zeros create just enough space for the remainder. Thus if the generator polynomial is of order n, the remainder will be, at most, of order n - 1 and will, therefore, contain no more than (n - 1) + 1 digits. So it is sufficient to append n zeros to the most significant end of the data string. These correspond to the LOWEST powers of P(X).

Thus, to summarise, the CRC checking procedure involves

    (i)   Appending n zeros to the end of the data stream.

    (ii)   Dividing the data stream by a generator polynomial (of order n).

    (iii)   Appending the remainder from this division to the data stream.

    (iv)   On recovery, dividing the whole recovered data stream by the generator polynomial.

    (v)   If the remainder in (iv) is zero, no errors have occurred.

All arithmetic operations are carried out "modulo 2".

This process may now be illustrated by a simple example. Very short data streams will be used to simplify the working.

Data stream = 1 1 0 0 1

Generator polynomial = $X^3 + X + 1 = P(X)$

Append n(=3) zeros to the data stream to form D(X)

New data stream = 0 0 0 1 1 0 0 1

$D(X) = X^7 + 0 + 0 + X^4 + X^3 + 0 + 0 + 0$

Dividing out using modulo 2 arithmetic throughout

$$
\begin{array}{r}
X^4+X^2 \\
\hline
X^3+X+1 \overline{\smash{\big)}\ X^7+0+0+X^4+X^3+0+0+0} \\
\underline{X^7+0+X^5+X^4} \\
-X^5 \\
X^5+0+X^3 \\
\underline{X^5+0+X^3+X^2} \\
-X^2 \\
X^2+0+0 = \text{REMAINDER } R(X)
\end{array}
$$

modulo 2

modulo 2

Thus the transmitted data stream is

```
From D(X)     0 0 0 1 1 0 0 1
From R(X)     0 0 1
              _____
              0 0 1 1 1 0 0 1  =  D'
              _____
```

If this is received uncorrupted we have

$$D'' = 0 0 1 1 1 0 0 1 = D'$$

and dividing $D''(X)$ by the generator polynomial gives

$$
X^3+X+1 \enclose{longdiv}{X^7+0+0+X^4+X^3+X^2+0+0} \quad X^4+X^2
$$

X^4+X^2

X^3+X+1 ⟌ $X^7+0+0+X^4+X^3+X^2+0+0$

$X^7+0+X^5+X^4$

$-X^5$

modulo 2

$X^5+0+X^3+X^2$

$X^5+0+X^3+X^2$

$0+0+0+0+0+0$ REMAINDER=0

∴ NO ERRORS

If, however, the data stream had been corrupted we might have

$$D'' = 1 0 1 1 1 0 0 1 \neq D'$$

and dividing this by the generator polynomial gives

X^4+X^2

X^3+X+1 ⟌ $X^7+0+0+X^4+X^3+X^2+0+1$

$X^7+0+X^5+X^4$

$-X^5$

modulo 2

$X^5+0+X^3+X^2$

$X^5+0+X^3+X^2$

$0 \quad 0 \quad 0 \quad 0 \quad 0 \quad 1$ NON-ZERO REMAINDER

∴ ERRORS PRESENT

It was mentioned earlier that the CRC character could be generated by a simple shift register. Figure 10.30 shows just such an arrangement for the generator polynomial used in the preceding example.

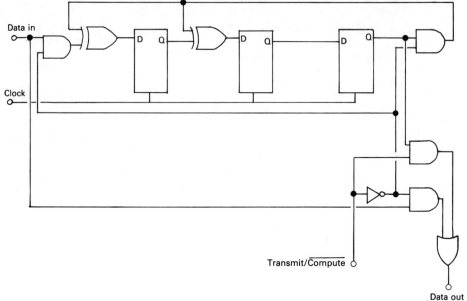

Figure 10.30: CRC Generator

The feedback taps used in the generator may best be understood by writing out the equation

$$P(X) = X^3 + X + 1 = 0$$

or

$$X^3 = -(X + 1)$$

$$= X + 1 \quad (\text{modulo } 2)$$

If shift register stage 1 is thought of as representing X^0, then stage 2 represents X^1, stage 3 represents X^2 and so that which is shifted from stage 3 (to a non-existent stage 4) represents X^3. But from the equation $X^3 = X + 1$ so the shifted out bit is returned to the X^0 and X^1 stages as shown.

In operation, the shift register initially contains all zeros and the data stream is applied to the 'DATA IN' terminal and the shift register clocked in synchronism. The 'TRANSMIT' terminal is held at logic '0' so the input stream appears also at 'DATA OUT'. When the data stream is complete, the CRC character is in the shift register and is shifted out to the 'DATA OUT' terminal by three clock pulses. The 'TRANSMIT' control is at logic '1' during this time. The AND gates in the input path and feedback loop are disabled at this time, thus ensuring that the system acts as a simple shift register.

The device may be used to check the validity of incoming data in which case the shift register should contain all zeros when the data stream is complete if no errors have occurred.

The generator polynomial used in the above example was necessarily rather simple. In practice a more complex polynomial such as

$$P(X) = X^{16} + X^{12} + X^5 + 1$$

is used. The shift register logic required for the implementation of this and similar polynomials may be obtained as a single device such as the Motorola MC8503.

10.5 Data Encryption

The discussion in the previous section concerned the protection of data, during transmission, against randomly occurring errors with a view to at least detecting those errors and possibly correcting them also. Because computing equipment has become so inexpensive, it is now widely used in many applications such as point-of-sale terminals, bank till units and the like. These provide immense operational advantages for the enterprises which use them since they are readily connected to a stock control or credit control system.

This connection may be of considerable distance (thus using serial transmission techniques) and may well use part of the public telephone system. As a result the data transmitted is subject both to random accidental errors and also to deliberate interception. This latter hazard may be carried out with a view to simply disorganising the data flow, but is much more likely to be for the purpose of illicit data gathering or so that different, but apparently correct, data may be substituted. These circumstances constitute a privacy and authentication problem which will become even more widespread if electronic mail distribution becomes commonplace.

In order to protect the privacy of data, it must be encyphered. To encypher data the original, non-encyphered material (PLAINTEXT) is processed according to a particular prescription which results in the generation of a protected CYPHERTEXT. This is received and subjected to another processing operation after which the original plaintext is recovered.

The security of this procedure depends on two factors:

(i)   The "bad guys" do not know the method used for encypherment/decypherment. That is, they are ignorant of the CRYPTOSYSTEM in use.

(ii)   The "bad guys" do not know the particular KEY
        used to encypher the message which they have
        intercepted.

If either of these conditions holds, then the security of the
data will not be compromised. The encyphered data may be
attacked in order to determine the plaintext but the methods
chosen for encypherment are such that the absence of either
one of the two factors defined above results in a
computational problem of such enormous proportions that the
solution is not feasible. It has been suggested that, at
present, any task which requires more than 10^{50} operations
is computationally unfeasible.

Considering the situation as it affects modern electronic
equipment, it is clearly not possible to provide every
organisation with a different method of encyphering data
since this would result in the production of a large number
of uneconomic one-off devices. Instead a common cryptosystem
has been widely adopted and the security of data is solely
dependent on the secrecy of the cypher keys. This
cryptosystem, which is now widely used, is called the US
Federal Information Processing Data Encryption Standard (DES).

The DES utilises a 56-bit binary key to achieve the
encypherment of data and the data is treated in 64-bit blocks.
Decypherment is achieved using the same 56-bit key. Special
purpose I/O processors are available for the implementation
of this algorithm, one example being the Intel 8294 Data
Encryption Unit which can handle data at a rate of 640 bits
per second.

Figure 10.31 illustrates how the DES processes plaintext into
cyphertext. Initially the 64 bits are scrambled to form a new
64 bit word which is then processed. The 64 bits are divided
into two halves. The first (left) half is processed by having
a modified form of the right half added to it. The
modification takes the form of combining the right half of
the data with an encyphering key, K , which is itself formed
from a subset of the 56-bit key. The processed left half then
becomes right half for the next stage. Likewise the right
half, which has not been processed, becomes the new left half.
This process is repeated a further fifteen times, at each
stage a different key is used but all keys are derived from
the basic 56-bit key. Finally, after a further stage of
scrambling the cyphertext is available.

Any system which relies on keys alone for its security is, of
course, subject to the problem of distributing the keys to
the "good guys" without the "bad guys" gaining possession of
them. The distribution of such keys could be by secure mail
and preferably they would be changed frequently. However, a
much more convenient method would be to use an ordinary public
channel to exchange keys. The objection to this is that the
"bad guys" can overhear the conversation but this need not be
a problem if ONE WAY FUNCTIONS are used to encode keys.

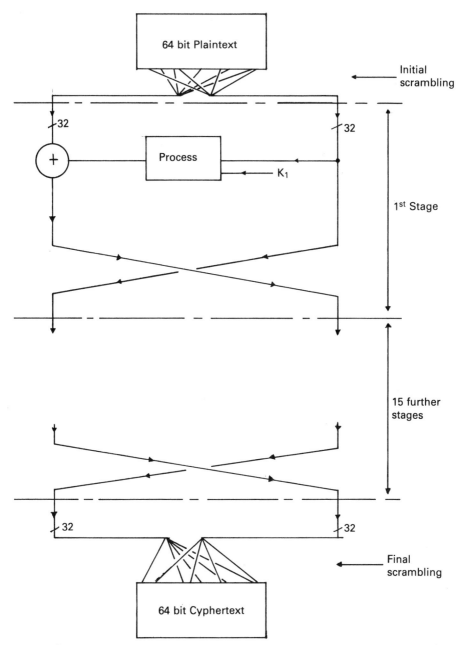

Figure 10.31: US Data Encryption Standard – General Scheme

A one way function may be defined as follows:

$H(X)$ is a one way function if, given $Y=H(X)$, it is easy to find Y for a given X but computationally unfeasible to determine X given Y.

This property may be used to allow two parties to a transaction, the "good guys", to agree on a key K with the "bad guys" listening even if the bad guys know which one-way function is in use.

The first party chooses a key K1 and transmits to the second party

$$K_1^* = H(K_1)$$

Likewise the second party chooses a key K2 and sends to the first party

$$K_2^* = H(K_2)$$

The information now available to the parties is

Good guys		Bad guys
1st Party	2nd Party	
$K_1^*=H(K_1)$	$K_1^*=H(K_1)$	$K_1^*=H(K_1)$
'K$_1$	K$_2$	
$K_2^*=H(K_2)$	$K_2^*=H(K_2)$	$K_2^*=H(K_2)$

If the one way function is chosen such that

$$K_1^* K_2 = K_2^* K_1 = K$$

both of the "good guys" have sufficient information to compute the encryption key K. However, the "bad guys" do not have this information since they do not possess K1 or K2 and they cannot discover it because of the one way properties of H.

10.6 Voice Communication Systems

Voice communication systems are becoming more common as the as the techniques of voice synthesis and voice recognition become developed. At present voice recognition techniques are not as well developed as voice synthesis and it is this latter area which is beginning to find commercial application.

Voice communication between machine and operator are valuable for a number of purposes such as giving warnings of action when the operator may not be expecting it and also to provide essential information when the operator's visual senses need to be concentrated away from conventional indicators etc. Examples of these application areas might be:

(i)   An automatic robot capable of giving an audible warning of its actions prior to carrying them out.

(ii)   An aircraft system capable of providing the pilot with, say, airspeed information during take off and landing when his attention needs to be directed out of the flight deck windows.

A number of approaches to the production of human-like speech are possible. The most direct method is simply to record, in an analogue fashion, the words and phrases required and then to replay them in the required sequence. This was the approach used by the early speaking clock machines. A direct development of this is the use of digital recording techniques to replace the analogue recording process. In this approach, the speech waveform is sampled at regular intervals and the resulting sample converted into a digital code. When the digitised word or phrase is required, the process is simply reversed. This approach requires the storage of approximately 10,000 bytes of data for every second of speech. Fortunately, the data can be compressed using various techniques but even the most economical digital recording requires between 1,000 and 2,000 bytes of data for every second of speech.

Speech, in fact, consists of two basic types of sound, the so-called "voiced" sounds and the fricatives. The former are responsible for the characteristic pitch of a voice and consist of an underlying pitch frequency while the latter are broadband and noise-like. (For example, sh!) Both basic sounds are modified by the vocal tract to give the audible sound. At any given time, the vocal tract may be modelled as an acoustic filter with a characteristic frequency response and may be simulated by a digital filter. Thus the sound being produced by a speaker at any given time may be described by

(i)   The presence or otherwise of fricative noise.

(ii)   The frequency of any pitched sound present.

(iii)   The coefficients of a digital filter which matches the characteristics of the vocal tract.

In a typical speech synthesiser based on this approach, the equipment applies the appropriate sound sources (i) and (ii) to a digital filter described by (iii) and the resulting waveform applied to an amplifier and loudspeaker.

Since the shape of the vocal tract is constantly changing, the filter coefficients used must also be changed. Likewise the presence or otherwise of fricative noise will vary as will the tension of the vocal chords. This latter revealing itself in changes in the pitched sounds. Consequently the data supplied to a speech synthesiser of this type must be constantly updated, a task which is usually carried out by the microprocessor driving the synthesiser. To maintain reasonable quality speech requires about 200 bytes of data for every second of speech - a considerable improvement over digital recording techniques. A typical device of the vocal-tract-modelling variety is the General Instrument SP-0250 which is readily interfaced to a microprocessor.

Using the above techniques, speech-like sounds may be produced. The question arises, however, of how the speech is to be divided up. The potentially most economical method is to divide the speech into phonemes. These are the basic building blocks of speech sounds and there are 44 such phonemes in the English language. By constructing a data base of the characteristics of each phoneme, it is, in principle, possible to build up any word or phrase by simply stringing together phonemes. Unfortunately, the actual sound of each phoneme is modified by those surrounding it and this considerably complicates the situation and reduces the quality of phoneme-based synthetic speech.

Alternatively the data base may be made up the characteristics of whole words. This inevitably means that there is considerable duplication of phoneme information but the context-dependent nature of each occurrence is maintained.

Finally the data base could be made up of whole phrases. Again efficiency drops but the quality of such synthesised speech is the highest obtainable.

10.7 Buffering of Data Input and Output

It frequently happens in real applications that the rate of production of data by one process is not synchronised with the rate of absorption of that data by the consuming process. Examples of such situations are not difficult to find, for instance, there is absolutely no reason why the rate at which an operator is able to provide keyboard input should be in any way related to the rate at which that data can be used.

Whenever this situation occurs, it is possible to decouple the processes to some extent by providing a data buffer. This is essentially a pool of data into which the data producing process puts its data and from which the data consuming process draws its data. The two processes can then proceed independently except for two situations:

(i)   When the buffer is full, the producer must stop.

(ii)   When the buffer is empty, the consumer must stop.

In a well designed system, the size of the buffer should be sufficiently well chosen so that these situations occur only rarely. On the other hand, the buffer size should not be so great that it is mostly empty as this would be a great waste of memory space.

In order to illustrate the concepts involved in the organisation of a buffer consider the situation which exists when a fast paper-tape reader is used to supply data to some consumer process. Because of the nature of the data items they are normally required in the order in which they were read thus the first item into the buffer is the first item out. This is completely different organisation of the storage area compared to that which applies for a stack. The buffer store (or First-In-First-Out store, FIFO) must have both an entry point and a removal point and therefore requires two pointers:

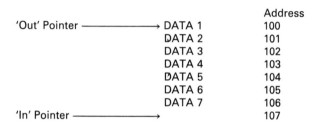

Figure 10.32: Use of 'IN' and 'OUT' Pointers

In Figure 10.32 the next item to be input will be inserted at location 107 while the next item to be extracted will come from location 100.

The two pointers will usually move at different rates with the result that the buffer will either grow in size or contract. One result of the simple structure shown above is that the "out" pointer follows the "in" pointer and the whole buffer gradually moves right through the memory! In this form of linear buffer, it is possible to tell when the buffer is empty simply by testing to see whether the "out" pointer has caught up with the "in" pointer.

The problem of the buffer moving through memory can be solved by noting that, after a while, the "out" pointer will probably have moved away from the starting position, thus freeing some of the early storage locations in the buffer. The "in" pointer can be re-positioned to start filling these spare locations.

In this scheme, the two pointers follow each other round in a circle - the so-called circular buffer (or ring buffer).

This, of course, makes the buffer a defined length and care must be taken to ensure that the "in" pointer does not overtake the "out" pointer, thus overwriting some entries in the buffer.

In ring buffers, there is the rather ambiguous situation that if the "out" pointer is equal to the "in" pointer the buffer is either completely empty, or completely full.

This difficulty can be overcome by maintaining a count of the number of words in the buffer.

Assuming that the paper-tape reader is operating under interrupt control, the two flowcharts (in Figure 10.33) will show how a circular buffer could be organised. It requires a "full" flag which is set when the buffer is full, an "empty" flag for the opposite situation and an "idle" flag to indicate that the tape-reader is ready to read, but is not doing so (perhaps because the buffer is full). A word count and "in" and "out" pointers are also required.

The initial values of the pointers etc., are:

```
"In" pointer      - Start of buffer
"Out" pointer     - Start of buffer
Empty flag        - Set (1)
Full flag         - Clear (0)
Idle flag         - Set (1)
Word count        - Zero
```

The flags referred to are not the hardware flags referred to in Chapters 7 and 8 but reserved memory locations used for communication between the producer and consumer processes.

Starting from the above initial conditions, the main program requires data and enters the section shown in Figure 10.33b. It finds the empty flag set and so checks the idle flag which is also set. Thus the main program causes the tape reader to run. The process of fetching a character takes some 5ms and so the main program idles around the loop testing the empty flag (which remains set) and the idle flag (which is now clear).

Eventually the empty flag is cleared and the main program may proceed to fetch the character from the buffer and to manipulate the word count and out pointer. The full flag is cleared since the main program has just extracted a word.

The out pointer is now tested to determine whether it exceeds the buffer limits. On the first pass this cannot be, but subsequently this situation can arise and the resetting process is needed to make the buffer, logically, a ring.

Next the word count is checked to see if the extraction process has emptied the buffer. If not the processing is complete, but if it has the empty flag must be set to prohibit any subsequent attempts to extract items from the buffer.

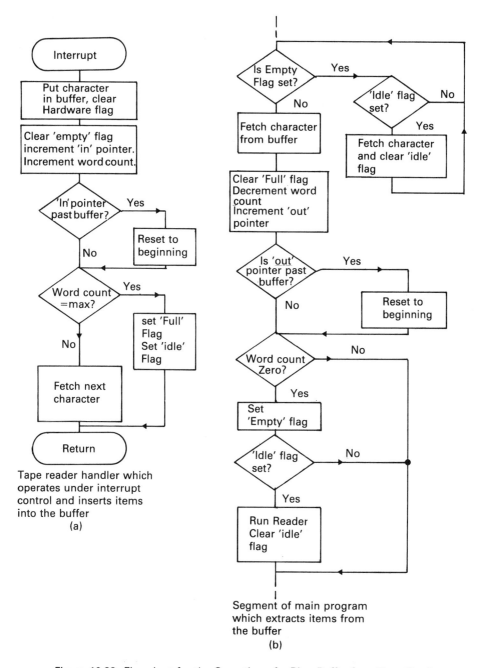

Figure 10.33: Flowchart for the Operation of a Ring Buffer for a Tape Reader

237

At this stage, if the tape reader is idle, no further items will be fetched and so to save time later, the reader is set running again. This task could be omitted in which circumstance, at the next attempt to obtain data from the buffer, the program would have to idle around the first loop as outlined above.

The main program would not normally contain the processing stages shown in Figure 10.33b at every point where data is required from the buffer. Instead this buffer emptying task would be written as a utility subroutine to be called when required.

The interrupt routine is quite simple. The tape reader is only allowed to run when the buffer is not full so the fetched character is placed directly in the buffer and the word count, "in" pointer and empty flag manipulated. The "in" pointer is checked to see whether it has gone outside the limits of the buffer and reset if necessary and finally, if the buffer is full, the full flag and idle flag are set. If the buffer is not full a further character is fetched.

It will be noticed that a number of flags and counters are shared between the two processes shown in Figure 10.33, and since it is possible for the interrupt routine to interrupt the main program it is possible that the two processes could both attempt to manipulate these flags at almost the same time thus confusing the situation. This is a fairly complex situation which often occurs between what are known as "co-operating sequential processes". It is discussed in a little more detail in Section 12.8.

The illustration given above implicitly assumes that the program has control of the producer device and can switch it off. This is clearly not always true, for instance, there is no way in which a keyboard operator can be turned off! This situation is usually handled by:

(i)   issuing a warning, and/or

(ii)   ignoring all further input and failing to acknowledge its receipt.

These are frequently combined so that subsequent keystrokes do not produce the normal echoed feedback of the character struck but instead an audible warning tone is issued for every ignored keystroke.

Finally a comment on buffer sizing is appropriate. The rate of production of data and its rate of consumption can be characterised by their average values. However, the arrival of data items and their removal are usually random events and there may be periods of time during which the actual arrival and departure rates vary from the average. It is for just this situation that buffers are required. The study of these situations makes use of queuing theory which takes account of the statistics of the data production and consumption processes. A study of this topic is beyond the scope of this

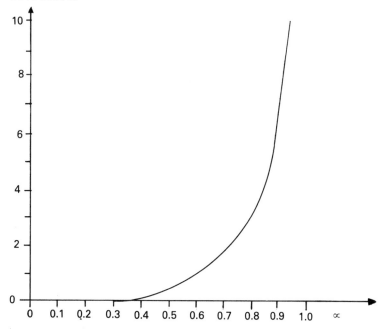

Figure 10.34: Average Occupancy of the Buffer

text but Figure 10.34 illustrates the way in which the steady-state number of items in a buffer varies with the ratio α defined as

$$\alpha = \frac{\text{average rate of production of data items}}{\text{average rate of removal of data items}}$$

It should be pointed out that Figure 10.34 gives the steady-state size of the buffer and the actual occupancy will vary from this figure.

Figure 10.35 shows the proportion of the time for which the buffer will contain more than a defined number of data items for various values of α.

Percentage of time for which the
buffer contains more than N data items

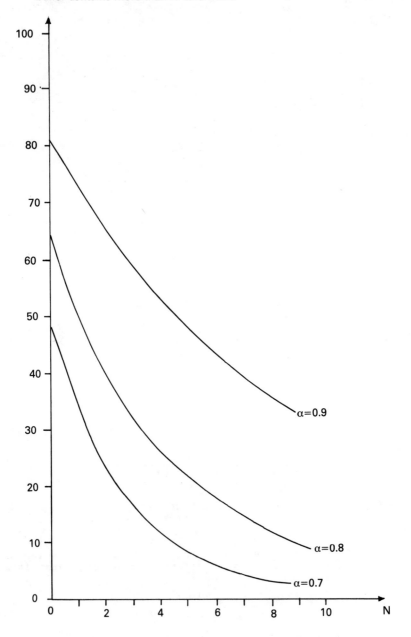

Figure 10.35: Frequency of Occurrence of a Given Buffer Occupancy

11. Techniques for Bulk Storage of Data

Although many microprocessors find application in relatively simple dedicated systems, a significant number are used in systems requiring the storage of large amounts of data or programs. It is not usually feasible to provide this storage in the form of ordinary read-write memory as discussed in Chapter 6 and so the system designer must resort to the use of various bulk storage techniques. These are frequently termed mass storage systems. Techniques which may be included under this heading are:

    (i)   magnetic drum storage
    (ii)   fixed head rigid disk storage
    (iii) moving head disk storage
    (iv)   "industry standard" digital tape storage
    (v)   floppy disk storage
    (vi)   digital cassette storage
    (vii) audio cassette storage
    (viii) "Winchester" disk systems
    (ix)   magnetic bubble storage

The first four classes of storage system are found only very rarely with microprocessor based systems. They represent the high cost, high speed, high reliability sector of the market and are most commonly found in general purpose minicomputer and mainframe computer applications. All methods except (ix) above involve high precision mechanical moving parts and so are inherently less reliable then solid state memory systems.

Because of this applications-balance, the discussion

presented in this Chapter will, in the main, be confined to cassette tape and floppy disk systems.

Before proceeding with the discussion of mass storage systems for microprocessor-based equipment, it is helpful to list some of the particular applications areas in which it may be necessary to make use of these techniques. Such applications might include

(i)   Data logging systems

(ii)   Systems where extensive set up data is required and the circumstances preclude the use of ROMs

(iii)   Systems where a large variety of applications programs are required but only one or two need to be executable at any one time

(iv)   Microcomputers.

11.1 Flexible Disk Storage Systems

The flexible disk (or diskette, or floppy disk) makes use of traditional magnetic tape technology. The disk consists of a 7.8" diameter disk of polyester material coated with a magnetic oxide recording surface. The whole unit is contained in a sealed sleeve with apertures for access as shown in Figure 11.1.

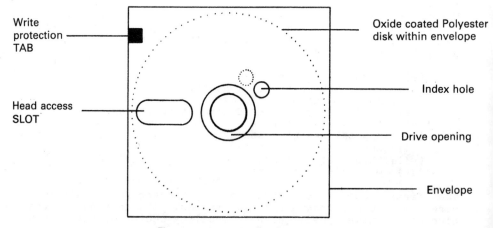

Figure 11.1: A Flexible Disk

To make use of the disk, it is inserted into the drive and the door shut. This operates the driving mechanism by causing a tapered cone to enter the drive hole in the centre of the disk thus clamping it to the motor drive. The polyester disk is now rotating at 360rpm.

Data is recorded on the disk in a series of 77 concentric tracks. The record/replay head is positioned over the required track by a stepper-motor-operated drive which rotates a threaded leadscrew or a flexible metal band. When the disk drive is first switched on, the motor drives the head to the very edge of the disk (track 00). Once this position is established, the head may be moved to any specified track by simply causing the leadscrew to rotate a certain number of times. Since stepper motors are pulse operated and always move the same distance for each pulse received it is a simple matter for the electronics of the system to keep track of the head position. This can also be verified from special identifiers which are subsequently read from the disk (see later). Should there be a disagreement between the drive electronics and the identifier information, the head is driven to the physical limits at track 00 and the system re-initialised. This is known as a RESTORE operation.

Once the head has been correctly positioned, it may be brought into contact with the disk through the slotted aperture in the envelope. Normally the head is kept out of contact with the disk to reduce wear on both the disk and the head. This procedure is known as HEAD LOADING and takes approximately 16ms. Now that the head is both positioned and loaded, data may be written to or read from the disk. Data is written in a bit-serial manner and up to about 42,000 bits may be accommodated on each track (5250 bytes). This is much more than may be conveniently handled by most systems and so each track is divided up into a number of sectors. Typically 8 sectors of 512 bytes, 15 sectors of 256 bytes or 26 sectors of 128 bytes may be used. This does not use the full capacity of 5250 bytes per track and the inefficiency arises because a sector identifying mark (containing other data also) has to be written at the start of each sector. A single absolute reference mark is provided by the index hole punched in the disk and sensed by a photosensor. Figure 11.2(a) shows this sectoring technique which is known as SOFT SECTORING.

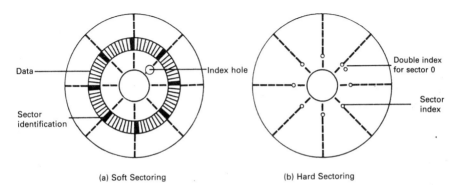

(a) Soft Sectoring   (b) Hard Sectoring

Figure 11.2: Disk Sectoring techniques

243

The inefficiency associated with soft sectoring can be avoided by making use of HARD SECTORING. This involves punching an index hole at each sector boundary and a double hole as a reference indicator.

Data may only be written to the disk or read from it in blocks, each block consisting of the contents of one sector of one track. In a soft sectored system, each block consists of a header section occupying 30 bytes followed by a data section of 128 (or 256 or 512) bytes plus three additional bytes which are used for timing and error checking. The header section contains information on:

(i)   Track number
(ii)   Sector number
(iii)   Size of sector
(iv)   Side of disk (for double-sided disks only).

This information enables the system to confirm that the head is correctly positioned and to initiate a restore operation if not. Both the data and the header are read and written as serial bit streams and are accordingly protected by cyclic redundancy check characters as described in Section 10.4.5.

The time taken to access data may readily be calculated. If the head is already loaded and on the correct track then, provided that the addressed sector is just arriving at the reading position, data can be extracted almost immediately. At the other extreme, the data may be required from the innermost track while the head is on the outermost one, the head may be unloaded and the required sector may just have passed. In this case the access time would be

(a)   76 x time to step one track (10ms)   = 76 x 10   = 760ms
(b)   time for one complete revolution at 360rpm   = 167ms
(c)   time to load head   = 16ms

Total Access Time   943ms

The terms (a) and (c) above are subject to variation between manufacturers and some drives have a track stepping time of as little as 6ms. Item (b) above is a function of the rotational speed which is standardised between manufacturers. However, a 2.4% tolerance is permitted so that the drive system can be reduced in cost by avoiding the need for servo controlled spindle motors. As a result there can be significant variations from one drive to another and, to ensure that the data can be read reliably, clocking information is carried on the disk along with the data. The technique most widely used on floppy disks is called DOUBLE FREQUENCY or FREQUENCY MODULATION recording and is shown in Figure 11.3.

In general, magnetic recording involves the establishment of small areas of magnetisation on the tape or disk surface. This magnetisation will have one of two directions (e.g. North magnetic pole to the left or right) which are indicated as positive or negative in Figure 11.3c.

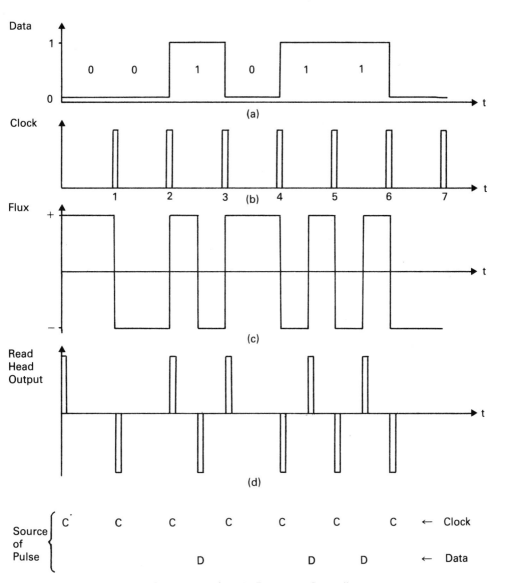

Figure 11.3: Double Frequency Recording

The problem of reading the data from a disk is very similar
to that of receiving synchronous serial data. The receiver
needs to know when to expect a data bit and this information
is provided by a local clock circuit which is held in
synchronism with the clock used for recording by clock data
on the disk track. At every clock edge the direction of
magnetisation is changed as shown for the first two clock
pulses in Figures 11.3b and 11.3c. In addition another change

of magnetisation is generated halfway between the clock
pulses if the data being recorded is a logic 1. This is shown
between clock pulses 2 and 3, and between clock pulses 4 and
6 in Figure 11.3c.

On reading the recorded data, a pulse will be output from the
reading head for every flux change as shown in Figure 11.3d.
Some of these pulses are due to clock information and some
due to data. In the receiving electronics, the clock pulses
are extracted and used to keep the local clock in synchronism.
This leaves the data-generated pulses which are extracted and
used to provide logic '1' levels in the output data stream.

Before this can be successfully carried out, the local clock
must be synchronised and this is achieved by a
synchronisation pattern recorded at the start of both the
header and data sections of each sector.

If a continuous logic '1' is present in the input data, the
magnetisation will change direction at twice the clock
frequency while if a continuous logic '0' is recorded, the
magnetisation changes direction at the clock frequency itself.
This gives the technique its name.

The maximum frequency that may be recorded is determined by
the rotational speed of the disk and the design of the
recording heads. It is approximately 500 kHz. This must
correspond to the double frequency recording and so that
maximum rate at which data bits may be recorded is the same
as the clock frequency, namely 250 kHz. If a method of
recording could be devised so that there was no need to double
the frequency of flux changes, then the data could be
recorded at 500 kHz and the disk capacity would be doubled.

This can, in fact, be done and the floppy disk is then said
to be being used in DOUBLE DENSITY mode. This is quite simply
achieved by deleting unnecessary clock pulses. Data bits are
recorded exactly as before with a flux change between clock
pulses for a logic '1' and no flux change for a logic '0'.
However, the clock induced flux changes are eliminated unless
two adjacent data bits are zero. Thus a continuous logic '0'
will record as flux changes at the clock frequency occurring
at clock pulse times and a continuous logic '1' will record as
flux changes at the clock frequency occurring between clock
pulse times. This recording technique is termed MODIFIED
FREQUENCY MODULATION (MFM) and is illustrated in Figure 11.4.

It will be noticed that the lowest output frequency occurs
when alternate '1's and '0's are recorded. The capacity of a
floppy disk system may be further increased to a total of 1.2
million bytes by using both sides of the disk.

The methods described so far conform broadly to the IBM 3470
format (single density) and the IBM system 34 (double
density) which have become industry standards. It is possible
to increase the disk capacity further by deviating from these
standards and it is currently possible to buy floppy disk
systems capable of storing two million bytes of data in a
double-sided, double-density format.

246

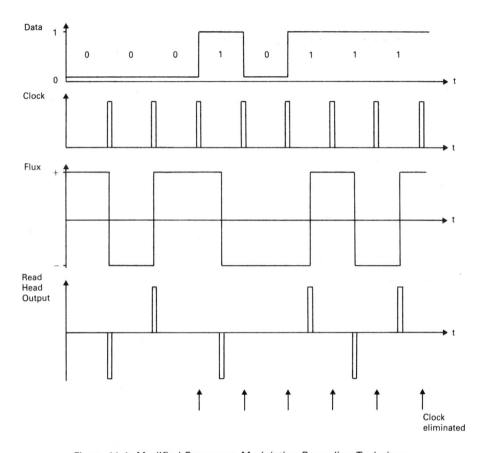

Figure 11.4: Modified Frequency Modulation Recording Technique

For small systems, reduced size floppy disk drives are becoming popular. These feature a maximum disk capacity of about 100,000 bytes on a 5.25" diameter single-sided, single-density disk and are popularly known as "mini-floppies".

The reliability of floppy disks is quite high considering that the devices are not protected by air filters. The life of a read/write head is of the order of 10^4 hours of head-to-disk contact and disk life is about 10^6 passes per track. Errors occur approximately one in every 10^9 bits, but many of these are so-called "soft" errors and can be recovered by re-reading the erroneous block of data. If this is done up to ten times, the proportion of errors remaining drops to about one in 10^{12} bits. The control of floppy disk drives is well catered for by some highly integrated interface adaptors such as Intel's 8271/8272 and Motorola's MC6843.

11.2 Digital Cassette Recording

Digital recording cassettes are very similar to their domestic audio recording counterparts being available in the same format and same tape width, 4mm. The tape itself is of a somewhat higher quality and each cassette contains from 50 to 100 metres of tape (compared with 175 metres in a C60 audio cassette). Information is recorded in a twin-track format and the use of a cassette-type enclosure provides enhanced protection and easier handling when compared with the 'industry standard' open reel tapes used in large main frame computer installations. This added protection and ease of handling is entirely appropriate for the type of use likely to be experienced in microprocessor based systems.

The most important single difference in operational characteristics between floppy disk storage and cassette tape storage is the greatly increased access time required for the latter. Data is stored on cassette in blocks, each new block being recorded after the last recorded block. Data may only be recovered in the form of whole blocks. The time taken to recover a particular piece of data is determined by its position relative to the read head. If the tape happens to be positioned so that the required block is the next one to come under the read head, then recovery will be instantaneous whereas if the required block is at the far end of the tape, a considerable time may elapse before the data is recovered.

In order to recover data the tape drive runs at a relatively high speed searching for the gaps between data blocks. These are counted and used to determine when the required block is reached. A typical drive might carry out this search operation at between 1 and 2.5 metres per second giving a worst case access time for a block of data of between 100 seconds and 40 seconds with 100 metre tapes. This is very much worse than that achieved by floppy disk systems.

Once the data block is located, the tape drive slows to its reading/recording speed of between 0.2 and 0.5 metres per second. At these rates data will be transferred from the tape at rates of 800 and 2,000 bytes per second respectively. This is much less than the 62,500 bytes per second obtainable from double-density floppy disks.

The recording of data on digital cassette tapes has been standardised at 30 bits/mm (800 bits/inch) by the American National Standards Institute (ANSI specification X3B1/579 1972), and this figure has been employed to calculate the above data rates. This standard also specifies the recording technique to be used and the size of the interblock gaps. If data is recorded in blocks of 256 bytes (the maximum allowed by the standard) only about 75% of the tape will be occupied by data. Thus the capacity of a 100 metre cassette may be determined as about 576K bytes or roughly twice as much as a single-sided, single-density floppy disk in IBM 3740 format.

The method used to write data onto the tape is known as PHASE ENCODING and is shown in Figure 11.5.

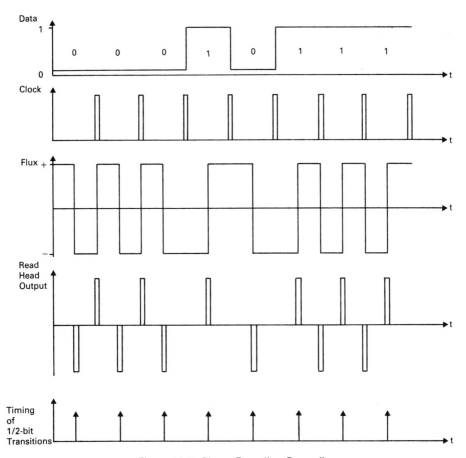

Figure 11.5: Phase Encoding Recording

It will be seen that the flux changes half way through each
bit time (1/2-bit transitions). For a logic '1' to be
recorded the transition is from - flux to + flux whereas for
a logic '0' to be recorded the transition is from + flux to -
flux. The transitions at the bit boundaries are not
significant. The flux changes sign at the basic bit rate when
alternate '1's and '0's are recorded and at twice this rate
if all '1's or all '0's are recorded.

To recover the data, the underlying clock must be obtained.
This is done by a phase-locked oscillator in the recovery
electronics. To initially synchronise this oscillator a
pattern of alternate '1's and '0's is recorded, as shown in
Figure 11.5. This provides a basic bit-frequency flux pattern
with transitions at the 1/2-bit time.

The standard recording format for a block of data consists of
an 8-bit synchronising pattern, a string of data bits of

between 32 and 2064 bits followed by a second 8-bit
synchronisation pattern which enables the electronics to
check that the clock is still in sychronism if required. The
contents of the data section will normally be between 2 and
256 bytes of data plus a 16-bit cyclic redundancy check
character.

In order to identify correctly a block of data, the control
system must be capable of finding the end of the tape. This
is achieved by the use of optical sensors which are activated
by the transparent nature of the non-magnetised leader tape.
In addition to the standard-sized cassette discussed above,
which is the same physical size as an audio cassette, others
are also available of different size. The 3M cartridge costs
slightly more than the standard cassette but is capable of
holding 2.5 million bytes of data with a data transfer rate
which is five times greater than that of a typical audio-
sized cassette. At the other end of the scale are the mini-
cassettes frequently used for pocket dictation machines;
these are capable of storing about 200,000 bytes of data. The
error rate for digital cassette storage is generally rather
greater than that experienced with floppy disk systems.

11.3 Audio Cassette Systems

For very low cost systems, a simple audio cassette recorder
may be employed and this approach is widely used in ultra
low-price systems. Reliability is generally much worse than
for professional quality digital recording. The data stream
is recorded as a sequence of tones representing the two logic
levels. In a typical system, a 1200 Hz tone may be used for
logic '0' and 2400 Hz for logic '1'. Each bit lasts for about
3.3ms giving a data transfer rate of 37.5 bytes/second and
this will be reduced to about 30 bytes/second if the data is
stored in standard asynchronous format (see Section 10.3.1).
The total capacity of a C60 audio cassette operated at the
standard speed is approximately 100,000 bytes. In practice,
this capacity is considerably reduced by the large inter-
record spaces that are usually left. Further, in an attempt
to improve reliability, some systems manufacturers duplicate
every record thus halving the available space. It must be
emphasised that this is a decision of the system manufacturer
and is not implicit in the design of the recording hardware.

11.4 Winchester Disk Systems

The objection to the use of rigid disks with microprocessor-
based equipment is that usually the environment would not be
sufficiently clean and the disk drive would not be
sufficiently rugged. These objections can now be overcome by

the use of "Winchester" disk systems which are appropriate if the speed or capacity of floppy disk drives is insufficient.

The Winchester disk is a rigid disk enclosed in a virtually airtight container and assembled under ultra-clean conditions. It therefore exists in its own micro-atmosphere and does not rely on extensive air conditioning for reliable operation. The disk driving spindle couples to an external drive motor via a sealing gland but otherwise there are no breaches in the sealing system, the Winchester module containing all of the head actuation mechanism.

As with virtually all rigid disks, the read/write heads are placed very close to the surface of the disk and 'fly' on the narrow boundary layer of air which circulates with the disk. Because there is no head-to-disk contact wear is very low and reliability correspondingly high with a mean time between failures of typically 9000 hours.

The more refined engineering of Winchester disks when compared with floppy disks permits both the tracks to be placed closer together and also the recording density (bits/inch) to be greater. The rotational speed of a typical Winchester drive is 3,600rpm or 10 times that obtained on standard floppy disk drives. Often more than one disk is mounted on the same spindle within the device. Each disk is termed a PLATTER and may be recorded on one or both surfaces. There is at least one read/write head per data surface and sometimes several heads are used to reduce the amount of space required by the head positioning device. For example, the use of four heads means that the travel of the positioning actuator is only 0.25 of the total width of the recorded surface. This, incidentally, also reduces the head positioning time.

A typical Winchester drive (Ampex Capricorn 165) employes five platters giving a potential of ten data surfaces. Only eight of these are used. There are two heads per surface and the worst case access time is 63.3ms. Data can be read from the disk at the rate of 1.2 million bytes per second and the total disk capacity is about 166 million bytes.

The reliability of Winchester disks is high with a soft error rate of 1 in 10^{10} and a hard error rate of 1 in 10^{12}. However, they are not without their problems. Because the disks are fully sealed in a clean environment, failure within the disk container requires that the unit be replaced and returned to a highly specialised repair facility. The data on the faulty disk may be recoverable but this cannot be guaranteed and anyway the data on the disk must be transferred to its replacement during repair if it is to be of any use. Since the disk units are not replaceable in the same sense as cassettes and floppy disks, there is an immediate problem of data security and back up which has not been adequately solved. This problem is, of course, compounded by the very large amount of data that can be stored on a Winchester.

11.5 Solid State Mass Storage Devices

All of the mass storage devices discussed so far in this Chapter have involved electromechanical mechanisms of one sort or another. Such mechanisms are far less reliable than solid state devices, they require maintenance, reasonably clean environments and cannot withstand vibration and shock to any great degree. A solid state mass storage device is, therefore, a very attractive proposition.

Two types of solid state mass storage systems have, in fact, been developed. The first is called a CHARGE-COUPLED-DEVICE (CCD) and makes use of small storage cells each capable of holding one bit of information in the form of an electric charge. The bit cells are arranged as long recirculating shift registers in which the data is continually shifted. This continual shifting is required to prevent data loss, a feature that is rather reminiscent of dynamic memory units (Figure 11.6).

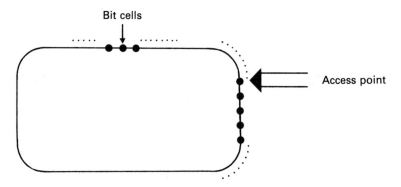

Figure 11.6: Single Ring CCD Memory

The organisation shown in Figure 11.6 is reminiscent of a single disk track and in fact a 16 Kbit CCD has a capacity approximately 40% of that of of a single track of an 8 inch single-density floppy disk.

In use, the organisation shown in Figure 11.6 would require the user to wait until the first bit of the required data block was available at the access point. When this occurs, the data is both recirculated and retrieved until the whole block has been read. This is the slowest organisation providing an access time of the order of 3.25 ms in the worst case.

An alternative architecture is to arrange the shift registers as a number of smaller loops; thus the time taken for data to reach the minor-loop access point is considerably reduced. Figure 11.7 shows a byte organised device of this type.

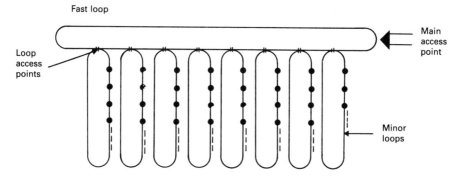

Figure 11.7: Byte Organized CCD Memory

Once the 8 bits of a particular byte of data are at the loop access points, they are shifted out to the main access point rapidly, before the next minor loop shift time. With such an organisation the access time for a particular block of data would be reduced to about 400 usec.

The major drawback of CCD storage devices is their volatility, which means that the power supply integrity must be guaranteed. The MAGNETIC BUBBLE MEMORY is a non-volatile alternative to the CCD. The storage cells consist of permalloy metalisation patterns laid down on a magnetic substrate (each cell is about 20 micrometres wide). The presence of a cylindrical magnetic domain within a cell denotes the storage of a logic '1' while the absence of a cylindrical 'bubble' indicates logic '0'. These bubbles may be shifted from cell to cell under the influence of a rotating magnetic field produced by small coils on the device. The data remains stored in the device in the absence of power provided that a steady bias field is maintained. In a typical device, this field is provided by a permanent magnet and so the device may be considered non-volatile.

The organisation of the shift register paths is very similar to that shown in Figure 11.7 and in the Texas Instrument TIB 0203 device there are 157 minor loops each holding 641 bits. Only 144 of the minor loops are used, permitting 13 defective loops in any device and thus enhancing the production yield. The total storage of 92,304 bits is roughly equivalent to 2.75 single-density floppy disk tracks. Data may be extracted from this device at a rate of about 6000 bytes per second, which is approximately 20% of that obtainable with a single-density floppy disk. The access time is about 9 ms in the worst case which is considerably better than a floppy disk. The storage cells for this capacity of memory can be housed in a single one inch square module although the control electronics must be separately accommodated.

Unfortunately, the development of bubble memory systems since they were first introduced in 1967 has been very slow and bedevilled by production difficulties. Indeed many manufacturers have discontinued their support of these devices recently.

11.6 Selection of Mass Storage Systems

From the previous sections in this chapter, it will be clear that the floppy disk is the most generally applied mass storage device combining reasonable reliability and access times with low cost.

For applications which are very demanding in terms of storage requirements and access time, the Winchester disk system offers a rugged and reliable medium which does not require a special environment, however, it is a relatively expensive solution and the disks cannot be exchanged by the user.

Where the nature of the application indicates that data will be accessed in a generally serial fashion or where access times are not very important, tape storage offers a low cost solution with acceptable reliability and the volume of storage can be adjusted by the correct selection of cartridge, standard cassette or mini-cassette.

For the most cost conscious applications, audio cassette recording offers a solution, albeit with a reliability that is lower than can be accepted in many applications.

Finally, where absence of moving parts is an attractive quality, solid state serial memories are a possible solution. The magnetic bubble memory is particularly attractive because it is non-volatile and could be packaged in the form of an exchangeable module.

Table 11.1 summarises some of the more important parameters of the memory systems discussed in this Chapter.

SYSTEM	Capacity (bytes)	Data transfer rate bytes/second	Worst case access time (seconds)
Winchester Disk	$8\times10^6 - 330\times10^6$	1.2×10^6	63×10^{-3}
Floppy Disk	$0.25\times10^6 - 2\times10^6$	$31,000 - 62,000$	1
Mini-Floppy Disk	$10^5 - 4\times10^5$	$31,000 - 62,000$	0.5
Digital Cassette	$0.2\times10^6 - 2.5\times10^6$	$800 - 6,000$	$40 - 100$
Audio Cassette	10^5 (C60)	30	Very variable
Magnetic Bubble	92,000 (per module)	6,000	10^{-2}

Table 11.1: A Comparison of the Characteristics of Bulk Storage Devices

12. Multi processor systems

Many pieces of modern electronic equipment incorporate more than one microprocessor unit in order to meet their design requirements most effectively. Until a few years ago multi-processor systems were rare and were most usually found in systems requiring high reliability or substantial computer resources. The very low cost of microprocessor circuits has meant that multi-processor solutions are now economically viable for a wide range of problems. They can result in a more effective and possibly cheaper finished product than that based on a single, concentrated source of processing power.

Once there is more than one source of processing power within a system, a number of issues arise immediately. These include

(i)   How, if at all, may the problem be partitioned between the various processor sub-systems ?

(ii)   How may the various processor sub-systems communicate with each other ?

(iii)   How may the physical resources of the system be allocated to processors at any given time ?

These issues are still the subject of considerable research effort and it is difficult to give exact answers to any of the questions posed above. This difficulty is exacerbated by the fact that multi-processor solutions may be selected for widely differing reasons.

One reason for choosing a multi-processor configuration is to match the processing capabilities of the system to the various disparate tasks that may need to be carried out in order to achieve the overall objective. Microprocessors, like minicomputers or mainframes, cannot be designed to be equally good at all tasks and so design compromises have to be made to produce a generally acceptable performance over a wide range of tasks. However, if several processors may be used then each can be purpose designed to achieve its best performance in one particular application area. Thus a system which incorporates several such processors and which allocates each to a part of the overall task appropriate to its particular specialisation will be significantly more effective than an equivalent system based solely on general-purpose processors.

Examples of specialised processors in the Intel range are:

Intel 8087	Mathematics co-processor
Intel 8089 Intel 8041	I/O processors
Intel 8051	Control microprocessor

The first is specifically designed to undertake complex mathematical operations, the 8089 and the 8041 are designed with instruction sets specifically geared to the data manipulations commonly required by I/O channels. The 8051 has an instruction set which includes excellent bit-manipulation capabilities, thus making it highly suitable for logic replacement and other control-type functions.

A second, and perhaps somewhat surprising, reason for using a multi-processor solution is to simplify the design. In a complex system, significant effort may have to be devoted to achieving adequate response times for each of the many tasks comprising the overall solution. The software may be further complicated by the need to switch between tasks and to maintain isolation between tasks. All these requirements lead to complex software and high software development costs.

By allocating a few (perhaps only one) individual tasks to one specific processor in a multi-processor solution, considerable simplification of the software may result and the reduced development costs could easily produce a cheaper overall solution despite the increased hardware costs.

The third possible reason for moving to a multi-processor design is to improve system reliability. This is much more problematical than the previous two reasons. It presupposes that the system will survive, albeit with reduced performance, if one or more processors fail. This is manifestly untrue if each processor is allocated different tasks, assuming that all tasks are necessary to the successful operation of the system. One is, therefore, forced to conclude that multi-processor systems will provide enhanced reliability only if the operating software permits dynamic re-allocation of tasks to processors under fault conditions or if the system is configured in such a way that under ALL conditions the tasks to be performed are allocated to those processors currently available to carry them out. This is true of distributed processing. The discussion above assumes that all processors in a system will be used; it is clearly possible to improve reliability by providing a second processor which remains quiescent until the first fails.

Multi-processor systems may be classified by the degree of co-operation between the processors. The degree of coupling has a strong influence on the type of communication system which needs to be provided between the processors.

At one extreme, there exist systems employing a main processor (e.g. an 8086) and a matching co-processor (e.g. the 8087 maths co-processor). This situation is illustrated in Figure 12.1 and operates as follows:

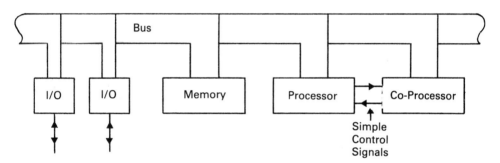

Figure 12.1: A System with a Co-Processor

The main processor fetches and executes instructions as required in the usual way. The co-processor monitors these instructions and ignores them. When an instruction requiring (say) a complex mathematical operation is fetched, the main processor ignores it and the co-processor "wakes up" and carries out the operation. This occurs even though it was the main processor which fetched the instruction.

The second, and still very close, degree of coupling occurs when several (perhaps identical) processors are connected to the main bus and share the remaining resources of the system as shown in Figure 12.2.

Each processor continues with its own tasks fetching instructions and data from memory and communicating with the system via the I/O ports. If the logic of the operation requires that the tasks running in processor 1 need to communicate with those in processor 2, then this has to be arranged in some agreed format. Typically, one processor will write a "message" to the other in a common "communications" area in memory. This message might consist of a block of

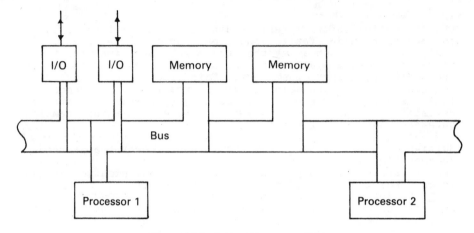

Figure 12.2: A Dual Processor System

data, a coded set of instructions or both. Once the message is written, the recipient must be advised that it has a message pending. This is most easily achieved by permitting the sender to issue a hardware interrupt to the recipient. An alternative would be the use of software flags. In either case, it will be necessary to prevent the message being overwritten before it is used or read while it is only half complete.

An obvious problem with this closely coupled arrangement is the fact that the two processors both share the system resources and, if one processor is using a particular resource, the second processor cannot. To allocate resources, it is necessary to have some sort of arbitration scheme which may be either centralised or localised. In most systems, the scarcest resource is the bus since it is through this that access to all resources is gained.

The effectiveness of such an arrangement depends very much on the amount of time, as a percentage of the whole, for which each processor requires use of the bus, and the pattern of such usage.

Much of the bus usage will be for data and instructions local to each processor and so much of the difficulty encountered by the system shown in Figure 12.2 can be overcome by a further loosening of the connection between processors. This is shown in Figure 12.3 where each processor sub-system has its own private memory bus and possibly I/O.

Clearly arbitration is still needed for use of the system bus but since most transactions are likely to take place on the private buses bus arbitration is less of a problem.

Each private system is, in effect, a small computer system and could be made up in a number of ways:

    (a) purpose designed system
    (b) single-board computer system

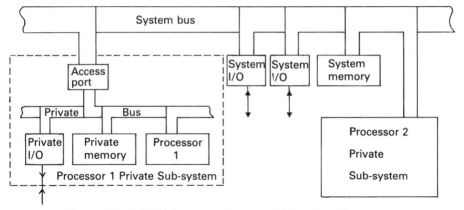

Figure 12.3: A Multi-Processor System with Localised Resources

(c) single chip processor (such as the 8051)
(d) single chip I/O processor (such as the 8041A)
(e) intelligent instrument

For moderately closely coupled systems, the main system bus
would be a typical computer-type parallel highway, preferably
designed specifically with the problems of resource sharing
in mind. A typical example of such a bus is the Intel
Multibus (R).

As the coupling becomes weaker (i.e. less traffic) the bus
can be changed to a simplified parallel bus such as the
IEEE-488 system (GP-IB) or a serial transmission link. In
such circumstances the bus may not even be hardwired, but
might well consist of a radio transmission channel.

12.1 The Structure of Bus Systems

Since the communication bus is such an important feature of a
multi-processor system, it is clearly important to study it.
In particular to look at the protocols involved in using a
bus, the way in which the use of the bus is granted to
specific transactions and the way in which such transactions
may be used to establish communication between tasks. In this
section, the first topic, that of bus protocol, will be
discussed.

Simple bus structures are usually synchronous and assume that
the desired information is present on the bus at the
appropriate time. No checking is carried out to ensure that
this is, in fact, the case and so it is possible for
communication to break down simply because the assumed timing

constraints have been violated. An example of such a bus structure was given in Section 9.4.1 in connection with the MC6800 family of devices.

By way of further illustration, consider the situation which exists when a computer is attempting to access memory via a synchronous bus system. If the communication system is a synchronous one, the computer will issue the address information and certain control signals (such as a "write" indicator) some little time after the beginning of the execution of the "memory write" instruction. A certain period of time later, usually shortly before the end of the instruction cycle, the input to the computer will be strobed, thus reading in data from the data bus. IT IS IMPLICIT THAT THE MEMORY UNIT HAS MADE THE DATA AVAILABLE AT THIS TIME; no check is carried out to see whether this is so. Thus, in the example illustrated below, memory device A will execute a proper data transfer, whereas memory device B, which is slower, will not make data available at the correct time and so "garbage" will be read.

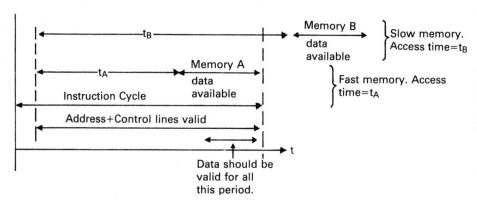

Figure 12.4: Operation of Fast and Slow Memories on a Synchronous Bus

Thus a synchronous bus system must be designed to operate sufficiently slowly to permit even the slowest device to communicate properly. This procedure, however, will slow down faster devices in an unacceptable fashion. The principal advantage of the synchronous system is its relative simplicity and the absence of large numbers of control signals. Synchronous buses are primarily used for communication between devices of like speed which are physically close to each other.

Where it is required to make more efficient use of the bus, a system must be developed which enables bus transactions to terminate as soon as the required data has been passed. Such a system is termed an asynchronous bus. In order to achieve asynchronous operation, it is necessary to provide an additional control line whereby the device being accessed can tell the accessing device that the data is available. This is the "data ready" signal shown in the example below.

260

If the above memory transaction was carried out asynchronously then the address and control information would be made available at the same time as in the synchronous case. After this the processor would enter a "wait" state and would exit from this only after receiving a "data ready" signal from the memory unit. Once this is received, the computer reads the data and concludes the instruction cycle, removing the control signals from the bus. This frees the memory and causes the data to be removed from the data bus. The situation for both fast and slow memory is shown below (Figure 12.5).

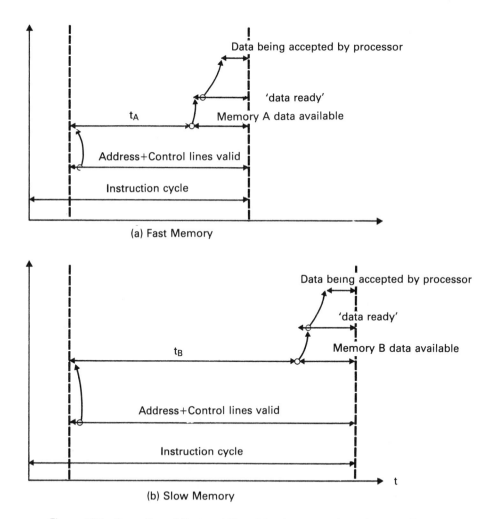

Figure 12.5: Operation of Fast and Slow Memory on an Asynchronous Bus

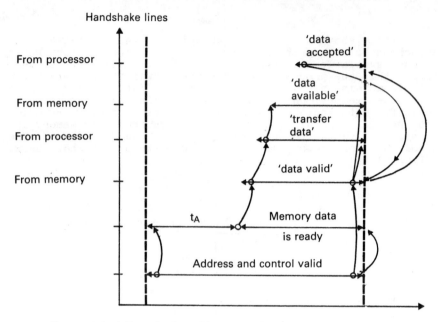

Figure 12.6: A Transfer from Memory to Processor Using 'handshaking'

Asynchronous communications are clearly more complex but they are independent of the device delays. This is especially important when the bus is long since the access time includes the time taken for control signals to reach the data source and return. Since signals travel at 3×10^8 metres/second, this limitation alone means that a synchronous system with an instruction cycle of 1 usec can only cope with a bus length of 150 metres which is inadequate for many purposes. In practice, electronic delays within the device could easily reduce this distance by a factor of 2 or 3.

Asynchronous systems are insensitive to transmission delays although such delays will reduce the speed at which the program within the processor proceeds.

In some circumstances, it can be advantageous to give the source of data a positive assurance that its data has been accepted. This requires a second control line, passing from the recipient to the data source. Such a protocol is called handshaking. The procedure is shown in Figure 12.6.

Using this procedure, the computer sets up the address and control lines. After the appropriate access time, (ta), the memory data becomes valid and the peripheral then issues the "data valid" handshake. On receipt of this signal the computer indicates its readiness to accept data by issuing the "transfer data" signal. The peripheral then responds by actually placing the data on the data bus and then signals the computer with "data available". Once the computer has received this signal it reads the data bus and then signals the peripheral that the transaction is over by asserting "data accepted".

Notice in all of the above operations that if a transmission delay exists it delays both the data being transferred and the signal which indicates the validity of the data. This it is impossible for any information to be read before it is valid.

A possible problem with handshaking is that, because all progress is dependent on a positive acknowledgement, it is possible for the system to "freeze" in the event of a fault condition inhibiting this acknowledgement. To guard against this all operations are normally monitored by a timer which sets a limit on the response time and causes a fault condition to be indicated if this limit is exceeded. In the above example "time-out" protection would be needed between the issuing of the address and the receipt of "data valid", also between the issue of "transfer data" and the receipt of "data available". Some handshaking systems omit one of the control lines if it is felt to be unnecessary. Often "data available" or "data accepted" will be omitted. If both are omitted, then the system reverts to the simple asynchronous arrangement shown in Figure 12.5. (The "transfer data" signal was not shown explicitly in Figure 12.5. It was assumed to be included amongst the control lines.)

12.2 The S-100 Bus

The S100 bus is so named because it comprises 100 signal lines. Originally used as the internal bus system in an early microcomputer it has since become very popular because a large number of companies market products which are designed to interface to it. S100 supports closely-coupled systems with multiple bus masters. One master is designated "permanent" and may be likened to the main processor system, the other masters are "temporary" and may be regarded as intelligent sub-systems with DMA-type access facilities to the bus. The signals provided by the bus are:

(i)   Address

At least 16 and up to 24 address lines are specified.

(ii)   Data

16 data lines are specified. These may be configured as two unidirectional 8-bit buses or a single bidirectional 16-bit bus.

(iii)   Status

8 lines which are output by the current bus master to indicate the type of bus operation in hand. For instance: memory read, I/O read, halted, interrupt acknowledge, etc.

(iv)   Control Output

5 lines output by the bus master primarily to synchronise bus transfer operations and to indicate when a temporary master may have use of the bus.

(v)   Control Input

6 lines controlled by the store (peripheral). Used to establish an asynchronous protocol and to request interrupts or use of the bus via the permanent bus master.

(vi)   DMA Control

8 lines. Four are address lines used to arbitrate between simultaneous requests and four are used to disable the bus drivers within the permanent bus master.

(vii)   Vectored Interrupt

8 lines used to permit vectored interrupts and to arbitrate between simultaneous requests.

(viii) Utilities

20 lines including ground, 3 power lines, master resets, etc.

Bus transfers in the S100 system are asynchronous and follow the pattern shown in Figure 12.5. The S100 has been the subject of a standardization exercise and is also known as IEEE-696.

12.3 Intel Multibus®

This is a more recent design than the S100 and was originally designed for use with the Intel range of single board computers. The bus specification makes provision for multiple bus masters to exist and so is highly suitable for multiprocessor applications. Provision is made for arbitration between bus masters competing for control of the bus and a number of resolution techniques (parallel arbitration, daisy-chaining) are supported. The bus itself employs a total of 86 lines, some of which are reserved for future development. The multibus is supported by a large number of product manufacturers and has become an IEEE standard (IEEE-796). When the bus is used to support single board computers (which have their own on-board bus structure) the system would be of the type shown in Figure 12.3. Multibus may be regarded as being suitable for the control of closely coupled and moderately closely coupled systems. The data transfer protocol is asynchronous and similar to that shown in Figure 12.5.

The signals defined for the multibus are:

(i)   Address

        20 lines.

(ii)   Data

        A bidirectional bus of width 16 bits is specified.

(iii)   Access Control

        8 lines used as follows:

        (a) 2 inhibit lines are provided; one is designed to inhibit read/write memory accesses and the other to inhibit ROM accesses. These may be used to permit substitute memory or I/O devices to respond, for instance during bootstrapping.

        (b) One data width control. This is used by the bus master to specify when the high order 8 bits of the data bus are in use (usually, when a 16-bit data item is being transferred).

        (c) Four transfer control lines, namely, memory read, memory write, I/O read, I/O write. These lines indicate the validity of the address lines and that data may be placed on the bus (read) or data is already on the bus (write).

        (d) One transfer acknowledge line. This is the response line from the slave by which it tells the bus master that the transaction is complete.

(iv)   Seven bus arbitration lines

        These lines are used to control the transfer of bus mastery from one device to the next, allowing for appropriate priorities to be imposed.

        (a) Two clock lines. Since the system may consist of many masters each with its own clock, a special "bus clock" is supplied so that all bus arbitration may be carried out synchronously. A second clock line is provided as a system "utility".

        (b) One "unbussed" signal provided to each potential bus master to indicate when there are no devices of higher priority on the bus.

        (c) One "unbussed" signal by which a bus master indicates that it does not require the bus. This

signal is connected to (b) above of the next
highest priority master when a "daisy-chain"
arbitration system is to be implemented.

(d) One "unbussed" bus request signal. This
signal is asserted by a potential bus master when
it requires use of the bus.

(e) One line to indicate to all devices when the
bus is in use.

(f) One line to indicate whether other devices
are trying to gain control of the bus.

(v)   9 interrupt control lines

The bus specifies eight separate prioritised
interrupt request lines. Interrupt vectoring is
achieved via a single "acknowledge" line which
causes vectoring information to be forced onto
the data bus.

(vi)   One system initialisation line

12.4 The IEEE-488 (GB–IB)® Bus

The IEEE-488 bus was originally proposed by Hewlett Packard
for the interconnection of "intelligent" instruments. As such
it supports a looser form of interconnection than the
interprocessor type buses discussed above. In general the
interconnection distances will be greater and the bus consists
of only 16 lines. Eight of these lines are used for data or
instruction transfer while the remaining 8 are dedicated to
bus control functions. The maximum transfer for data is about
250,000 bytes/sec and the maximum length of the bus is 20
metres subject to the restriction that there may not be more
than 2 metres of bus between "instruments". The maximum
number of "instruments" is set at 15 and an asynchronous
handshaking protocol is used. A particular feature of the
protocol, and the signals used to control it, is that it
automatically adjusts to the speed of the slowest device
involved in the transfer.

The bus specifies three classes of device which may be
connected to it, namely:

Controller:

This device defines which other devices may use the bus
for transaction by defining them as "talkers" or
"listeners". The controller uses five of the bus control
lines. There can only be one active controller at any
given time.

Talker:

> This device places data on the bus for reception by "listeners". It uses one of three handshake lines (DAV) in the control section of the bus. There may be only one active talker at any time.

Listener:

> This device receives data from the bus and uses two of the three handshake lines (NRFD and NDAC) in the control section of the bus. There may be many active listeners on the bus at any given time.

The signals specified for the bus are:

(a)   8 data lines:

> DIO1 - DIO8. These are used for the transfer of data between talkers and listeners when the ATN (attention) control line is at a TTL high level and for the transfer of commands from the controller when ATN is at a TTL low level.

(b)   3 handshake lines:

> Two of these are operated by listeners and one by the talker.

(c)   5 bus control lines:

> IFC (interface clear) acts as a system reset command.

> ATN (attention) indicates whether the data bus is being used for data transfer or for command transfer.

> SRQ (service request) indicates to the controller that a device wishes to make a data transfer.

> REN (remote enable) is intended to disable the front panel controls of an instrument and to prepare it to receive commands over the bus.

> EOI (end/or identify) is used by a talker to signal the end of a transaction and by the controller to request that a device requiring service identify itself by asserting one of the data lines.

Using the bus signals the controller can carry out the following operations:

> make a particular device a talker
> make a particular device a listener
> disable the current talker
> disable all the current listeners
> send one of 16 commands (specified by a binary code on the data bus) to all devices
> send one of 16 commands (specified by a binary code on the data bus) to all active listeners and talkers.

In addition the operations specified for REN, EOI and IFC are available.

The interlocked handshake protocol used by the IEEE bus requires three handshake lines, namely:

DAV - Data Valid, from talker
NRFD - Not ready for data from listeners
NDAC - Not data accepted

The electrical specification requires that if the condition implied by the name is TRUE then the line must be at TTL low (<0.8 volt) level. This facilitates the wired-or configuration (Appendix C) of the listener lines and permits the data transfer rate to adapt to that required by the slowest active listener. The protocol existing between a talker and a single listener is shown in Figure 12.7.

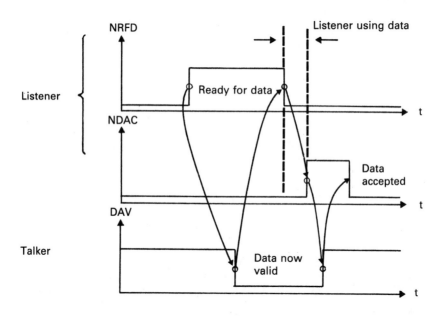

Figure 12.7: GB-IB Protocol-Single Listener

The first stage in the transfer occurs when the previously designated listener indicates its readiness by letting the NRFD line go high.

The talker, which is monitoring NRFD, then places data on the bus and signals its availability by taking DAV low. The listener monitors this line; when DAV is low it proceeds to input (and possibly process) the data. The business of the listener is indicated by NRFD going low. Once the data has been input, the completion is signalled by the listener letting NDAC go high. The talker monitors NDAC and when it

268

goes high it knows that the data has been used. It therefore proceeds to prepare new data and signals this by taking DAV high. The talker completes the transaction by taking NDAC low.

When several are active on the bus they are connected to NRFD and NDAC in a "wired-or" fashion. This ensures that these lines are held at a low level unless released by ALL listeners. As a consequence, since the talker cannot put data on the bus until it sees NRFD go high, the data is only placed on the bus when all active listeners are ready.

Likewise, the data will remain on the bus until all listeners have indicated that they have finished. This happens when NDAC goes high, which can only happen if each and every listener has released it.

It must be emphasised that the "wired-or" configuration is one in which the signal line goes low if any of the devices connected to it request a low level. A high level results only if all devices have set a high level.

The IEEE bus system supports multiple processors since every device (talker or listener) may include significant processing power. Usually systems include a single controller; certainly only one controller may be active at any given time. However, it is possible for the current controller to pass a command to a specified listener to instruct it to assume the role of controller. The original controller would, of course, cease operations once the transfer command had been issued.

Interfacing microprocessor systems to the IEEE-488 bus is simplified by the availability of special purpose interface adaptors which may be placed between the microprocessor bus and the IEEE-488 bus. Among these are:

Motorola MC68488 - Provides talk/listen functions for MC6800 bus systems

Intel 8291 - Provides talk/listen functions for 8080/8085 bus systems

Intel 8292 - Provides controller functions for 8080/8085 bus systems.

12.5 The CAMAC Bus

The CAMAC (Computer Aided Measurement And Control) bus was developed as the standard bus for instrumentation systems by the members of EURATOM. It has become a widely used standard for this purpose. The bus is not specifically designed for multiple processor situations, but there is no prohibition on individual modules being "intelligent". However, the structure of the bus is centralised in the crate controller and connection between this and the individual modules is reminiscent of a separate I/O bus structure between a processor and its peripherals (Chapter 7). There is no provision for multiple bus masters.

The organisation of CAMAC centres around the crate which is a standardised structure housing up to 23 peripheral modules plus a mandatory crate controller. The function of the crate controller is to organise transfers on the standard bus which is wired into the crate. The crate controller could well be a microprocessor based unit designed to gather data down the standard bus and forward it to another, external, processor. Alternatively, the crate controller may perform functions in addition to the control of the crate such as data reduction, printing and other computing functions.

The CAMAC bus consists of 67 bussed lines plus 2 interrupt like lines which run from EACH module to the controller. In addition, there are power lines and unbussed user definable lines.

These bus signals are:

(a) Data lines:

> 24 for the transfer of data from the controller to the modules. 24 for the transfer of data from the modules to the controller.

(b) Sub-address lines:

> Four to identify the destination or source of data within an addressed module (see below).

(c) Function lines:

> Five to specify the particular operation required of an addressed module.

(d) Control lines:

> Eight for various purposes such as synchronisation and control of the bus, acknowledgement of receipt of command etc.

(e) Undefined:

> Two lines for designer use.

In addition to the above, each module in the crate has what amounts to an individual interrupt line ("look at me") by which it requests service, and an individual module select line by which the controller addresses it.

12.6 Serial Connected Networks

Once communication distances become greater than a few metres, the cost of parallel busses becomes too great for many applications. In these cases, all communications must be carried out via a serial link as discussed in Chapter 10. Nevertheless, it is necessary to establish a protocol concerning the error checking to be carried out, the different types of character or packet of data to be transmitted (e.g. control or data), etc. In this way each character received is checked for errors. If it is found to be error free, it is inspected to see whether it is a command or data. If it is a command, the appropriate actions will be carried out by the recipient; if data it will be processed according to the program stored in the recipient.

The intelligent nodes of a network may be interconnected as shown in Figure 12.8.

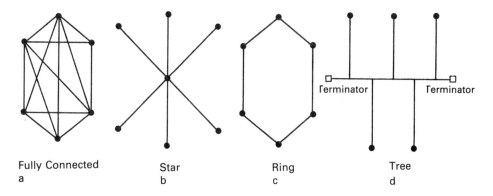

Fully Connected
a

Star
b

Ring
c

Tree
d

Figure 12.8: Network Interconnections

The fully connected system involves the shortest delays, and is the most secure against faults because of its re-routing possibilities, but it becomes untenable for even moderate numbers of nodes.

The star connection is much more economical and involves only moderate transmission delays. However, it is totally dependent on its switching centre S which may, or may not, allow simultaneous transactions to proceed.

The ring system is attractive because of its simplicity and the absence of a switching centre. However, the breakdown of a node will cause the system to fail unless it is entirely passive. By using suitable techniques, it is possible to permit several transactions to proceed at one time. An example of a ring system is the CAMBRIDGE RING which will be explained briefly by way of illustration of the general principles involved in a ring structure.

The tree structure is essentially a serial bus and is exemplified by the Ethernet system.

12.6.1 THE CAMBRIDGE RING

Information on the Cambridge Ring is transmitted in packets consisting of a 3-bit header, an 8-bit destination address, an 8-bit source address, two 8-bit bytes of data and a 3-bit trailer. The ring is organised rather like a carousel slide tray with each slot containing one packet of data. The slots rotate continually and are intercepted at each ring node. As the packet is intercepted its destination address is checked. If the packet is not addressed to the node it is simply re-transmitted into the next section of the ring. If, however, the destination of the packet corresponds to that of the node then two things happen:

(i)   The packet is re-transmitted onward round the ring.
(ii)   The packet is copied into the node.

The first action may seem rather strange; however, it does permit the packet to travel back to its source so that the correct transmission around the ring can be determined by comparison with a copy of the original which is retained in the source node. Secondly, making every packet travel right round the ring helps to ensure that all nodes have an equal opportunity to transmit into the ring.

If a packet arrives at a node and its source address is identical to that of the node, two actions occur:

(i)   The packet is copied into the node and compared with the original for error detection purposes.

(ii)   The packet has one bit in its leader changed to indicate that it is now empty and the resulting empty packet transmitted into the ring.

The latter procedure is necessary to maintain an ordered arrangement of slots in the ring. If a used packet were simply annihilated, then stations that want to transmit would simply look for a vacant space and insert a packet. Small errors could build up and result in the tail of a new packet overwriting an existing packet.

If a node wishes to transmit data, it first assembles the required packet complete with leader, trailer, source address and destination address. The node then monitors the ring and behaves as outlined above until an empty packet is seen. As the empty packet is intercepted by the node, the node's own packet is transmitted in its place on a bit for bit basis and the generation of a new packet involves no greater delay than the re-transmission of a full one.

12.6.2 ETHERNET

Information is transmitted around the Ethernet system in the form of data packets consisting of a 64 bit preamble for synchronisation purposes, followed by a 48 bit source address, a 16 bit "type field", an N-byte data field and a 32 bit CRC error check sequence.

The transmission medium was originally designed to be a simple coaxial cable but the system is readily modified to accommodate fibre-optic and other forms of transmission. Each node on the system is a simple tap (rather than a re-transmission system as used by the Cambridge ring) and so the integrity of the system is not generally compromised by the failure of a node.

Each frame of data on the Ethernet system is separated by a gap of at least 9.6 usec. When a node wishes to transmit data, it listens to the transactions on the network. When the network is idle, as determined by the absence of a carrier signal, the transmitting node waits for the interframe gap to expire and then starts its own transmission. It is clearly possible for more than one node to have traffic for the network and all such nodes will attempt to transmit once the network is seen to be idle. This is a potentially disastrous situation called a collision. All nodes contain logic which enables them to sense when a collision has occurred. When collision is detected, the nodes all "back off" and then attempt to re-transmit some time later. The back off period is randomised so that repeated collisions should not occur.

12.7 Bus Arbitration Techniques

In the previous section, a number of bus structures were discussed. Some of these permit different devices to become bus masters as the situation demands. To permit this, there has to be a defined protocol for transferring control from one master to another and also for deciding between competing demands for use of the bus (bus arbitration).

Bus arbitration techniques may be classified in a number of ways:

    (i)   Hardware or software implementation
    (ii)   Centralised or distributed implementation
    (iii)   Request driven or non-request driven
    (iv)   Serial or parallel arbitration

The distinction between the possibilites for (i) above are obvious. Either the special purpose decision-making hardware is built or the decision-making is carried out by a program running in a sequential processor (which may, or may not, be dedicated to this task). Clearly the software approach is slower and would only be suitable for low speed systems or systems which are loosely connected.

The implications of centralising the arbitration function are that the whole system becomes dependent on this piece of

hardware. This situation is highly undesirable when
multiprocessor systems are being used to implement high
reliability distributed computing facilities. Often, however,
the centralised approach is acceptable although it will not be
so easy to expand a centralised system as to expand a
distributed system. This is because the centralised facility
must be provided for the system ab initio and so will usually
be designed with some maximum capacity in mind.

In a request driven system, the transfer of control occurs in
response to a request issued by a potential bus master. By
contrast, the non-request driven system relies on the current
bus master offering the bus to other potential bus masters at
intervals.

Before discussing the final distinction (serial versus
parallel arbitration) a bus master transfer protocol must be
established. Figure 12.9 shows a pair of potential bus
masters with their relevant control signals.

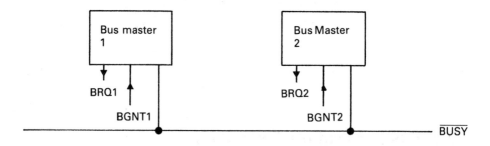

Figure 12.9: Two Potential Bus Masters

The signals involved in the bus transfer are:

BRQ:

> Bus request. The potential master requests the bus on
> this line and maintains it throughout its command of the
> bus.

BGNT:

> Bus Grant. Only one potential master will receive this
> signal which is originated by the arbitration network.
> No bus master actually achieves control of the bus until
> it has received a valid bus grant signal.

$\overline{\text{BUSY}}$:

> A "wired-or" which indicates that the bus is in use.
> During a transfer of control the outgoing master will
> lose its grant signal. However, it must complete its
> current transaction so it will not release $\overline{\text{BUSY}}$. The new
> master cannot gain control of the bus until:

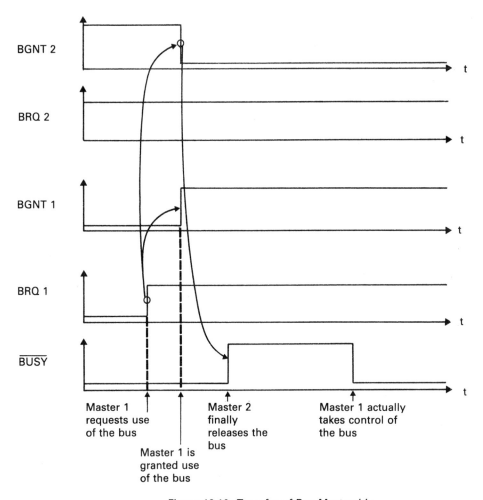

Figure 12.10: Transfer of Bus Mastership

(a)   it receives a grant signal
(b)   BUSY is released

Obviously   the   new   master   re-asserts   BUSY   almost
immediately.

The   progress   of   a bus transfer from master 2 to master 1 is
shown in Figure 12.10.

Notice that master 1 must be presumed to have higher   priority
than master 2,   otherwise it would not have been given control
of the bus.   Notice also that   master   2   never   releases   its
request.   It has, been interrupted and so, presumably, it still
requires use of the bus.

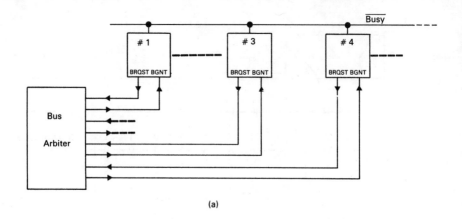

(a)

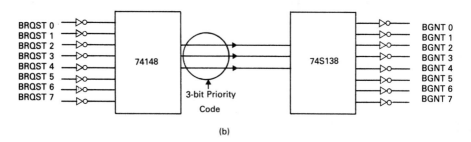

(b)

Figure 12.11: Circuit and Connection of a Practical Bus Arbiter

Figure 12.11a shows the general arrangement of a centralised parallel arbitration system. All of the request lines from the potential masters are directed to the bus arbitrator which selects the highest priority and issues a grant signal on the corresponding line. Only one grant signal is active at any given time. Thus if BRQ1, BRQ3 and BRQ4 are all active the bus arbiter will issue a grant signal (logic 1) on BGNT1 only (low numbers = high priority).

Figure 12.11b shows how such an arrangement may be realised using two 74-series TTL logic packages plus some logic inverters.

The 74148 device is a priority encoder which outputs a 3-bit code according to the active (logic 0) inputs which it is receiving. If BRQST0 is active the code output is 000 irrespective of the other inputs. Likewise if BRQST0 is inactive and BRQST1 is active, the code 001 is output irrespective of other inputs. This is summarised in Table 12.1.

The 74138 is a simple numeric 1-out-of-8 decoder which activates the output line corresponding to the binary number residing on the input code lines. Again an active output is

INPUT (BRQST)								Code Output		
0	1	2	3	4	5	6	7	2	1	0
0	X	X	X	X	X	X	X	0	0	0
1	0	X	X	X	X	X	X	0	0	1
1	1	0	X	X	X	X	X	0	1	0
1	1	1	0	X	X	X	X	0	1	1
1	1	1	1	0	X	X	X	1	0	0
1	1	1	1	1	0	X	X	1	0	1
1	1	1	1	1	1	0	X	1	1	0
1	1	1	1	1	1	1	0	1	1	1

X=Don't care

Table 12.1: Operation of 74148

Code Input			OUTPUT (BGNT)							
2	1	0	0	1	2	3	4	5	6	7
0	0	0	0	1	1	1	1	1	1	1
0	0	1	1	0	1	1	1	1	1	1
0	1	0	1	1	0	1	1	1	1	1
0	1	1	1	1	1	0	1	1	1	1
1	0	0	1	1	1	1	0	1	1	1
1	0	1	1	1	1	1	1	0	1	1
1	1	0	1	1	1	1	1	1	0	1
1	1	1	1	1	1	1	1	1	1	0

Table 12.2: Operation of 74S138

at a TTL logic '0' level. The truth table for the 74138 is shown in Table 12.2.

To implement a parallel distributed system, the bus request signals would have to be routed to each master which would then contain its own replica of the bus arbitration circuit (Figure 12.11b). The grant signals would be internal to the masters.

To implement a serial arbitration scheme, each master has to have a bus priority output signal (BPRO) in addition to those previously described, and the bus request signal is no longer used outside the master itself. The bus masters are then arranged in a daisy-chain fashion as shown in Figure 12.12.

The system functions as follows. A potential master receives the grant (BGNT) input, and assuming that it does not itself want to use the bus, it passes the grant signal on down the daisy-chain to the next master.

If, however, the master wishes to gain control of the bus (i.e. its internal BRQST = 1) it outputs '0' at BPRO thus inhibiting any lower priority masters. It then examines its BGNT input. If this is at logic '0' the requesting device

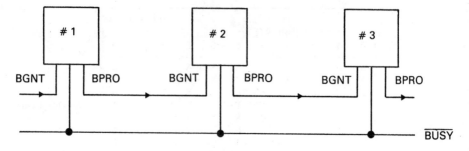

Figure 12.12: Serial Arbitration

waits. If the grant is logic '1', the master monitors the
BUSY line until it goes to logic '1' (not BUSY). The new
master then commences operations and takes BUSY back to logic
'0'.

A bus master which currently has control of the bus must
surrender it as soon as its grant input (BGNT) becomes logic
'0'. It will then complete its current transaction and
release the BUSY line back to logic '1'.

12.8 Inter-Process Communication and Resource Sharing

The preceding sections have concentrated on the hardware
aspect of multiprocessor systems. However, the processes
running on the various processors must communicate and will
also have to share resources other than the main bus (printer
facilities, for instance).

Inter-process communication can be carried out by designated
areas in the shared memory. Thus data may be deposited in a
buffer for subsequent use by another process. The consumer
process will be informed of this event either by the setting
of a software flag in the shared memory or via a hardware
interrupt to the processor in which it resides.

Likewise, "instructions" may be passed from process to
process by the writing of prescribed binary patterns into
mutually agreed memory locations. The concept of a dual-
ported memory will now be introduced because it provides a
means whereby processors may communicate without excessive
use of the main bus. Figure 12.13 illustrates the concept.

Units connected to the private bus may access the memory via
port A while those on the main bus make accesses via port B.
The accesses at either port are made without any regard to
the activities at the other one. All such activities conform
to the timing requirements of the bus in question. In order
to achieve this, the actual memory devices used in the memory

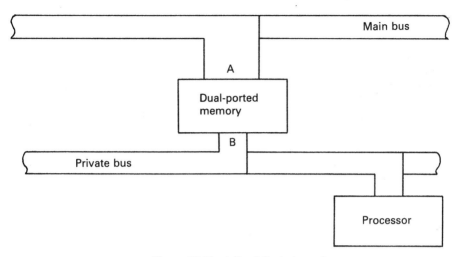

Figure 12.13: A Dual-Ported memory

must be faster than the bus timing requirements of the
overall system. Internal electronics timeshares the memory
between the ports in a way which is completely invisible to
the outside world.

By using dual-ported memory, the transfer of each word
requires only one main-bus transaction rather than the two
needed for communication via a shared single-ported memory on
the main bus.

It is often the case that the maintenance of information
concerning the status of a system requires the coordinated
manipulation of a number of variables. If several different
processes require to carry out this updating procedure, there
is always the danger that the maintenance function being
carried out by a process P1 can be interrupted by P2
acquiring the bus in order to carry out the same function.
Since the whole maintenance operation needs to be carried out
in a coordinated fashion, there is a considerable danger of
the status variables being left in disarray.

For example, consider two independent processes which, when
complete, have to update a counter. The code to be obeyed in
each case might be:

    Load "counter" to accumulator in processor
    Increment accumulator
    Store accumulator in "counter"

If a processor P1 commences this routine, with the counter
initially at 1 and is subsequently interrupted by processor
P2 carrying out the same operation, the situation would be as
shown in Figure 12.14.

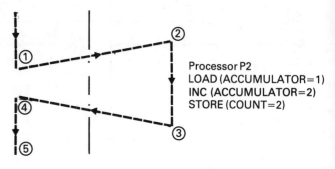

Processor P1
LOAD (ACCUMULATOR=1)
INC (ACCUMULATOR=2
STORE (COUNT=2)

Processor P2
LOAD (ACCUMULATOR=1)
INC (ACCUMULATOR=2)
STORE (COUNT=2)

Table 12.14: An Example of Co-operating Sequential Processes

The resulting value of "counter" is 2 not 3 as it should be. This occurred because P1, when it resumed operations at 4, was working on the out of date value of count (=1) rather than the value updated by P2 (=2).

This can be cured by forcing a strictly sequential execution of this critical sequence of code so that if a processor has entered the critical sequence it will complete it before relinquishing control to another.

This would naturally occur if the sequence of instructions were combined into a single "increment memory" instruction (provided that another processor could not gain the bus part way through an instruction). Certain microprocessors provide the facility to lock the bus during critical code sections thus making it impossible for another processor to break in.

If neither of these hardware solutions is available then software protection by the use of flags must be resorted to. This appears on the surface to be a simple solution - simply set a flag when the critical section is reached and unset it at the end. All processes wishing to execute the critical section must check the flag first. However, unless the operations of checking and then setting the flag can be made indivisible as outlined above, this simple solution does not work. Simple solutions to this problem are invariably found to be unsafe under some circumstances, either not adequately protecting the critical section or being liable to deadlock (the "no, after you!" syndrome).

One solution which does work is shown in Figure 12.15 but readers are referred to more complete texts on the subject for a fuller treatment.

Note that the two delays, D1, D2 (D1 not equal to D2) are needed solely to avoid the unlikely possibility of the two processors being synchronised and of identical types. If this asynchronisation is not introduced via D1 and D2, there is a remote possibility of a deadlock situation.

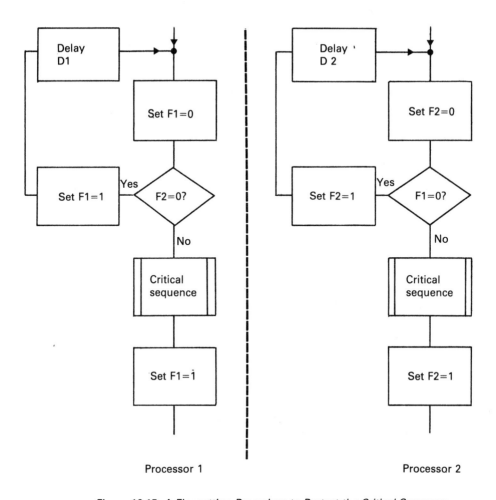

Figure 12.15: A Flagsetting Procedure to Protect the Critical Sequence

13. Memory Management

The latest generation of microprocessors has been designed to support very large memory spaces. This is a recognition of the fact that in some applications microprocessors will be used to control systems which are complex and which contain many sub-tasks. A problem with such systems is the organisation of the memory space and the protection of one task from illegal access by others. These are the two primary functions carried out by memory management systems.

Memory management was first introduced on large mainframe computers, particularly those designed with multi-user time-sharing environments in mind. Recently they have been applied to minicomputer systems and, since mid 1979, they have been available for some of the new generation of 16-bit "super-micros".

13.1 The Functions of Memory Management

As outlined above, memory management has two primary objectives:

(i)   The organisation of the allocation of memory space.

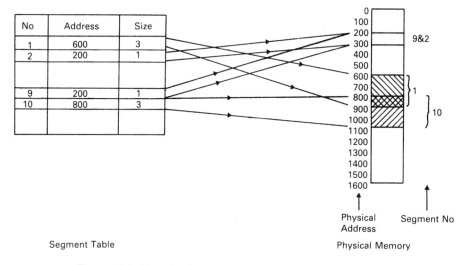

Segment Table   Physical Memory

Figure 13.1: Mapping Logical Addresses to Physical Addresses

(ii)   The control of access to particular areas of
        memory with the purpose of preventing
        interference between independent tasks and also
        preventing the corruption of data or the carrying
        out of illogical operations (such as executing
        data!)

Consider first the allocation of memory space. In most
management systems, the memory space is considered to be made
up of segments. These segments are made up of blocks of
memory locations the size of which varies from system to
system (typically 16 bytes to 256 bytes). Segment boundaries
always occur on block boundaries, but none of these
boundaries necessarily reflect the way in which the memory is
constructed from integrated circuits.

The user writes his program using "logical addresses". These
logical addresses in no way reflect the actual physical
storage addresses that will later be used during execution of
the program. The logical address will consist of two separate
parts.

(a) A segment number which will be used during execution to
determine the base address of the segment being accessed.

(b) An offset which specifies how far into the segment the
actual address being accessed is.

It must be clearly understood that the base address of a
segment is not determined directly by the segment number
associated with it. The segment number is simply a reference
number which is used by the memory management hardware to
enter a table (which is pre-loaded under program control)

283

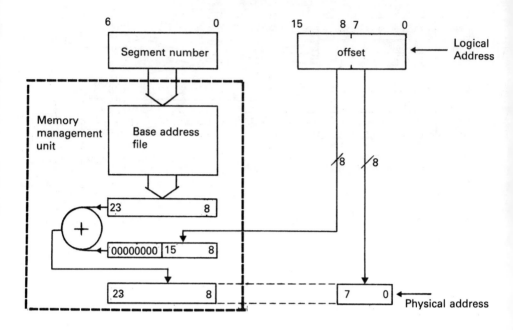

Figure 13.2: Z8010 Memory Management

from which the base address is extracted. Thus it is possible for several differently numbered segments to access the same physical area of memory. Note also that the sizes of segments can vary. This situation is illustrated in Figure 13.1.

The actual process or memory mapping is best illustrated by an example, in this case the Z8010 memory management chip designed by ZILOG for their Z8001 processor (Figure 13.2).

The memory management chip is placed between the processor and the address bus. The processor generates a 7-bit segment number which is supplied to the memory management unit, and a 16-bit offset. The lower 8-bits of this address are supplied directly to the address bus while the upper 8-bits go to the memory management unit to be added to the segment base address. Thus the following calculation is carried out:

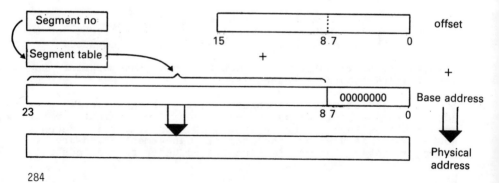

Note that since the least significant 8-bits of the base address are assumed zero they do not actually take part in the addition. This also implies that the block size for the Z8010 system is $2^8 = 256$ bytes, and that the maximum memory size that may be supported is $2^{24} = 16$ Mbytes.

The contents of the segment table consist of the base address and also some access control information (see below). This table is loaded under program control, usually by the operating system in a multi-task environment. If a particular program is used many times and is held on a backing store when not in use, the program is likely to be loaded at different locations each time it is used, the segment table will have to be updated each time this happens.

The control of memory access is another important role of a memory management system. The contents of each segment may be designated as being available only for limited access. For instance, the segment may be designated 'execute only' in which case only read operations during an instruction fetch would be permitted thus prohibiting any inadvertent changes to the program code. A segment may alternatively be designated 'read only' thus permitting access to data table but protecting them from corruption.

Since different programs may access the same physical memory, but with different segment numbers, their privileges may be quite different. For instance, a data logging task might have read-write access to data tables but the analysis programs would only be allowed read-only access.

Another important class of access is "system" as opposed to "user". Most processors which are designed to support multi-task operations have the facility to run in either system or user mode. System mode is reserved for the operating system. In this mode the programs have unrestricted access to all machine facilities. In user mode, access to certain facilities, such as I/O instructions, is prohibited. By reflecting this distinction in the memory management unit also, it is possible to stop user programs from executing operating systems or from changing the data tables used by the operating systems.

To summarise, the segment table has associated with it a list of attributes for each segment which would typically include the following:

Read only
Execute only
System only

If an attempt is made to violate these constraints, the memory management unit will inhibit the access and cause the processor to be interrupted.

13.2 Other Functions of a Memory Management Unit

Because the memory management unit monitors every address transaction, it is capable of providing a number of other pieces of information.

Included in this category would be the monitoring of the number of accesses to a particular segment. If no memory reads or writes have taken place within a specified time, this could indicate that the task in that area is of low priority and can be removed to backing store if more space is needed, or it might indicate that a program has got "hung up".

The monitoring of write access alone is also useful to an operating system since a segment which has not been written to since it was loaded is identical to its image on backing store and therefore need not be transferred out before being overwritten in memory.

Some memory management systems have provision for segments which are not resident in main memory. If a reference is made to such a segment the access is deferred while the relevant data is brought in from backing store. Thus, the user program can appear to have an almost limitless amount of "virtual" memory.

Many memory management systems can keep track of how much space remains in a given segment and provide a warning to the user when this area reaches a pre-defined minimum. This is particularly useful for protecting the system against stack overflow. It could also be used as the signal to move a buffer of data out to backing store (in say, a data-logging application).

Related to these calculations of space left in a segment is the actual prohibition of access outside a segment. Consider a segment which is 512 bytes in length. If an attempt is made to access this segment with an offset of 600, the access will be inhibited and a warning raised. The access WILL NOT be made 88 bytes into the adjacent segment.

13.3 Available Memory Management Systems for Microprocessors

Most of the above discussion, with the exception of the virtual memory concept, has been modelled on the facilities provided by the Z8010 memory management chip designed by Zilog for use with their Z8001 CPU. Memory management is also available for the Intel 8086/8088 processors but this is

286

provided on-chip with the processor and is not a separate entity. These devices can address up to 1 Mbyte of memory and use a segmentation scheme with segments made up of multiple 16-byte blocks. Only four separate segments are provided at any one time; one of these is used for accessing program code, one for accessing operand data, one for stack operations and one "extra segment" for any other use, typically the implementation of inter-task common data areas. The comprehensive memory control features outlined in previous sections are not present but it has been hinted that they might be added later. The advantage of using only four segments with each having its own implied use is that the instructions codes can be shorter since they do not have to specify the segment number.

14. Peripheral Support Devices for Use with Microprocessors

It will be recalled that, in Chapter 9, it was pointed out that a microprocessor requires quite a lot of hardware and software to turn it into a microcomputer. The majority of microprocessors are not incorporated into such units. Instead the system designer embeds a microprocessor system within his product so that the latter fulfils its design requirements most effectively. Used in this way the flexibility is put to work to the advantage of the equipment manufacturer and is not made available to the end user. This is in complete contrast to the situation which obtains between a computer (or microcomputer) manufacturer and his customer.

It will, therefore, be apparent that the microprocessor and its supporting hardware must be designed so that the equipment manufacturer's and system designer's priorities are reflected in their facilities. These priorities would include:

    (i)   low cost
    (ii)   high reliability
    (iii) minimum of special-purpose electronic design
    (iv)   small size
    (v)   small number of distinct units

In order to design a complete system, it is necessary to add both memory and peripherals. The first of these is a fairly standard item which, because of its large scale production, readily meets requirements (i) and (ii) and, because memory systems are not much different from one system to the next, requirement (iii) is met. Memories have been discussed fairly fully in Chapter 6 and so they will not be reviewed further here.

Peripherals, however, would seem to present a very different problem. It is, after all, the peripherals which are largely responsible for the differences between one system and the next. It is clearly impossible to devise a range of packaged circuits which will meet all the various input/output requirements of users and at the same time ensure that there is a sufficient bulk of production to keep costs down. One possibility would be to let designers devise their own special purpose interface hardware and to connect it to the system bus. This, to some extent, is the situation which exists with minicomputers and the reason that the interfacing costs of minicomputer systems tend to be very high. It is not acceptable for microprocessor systems since:

(a) A large number of small - and medium - scale integrated circuits would be used resulting in a high package count and a bulky finished product.

(b) As a result of (a) there would be a large number of connections. This tends to lead to poor hardware reliability.

(c) Assembly and design costs will be high, as will the cost of design changes.

(d) It will take a relatively long time between specifying the functions of an interface and producing the first proven prototype.

Because the two extreme solutions which have been outlined above do not meet the requirements, a third and more useful path has been followed by most manufacturers.

It has been recognised that there are two broad classes of peripheral. Namely those that transfer their data in serial mode and those that transfer their data in parallel mode. Having drawn this distinction, the way is open for the manufacture of a single large scale integrated circuit which will transmit data between the bus and the outside world in parallel format. Similarly, a device is required which will do the same job but will convert parallel data from the bus into serial format on the way out and similarly change serial data to parallel on the way into the bus. Such functions will perform the work of a circuit consisting of many MSI and SSI circuits and will this achieve objectives (ii), (iii) and (iv) above. Also, because these peripheral adaptor circuits are of general applicability, they can be expected to be produced in large quantities thus reducing the costs considerably.

The similarities between different devices which have been outlined above may have served to obscure those features which differentiate between the various peripherals. One of these differences is the voltage levels and power requirements of the various devices. These differences will always exist and therefore special purpose electronic circuits will be required to resolve the differences. Fortunately, such circuitry is not usually either complex or difficult to design.

The second difference is one of information requirements. Peripherals vary widely in the control signals which they require, some requiring just one simple flag while others require several.

To resolve these differences, a certain amount of adaptability must be incorporated into the special peripheral circuits supplied for use with microprocessors. This facility usually takes the form of one or more control registers within the peripheral adaptor, the contents of which define the detailed operation of the device. For instance, one bit of the register might determine whether a flag is set on a '1' $\longrightarrow$ '0' transition or on a '0' $\longrightarrow$ '1' transition.

These control registers may be loaded under program control and this will normally. take place during the 'power-on' initialisation routine. There is, however, no reason why the contents should not be changed during the execution of a program if this is advantageous.

The general classification of peripheral devices is illustrated below in Figure 14.1. In addition to devices concerned with data transmission, there are also some support devices which simplify the use of a microprocessor or expand its capabilities. Typical of such circuits are clock generators, interrupt controllers and bus arbitrators. Some of these devices will be discussed later in the chapter.

There is also a class of support circuits designed for very specific types of peripheral. Thus keyboard controllers, floppy disc controllers and CRT display controllers will all be found as single-chip circuits. These highly specialised circuits are available because of the very large number of systems which incorporate such peripherals and so they may be produced in the large quantities needed to make a semiconductor product viable. These devices will not be discussed here, but the principles of operation of some of the peripherals supported by these specialised circuits have been discussed in Chapters 10 and 11.

Recently there have emerged a number of peripheral controllers which may be programmed by the system designer. Such devices contain processors and memory (ROM and EPROM) and as such are essentially single-chip microprocessors (Chapter 17) with instruction sets and architectures designed specifically to permit them to interface complex peripherals to the system. One example of such a device is Intel's 8041.

The remainder of this chapter is concerned with an examination of some of the support devices provided by Motorola for the MC6800 (including related microprocessors). Readers who are more interested in devices related to the Intel 8080/8085 family should refer to Appendix B.

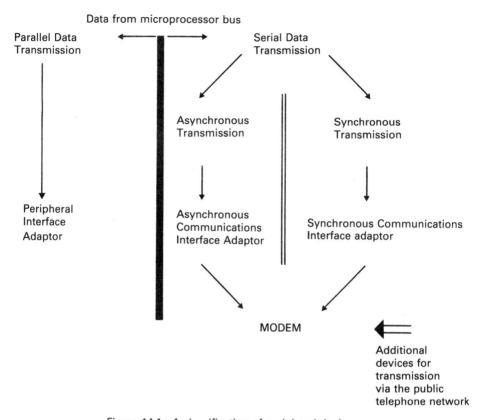

Figure 14.1: A classification of peripheral devices

14.1 Parallel Data Transmission

For parallel data transfer, the MC6800 is provided with a
Peripheral Interface Adapter (PIA). This is capable of
transmitting 8 bits of data from the bus to the peripheral
and vice versa. In addition to the data register, there are
two flags which may be set by external events and may cause
interrupts. The direction of data flow and many other aspects
of the PIA performance are determined by the contents of the
control register.

14.1.1 THE 6820 PERIPHERAL INTERFACE ADAPTER

The PIA consists of two near-identical halves (the difference
between these halves is small and will be explained as
appropriate). Each half of the PIA is capable of transferring
data, 8 bits at a time, between the external device and the
microprocessor data bus. In addition, two control lines are

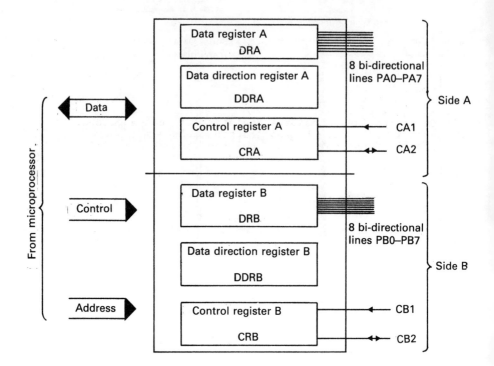

Figure 14.2: Block Diagram of PIA

provided for connection to the external device. One of these control lines acts as an input only and the second line can be made to act as an input or as an output. The way in which the control signals operate and influence the behaviour of the PIA, and the direction of data transfer between the data bus and the outside world, is controlled by the contents of two registers within each section of the PIA. These registers are termed the Data Direction Register (DDR) and the Control Register (CR). The provision of these registers gives the PIA its flexibility.

A simplified block diagram of the PIA is given in Figure 14.2 where it can be seen that there is a third register in each half of the PIA. It is through this that the data is transferred.

All of the internal registers of the PIA can be accessed as if they were memory; thus no separate Input/Output instructions are used in MC6800 systems. Ordinary "STORE" and "LOAD" instructions are all that are required.

As will be seen from Figure 14.2, the PIA ought to have six memory addresses allocated to it. In fact, only four are allocated - two for the A-side and two for the B-side. One of these addresses is allocated to the Data Register DR or Data

Direction Register DDR, while the second is allocated exclusively to the Control Register. The selection between the DR and the DDR is determined by one of the bit positions in the control register.

When this bit in the control register is set to '0', the Data Direction Register will be accessed when the appropriate PIA address is referenced. However, when this control register bit is set to '1', the Data Register will be accessed. This procedure may seem to be rather cumbersome; however, in practice it turns out not to be too troublesome since the Data Direction Register is only very rarely accessed in most systems.

14.1.1.1 DATA DIRECTION REGISTER (DDR)

The control of the data lines as inputs or outputs is exercised by the Data Direction Register; this is an 8-bit register. When a particular bit of the Data Direction Register is set to '1' the line connected to the corresponding bit in the Data Register is configured as an output. If a bit in the Data Direction Register is set to '0', the corresponding line is configured as an input. All eight connections to the Data Register may be configured individually.

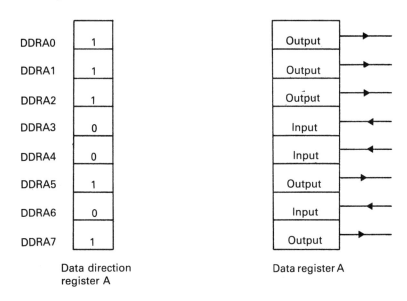

DDRA0	1	Output	→
DDRA1	1	Output	→
DDRA2	1	Output	→
DDRA3	0	Input	←
DDRA4	0	Input	←
DDRA5	1	Output	→
DDRA6	0	Input	←
DDRA7	1	Output	→

Data direction
register A

Data register A

Figure 14.3: Use of Data Direction Register

14.1.1.2 CONTROL REGISTER

The control register is also an 8-bit register whose structure is as shown in Figure 14.4.

293

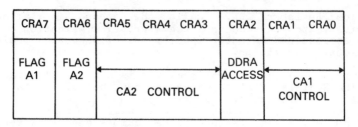

CRA7	CRA6	CRA5 CRA4 CRA3	CRA2	CRA1 CRA0
FLAG A1	FLAG A2	CA2 CONTROL	DDRA ACCESS	CA1 CONTROL

Figure 14.4: Layout of Control Register A (CRA)

Bits 6 and 7 (CRA6, CRA7) of the control register do not actually control anything. As noted elsewhere, it is often necessary to employ one or more flags in a peripheral device to indicate its current status. Bits 6 and 7 serve this function. Bit 6 (Flag A2) can be set to '1' if the signal on control input line C2 changes in an appropriate fashion and if C2 has been set up as an input (see below). Similarly, bit 7 (Flag A1) can be set to '1' if the signal on control line C1 changes appropriately. These flags can be made to cause an interrupt if some of the other control register bits are set appropriately. The status of these flags is tested by reading the whole of the contents of the control register into the microprocessor where it can be tested under program control. The act of reading the data register resets both flags to '0'.

Bit 2 of the control register is used to select either the Data Direction Register A or the Data Register A as explained above. A logic '1' in this position selects the Data Register and a '0' selects the Data Direction Register.

Bits 1 and 0 are used to control the operation of control line CA1 as shown in Figure 14.5.

Bit 0='0'	INTERRUPTS ARE DISABLED. If an event occurs on control line CA1 so that Flag A1 is set, no interrupt is generated.
Bit 0='1'	INTERRUPTS ARE ENABLED. If an event occurs on control line CA1 so that Flag A1 is set an interrupt *is* generated.
Bit 1='0'	Flag A1 is set to '1' when the signal on control line CA1 goes from Logic '1' to logic '0'.
Bit 1='1'	Flag A1 is set to '1' when the signal on control line CA1 goes from Logic '0' to logic '1'.

Figure 14.5: Use of Bits CRA0 and CRA1 of Control Register A

Control over line CA2 is exercised by bits 3, 4 and 5 of the control register. It is necessary to use 3 bits since control line 2 can be used as either an input or an output. To use CA2 as an input, bit CRA5 must be set to '0'. When CA2 is used as an input, bit CRA4 performs the same function for CA2

as bit CRA1 does for CA1. Similarly, CRA3 is functionally
equivalent to CRA0.

When CA2 is to be used as an output control, bit CRA5 must be
set to '1'. When used as an output control line, CA2 can
carry a pulse-type output or it can simply follow the logic
state of bit 3 of the control register. This latter mode of
operation is the simplest to understand.

If bit CRA5 = 1 (CA2 is an output)
    CRA4 = 1 (simple output mode selected)

Then the output on line CA2 follows the logic state of bit
CRA3.

i.e. The output on CA2 is '1' when CRA3 = '1'
     The output on CA2 is '0' when CRA3 = '0'

Thus a device connected to control line CA2 could be switched
on and off by simply storing a '1' or a '0' in bit CRA3 of
the control register.

The final mode of operation for control line CA2 is the pulse
mode (handshake mode) which is selected when

    CRA5 = 1 (CA2 is an output)
    CRA4 = 0 (Pulse mode selected)

There are two types of pulse operation. The first occurs when
bit CRA3 is '0'. This mode is illustrated in Figure 14.6.

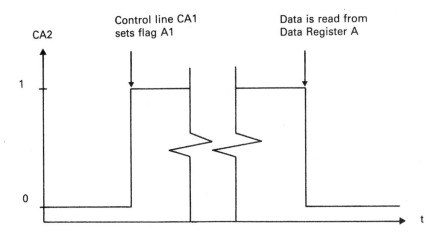

Figure 14.6: Pulse Mode Output on CA2 when bit CRA3=0

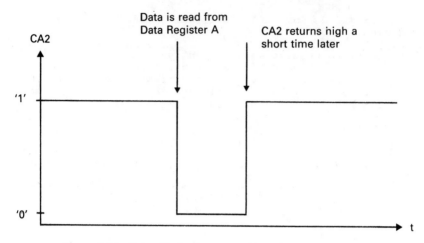

Figure 14.7: Pulse Mode Output on CA2 with bit CRA3=1

The generation of the pulse is controlled by events not
directly connected with control line CA2. The output on the
control line goes to a logic '1' level when some event on
control line CA1 causes its flag, flag A1, to set. The output
is restored to zero when data is read from the associated data
register. This mode of operation permits a 'handshaking'
protocol to be established during input operations.

The second pulse mode occurs when bit CRA3 is set to '1'.
This mode of operation is illustrated in Figure 14.7.

The mode illustrated in Figure 14.6 would be most useful if
flag A1 was set when data was applied to the PIA. The output
of control line CA2 could be used to inhibit any further data
until the first data is read. Likewise the mode illustrated
in Figure 14.7 could be used to apply a 'trigger' pulse to a
peripheral, automatically initiating the fetching of fresh
data once the first piece of data has been read.

The pulse modes described above apply only to the A-side of
the PIA. The B-side has similar modes of operation except
that it is the WRITING of data to the PIA which is important,
not the reading of data from it. Thus the B-side supports
output handshaking.

14.1.2 AN EXAMPLE OF THE USE OF A PIA

As an example of the use of a PIA, consider the interface
between a paper tape reader and a microprocessor.

The tape reader provides the following signals:

D_0–D_7	Data lines representing the character
Step input	A negative transition on this input causes the next character to be fetched.
Ready output	A '1' level on this output indicates that the new character is available.

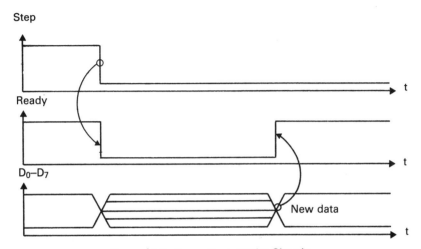

Figure 14.8: Paper Tape reader Signals

Clearly there are two control lines needed, the "step" signal which is an output and must, therefore, be connected to control line 2 since this is the only output control line, which leaves the 'ready' line to be connected to control line 1. The arrangement is shown in Figure 14.9 assuming that the A-side of the PIA is in use.

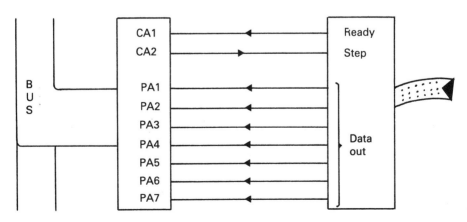

Figure 14.9: Connection of PIA to a Tape Reader

The settings of the DDR and the control register must now be decided. Clearly the DDR is set to 00(16) since all bits are being used as inputs. The control register is a little more complex, however, and must be taken one bit at a time.

CRA0 = 1	Assuming that interrupt operation is desired.
CRA1 = 1	Because the flag is to be set when ready goes from '0' to '1'.
CRA2 = 1	Selects data register (needs to be 0 during initialisation only).
CRA3 CRA4 }	Depends on mode of operation. See below.
CRA5 = 1	(Control line 2 is an output).
CRA6 = X	(Flag 2 - read only, irrelevant in this application).
CRA7 = X	Flag 1 - read only. Set to 1 when a new character is ready.

The setting of bits 3 and 4 governs the way in which the tape reader is used. The simplest method is to set CRA4 = 1 (simple mode). In this mode the reader is made to step by writing 1 to bit 3 followed by a write of 0 to bit 3. Since CA2 follows bit 3, this produces the necessary negative transition to step the reader. This method is, however, rather inefficient and the reader can be made to operate automatically by using pulse mode.

If CRA4 = 0 (pulse mode) then setting CRA3 = 0 results in the following action:

The reader fetches a character. When it is ready the "ready" line goes high and sets flag A1. This will cause:

(i) an interrupt
(ii) control line 2 to go from 0 to 1 (Fig 14.6)

Eventually the program reads data from the A data inputs. The act of reading automatically causes control line 2 to go from '1' to '0', thus setting the reader in motion without direct program intervention.

14.2 Serial Data Transmission

As has been discussed in Chapter 10, serial transmission consists of sending data bit-by-bit over a single pair of lines rather than over a set of 8 lines as would be required for the parallel transmission of an 8-bit word. Reliable serial transmission requires that both the transmitter and receiver remain in synchronism and various techniques exist to achieve this. Also the data usually needs to be protected by some sort of error checking. Because of the variety of methods used to implement serial transmission systems, it is not viable to manufacture a communications adaptor for each of the possible methods that could be used. Instead a single adaptor is manufactured which incorporates sufficient flexibility to be configured for each situation. The Motorola 6800 family of parts incorporates a number of serial data transmission adaptors to meet most requirements:

MC6850 Asynchronous Communications Interface Adaptor (ACIA)
MC6852 Synchronous Serial Data Adaptor (SSDA)

The MC6850 is an example of a type of device widely available from many manufacturers called a universal asynchronous receiver/transmitter (UART). There also exist devices which cover the functions of both the MC6850 and the MC6852. These are commonly called universal asynchronous/synchronous receiver/ transmitters (USART). By way of illustration the capabilities of the MC6850 ACIA will be described.

14.2.1 THE INTERFACING AND USE OF AN ACIA

In this Section, the connection of a Motorola MC6850 ACIA to an MC6800 microprocessing unit will be discussed. The ACIA is supplied as a 24-pin dual-in-line package. A simplified block diagram of the ACIA is shown in Figure 14.10.

All data transfers between the ACIA and the microprocessing unit take place via the Data Buffer. As can be seen from Figure 14.10, data may be written either into the transmit data register (i.e. a character to be sent) or into the control register, which establishes the format of the character to be transmitted, enabling of interrupts etc. Data cannot be read from these registers as no purpose would be served by doing so.

Data may be read from the receiver buffer (i.e. an incoming character) and from the status register. The latter contains information about errors which may have occurred during the transmission and reception as well as an indication of whether a new character is available to be read.

One feature of note is that the device is DOUBLE BUFFERED. That is, a character for transmission is placed first in the transmit data buffer and, if the transmission unit is free, it is automatically transferred to this. Once the transfer has taken place, new data may be put in the transmit data buffer even if the first character is still being sent. Once the first character is completed, the second will automatically be transferred and sent. The ACIA automatically adds the start, stop and parity bits to the data as required.

A similar situation exists on the receive side. A character is taken into the receiver unit and all synchronisation and parity bits removed. It is then transferred to the receive data buffer and the ACIA is free to receive the next character even before the first character is read into the microprocessor unit.

The ACIA also has other inputs for clocks, power supply and to permit it to be selected from amongst all the other peripherals and memory which may be connected to the microprocessing unit.

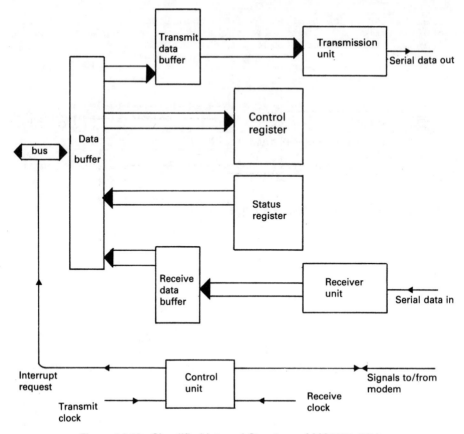

Figure 14.10: Simplified internal Structure of MC6850 ACIA

14.2.1.1 CONNECTION OF ACIA TO THE BUS

The connection of an ACIA or, for that matter, any other peripheral adaptor, to the bus is extremely simple as shown in Figure 14.11.

As will be seen from the Figure, interfacing this device consists, for the most part, of connecting together like-named signals.

The data bus of the microprocessor is connected directly to the data pins of the ACIA. The address bus is connected to an address decoder which is wired up so that only the occurrence of the particular address chosen for the device causes a '1' at its output. The device is essentially a large "and" gate though it would probably be constructed of one or more medium-scale-integration devices designed specifically for this type of job. The output of the decoder is applied to CS0 (Chip select) in order to control the selection of the ACIA.

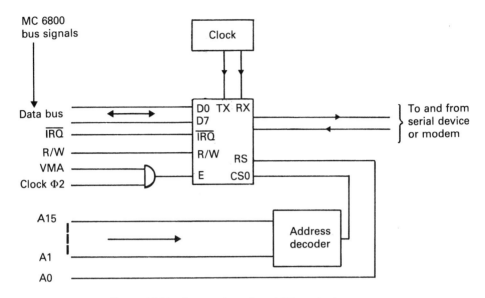

Figure 14.11: Connection of an ACIA to the bus.

The ACIA has four internal registers each of which must be
individually addressable. This would seem to imply the use of
two address lines to select a particular register. However,
two of the registers are write-only (transmit data and
control) and the other two are read-only (status and receive
data) and so the read/write line may be used as one of the
selector lines. In Figure 14.11, address line A0 is not taken
into the address decoder so the ACIA will be selected by
lines A15 to A1 inclusive, irrespective of the state of A0.
A0 is then used to select a particular register from the
read-only or write-only pair.

A0	Read	Write
'0' '1'	Status Receive Data	Control Transmit Data

The enable input (E) has the special function of both
enabling the device and also synchronising the data transfers
with the microprocessor. For this reason, the Phase 2 clock
is used. The valid memory address signal (VMA) is AND-ed with
this to avoid spurious read and write operations. The use of
an "enable" for synchronisation is a peculiarity of the MC6800
system.

The ACIA's interrupt request line IRQ is connected directly
to the IRQ line of the bus and will, therefore, cause an

interrupt in the system provided interrupts are not masked. This line could, equally well, have been connected to the Non-Maskable-Interrupt line ($\overline{NMI}$) if it had been desired that the ACIA interrupts should not be turned off.

A separate clock generator is provided to time both transmission and reception. Provision is made for two separate rates, one for transmission and one for reception.

14.2.1.2 PROGRAMMING THE ACIA

As was mentioned above, the exact format of an asynchronously transmitted serial character is subject to considerable variation. The ACIA is programmed to adopt one of a number of formats by using the control register. In addition, this register controls the relationship between the external clock and the transmission rate, the receive and transmit interrupt status and the level of one of the modem control signals. The control register is 8-bits wide and functions as follows:

bits 0 and 1	Control the transmission rate (see table 14.1)
bits 2, 3 and 4	Control the format of the data being transmitted and received (see Table 14.2)
bits 5 and 6	Control the transmitting interrupt conditions and the 'Request to send' line
bit 7	Controls the receiving interrupt conditions. (0=disable)

CR0	CR1	FUNCTION
0	0	Transmission Rate is same as clock rate
0	1	Transmission Rate is 1/16 of clock rate
1	0	Transmission Rate is 1/64 of clock rate
1	1	Reset

Table 14.1

CR2	CR3	CR4	Character Format
0	0	0	7 bits+Even parity+2 stop bits
0	0	1	8 bits+2 stop bits
0	1	0	7 bits+Even parity+1 stop bit
0	1	1	8 bits+Even parity+1 stop bit
1	0	0	7 bits+Odd parity+2 stop bits
1	0	1	8 bits+1 stop bit
1	1	0	7 bits+Odd parity+1 stop bit
1	1	1	8 bits+Odd parity+1 stop bit

Table 14.2

The status register is not used as a means of controlling the operation of the communications. It is used to register the various errors that may occur during serial transmission. The status register is also an 8-bit register.

Bit 0:

> This indicates, when set, that a character is available in the receive data register. If receiver interrupts are enabled by the control register it will cause an interrupt.

Bit 1:

> This indicates, when set, that the transmit data register is available for a new character. It will cause an interrupt if the control register has enabled transmitter interrupts.

Bit 2:

> This bit will be set if the modem indicates that it has lost contact. An interrupt will occur if receiver interrupts are enabled.

Bit 3:

> When set, this indicates that the modem is ready to transmit daţa.

Bit 4:

> When set, this indicates that a FRAMING ERROR has been detected by the receiver. This means that the receiver has not detected a stop bit due to some fault in the transmission or loss of synchronisation.

Bit 5:

> When set, this indicates an OVERRUN ERROR. This is the loss of characters in the data stream due to the receive data register not being read before the next character overwrites it. An interrupt will occur if receiver interrupts are enabled.

Bit 6:

> If the parity of the received character is not as specified by the control register this bit will be set.

Bit 7:

> Interrupt request. This bit is set if an interrupt has been requested by the ACIA. It is used by the microprocessor program when polling devices to determine which one has caused an interrupt.

The transmission of serial data over the public network requires the use of modulated carrier techniques rather than D.C. transmission. This facility takes the form of frequency shift keying (mark sent as one frequency and space as another) or phase shift keying. The 6800 family includes two modem (modulator-demodulator) devices which transform the serial data provided by the ACIA or SSDA into the appropriately modulated form for transmission via the public network.

The MC6860 modem is a frequently shift keying device which synthesises the output modulated waveform digitally. The 6862 modem is a phase shift keying device which also generates its output modulated waveform digitally. In this case, however, the output is provided as a 6-bit digital output which is then applied to a D to A convertor and filter before transmission.

14.3 Counter and Timer Circuits

Many microprocessor systems require to measure time intervals or to count events as a part of their operations. These operations can be carried out under software control but this solution can be unnecessarily demanding on processor time and so a hardware solution is often to be preferred.

To meet this requirement, the MC6840 counter-timer circuit is available. The use of the 6840 avoids having to construct timer circuits out of a relatively large number of MSI and SSI devices and is, therefore, to be preferred in microprocessor systems.

The MC6840 counter-timer contains three similar sets of timing circuitry each of which operates independently of its neighbours. Figure 14.12 shows a block diagram of one of the timer units.

Under program control it is possible to write to the 16-bit latch and to the 8-bit control register; and it is possible to read the contents of the counter (16 bits) and the status register. The latter is an 8-bit register which is shared by all three counter circuits.

On initialisation, the contents of the latch are transferred to the counter which is then decremented on each negative going edge of the selected clock source. The clock may be derived from the system clock $\phi2$ or it may be provided by an external source connected to the "C" input. The gate input is used in the various operating modes to initiate and to inhibit the timer.

Various operating modes are available and are selected by loading the appropriate bit pattern to the control register.

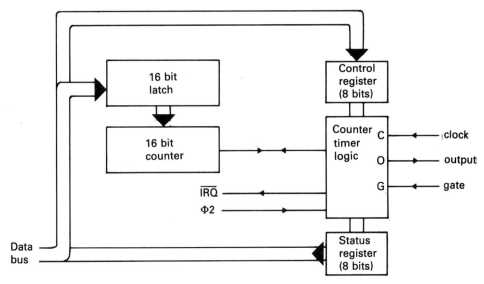

Figure 14.12: Simplified Diagram of one section of MC6840 Timer Unit

14.3.1 CONTINUOUS COUNTING

This is available in 16-bit or 8-bit modes. In the 16-bit mode the contents of the counter are decremented by each clock cycle until the counter contains zero, when it is said to have "timed-out". When this happens, the counter is reloaded from the latch and the counter flag in the status register is set. An interrupt will be generated if interrupts for the particular counter have been enabled.

The initialisation of the count can occur, under the control of external hardware, by a high to low transition on the gate input, G. This must remain low for the duration of the count. If G goes high, the count is lost and the counter will be re-initialised on the next high-low transition. Alternatively the counter can be started under program control (if bit 4 of the control register is 0). Using this method, the act of writing to the latch also transfers the latch contents to the counter and starts the counting.

Each counter has an output to external hardware which, if enabled, is toggled each time the counter times out (Figure 14.13).

In addition to the 16-bit mode, there is an 8-bit counting mode. In this mode the 16-bit contents of the counter are treated as two 8-bit numbers. The least significant number is decremented to zero AND THEN RESET TO ITS ORIGINAL VALUE (not FF). At the same time that it is reset, the most significant 8-bit number is decremented.

This process continues until the most significant number reaches zero when the counter times out as above.

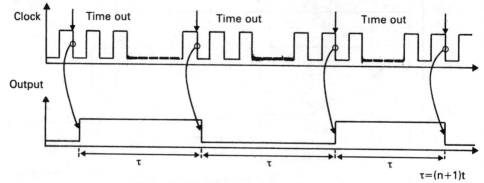

Figure 14.13: Waveform at Counter Output

If the output is enabled, a most interesting waveform is generated (Figure 14.14). The output goes low on initialisation and comes high again when the least significant number is reset for the last time before the time out. The output is set low again at the time out. In this way, by varying the relationship between the most significant and least significant number, a variable mark-space ratio waveform can be generated.

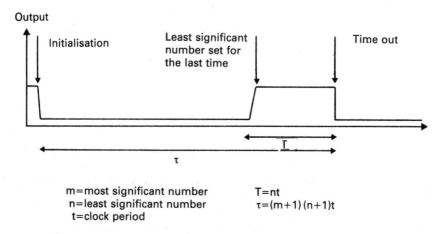

m=most significant number   T=nt
n=least significant number $\tau=(m+1)(n+1)t$
t=clock period

Figure 14.14: Output Waveform in 8-Bit Counting Mode

14.3.2 SINGLE-SHOT MODE

This is a mode which allows a single pulse of defined width to be generated at the output. With the output enabled, the output makes a low-high transition one clock period after initialisation and goes low again at time out. No further changes then take place on the output although the timer continues to operate (Figure 14.15).

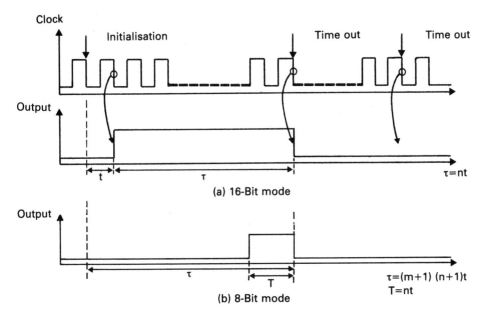

Figure 14.15: Timer Output in Single-Shot Mode

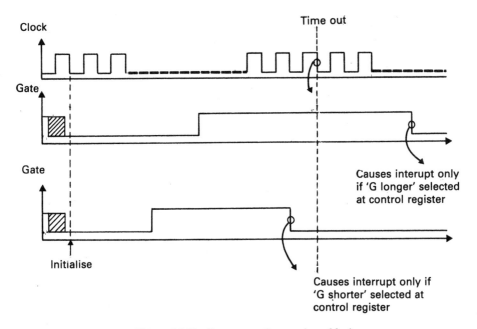

Figure 14.16: Frequency Comparison Mode

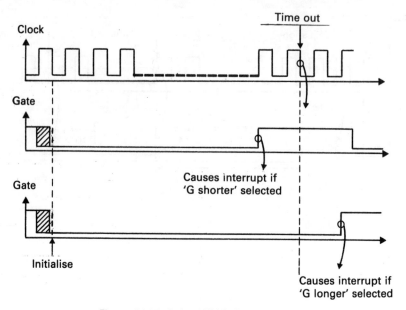

Figure 14.17: Pulse Width Comparison Mode

14.3.3 FREQUENCY COMPARISON AND PULSE WIDTH MEASUREMENT MODES

These modes are used to enable external waveforms, presented
to the counter-timer on its G input, to be compared with the
internally generated period (from initialisation to time out)
of the counter.

In frequency comparison mode, the period of one cycle of the
G waveform is compared with the timer period and an interrupt
may be generated either when the G waveform period is longer
than the internal period, or when it is shorter. The
selection is made by the setting of the control register
(Figure 14.16).

In pulse width comparison mode, it is the time for which the
G input is low that provides the external period in the
comparison (Figure 14.17).

14.3.4 CONTROL REGISTER

Each timer section has its own control register which is
accessible to the programmer and which he may use to select
the various counting modes. The layout of this register is
given in outline below (Figure 14.18).

14.3.5 STATUS REGISTER AND TIMER ADDRESSING

The status register of the 6840 is very simple, having one
bit allocated to each of the three timers and a fourth bit

308

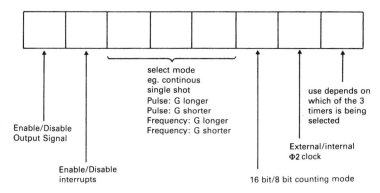

Figure 14.18: Control Register for one 6840 Timer

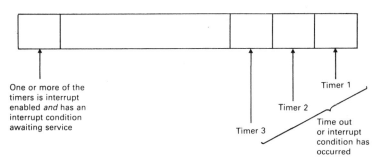

Figure 14.19: Status register of 6840 Timer

allocated to show whether there are any interrupts pending from the device.

The single status register does, therefore, serve all three timers.

Each timer has one 8-bit control register and one 16-bit latch which may be written to and one 16-bit counter that may be read. Thus each timer requires three 8-bit (write) address and two 8-bit (read) addresses.

In total, therefore, the 6840 has nine write-only locations (including the status register) and seven read-only locations.

The 6840 is provided with three addressing lines giving eight possible read-only and eight possible write-only locations. The read-only locations are simply given sequential locations but two of the write-only locations have to share an address. This is achieved in a manner similar to the Data Register and Data Direction Register in the 6820 PIA, in this case the selection between the two identically addressed locations is determined by the setting of bit 0 in the control register of timer 2.

14.4 Clock Circuits

The MC6800 processor does not contain any on-chip clock circuitry. This is provided by a separate device, the MC6870A, which provides ∅1 and ∅2 clock signals in NMOS compatible form plus a ∅2 clock output suitable for driving TTL circuitry. The clock frequency is internally set to 1.0 MHz.

The MC6871A is a slightly more flexible device which has two control inputs. The first "HOLD 1" causes the clock waveforms to be lengthened with ∅1 held high (and ∅2 low) as required for use of the "Tri-state control" input of the processor (Section 9.4.3) while the second input "MEMORY READY" causes the waveforms to be lengthened with ∅2 high (and ∅1 low).

The stretching of the ∅2 clock by "MEMORY READY" is used to lengthen the second half of a processor cycle when slow memory is being accessed. Since data is absorbed by the processor when ∅2 goes from high to low the stretching of ∅2 delays this time and thus allows more time for the memory to respond. MEMORY READY is a signal supplied by the decoding circuitry of the memory being accessed.

The "HOLD 1" and "MEMORY READY" signals must be synchronised with the main ∅1 and ∅2 clocks. This is achieved by external circuitry and by the two other signals made available from the 6871A (an unstretched ∅2 signal and a double clock frequency signal).

The 6871B clock circuit is broadly similar to the 6871A.

The most sophisticated clock circuit in the range is the MC6875. This circuit provides for external determination of the clock frequency by crystal, by R-C circuit or by some external waveform. It also contains all of the necessary synchronisation circuitry for the "MEMORY READY" signals etc. and therefore removes the need for any external circuits.

14.5 Composite Support Devices

It frequently happens that small systems do not fully utilise the facilities provided by the support devices described so far. To serve the needs of these smaller systems there exist multi-purpose support circuits which typically include a selection of resources including read/write memory, read-only memory, programmable ROM, timers and I/O ports. In the 6800 family the multi-function support device is the MC6846 which incorporates 2K bytes of ROM, a timer, and a parallel 8-bit I/O port. The MC6846 may be used as a general support device for all 6800-family processors although it is specifically designed as the second item of the MC6802 2-chip processor system.

The parallel I/O section functions in a fashion which is very
similar to one half of the MC6820 PIA discussed earlier. The
timer unit, likewise, is very similar to one of the units
incorporated into the MC6840. In both cases there are minor
operational differences which need to be taken account of.

14.6 Interrupt Control Devices

As described earlier, the MC6800 has two interrupt lines, one
maskable and the other non-maskable. As a rule most devices
will be connected to the maskable interrupt ($\overline{IRQ}$) line.

An interrupt occuring on this line causes a vectored jump to
a service routine, the address of which is stored (usually in
ROM or PROM) at locations FFF8 and FFF9. Where many devices
are connected to the $\overline{IRQ}$ line the service routine will have
to poll them before deciding which to service. This is a time
consuming operation which can be avoided if each device has
its own vectoring location.

The MC6828 priority interrupt controller provides just this
facility by expanding the single $\overline{IRQ}$ line of the 6800 into 8
vectored interrupt lines. This is achieved by modifying the
information on address lines A4 - A1 when the processor
attempts to read from FFF8 and FFF9, causing accesses to be
made to other addresses in the range FFE8 to FFF7. The actual
addresses used are controlled by which of the interrupt lines
has initiated the vectored interrupt. The general arrangement
of the system is shown in Figure 14.20.

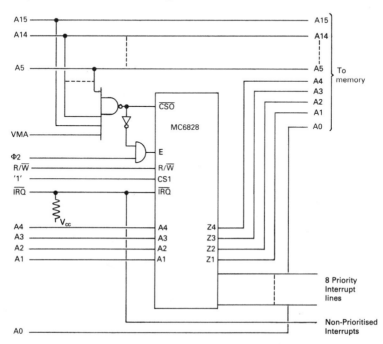

Figure 14.20: Use of MC6828 Priority Interrupt Controller

The 6828 is selected under the following conditions:

$\overline{CS0}$	CS1	R/$\overline{W}$	A4	A3	A2	A1
0	1	1 (read)	1	1	0	0

If CS1 is connected to VMA and CS0 is connected to the NAND of A15 to A5, the 6828 will only become operational when the processor is attempting to READ from either FFF8 or FFF9 (which only happens on an interrupt service). At all other times, the 6828 is deselected and the information on address lines A1 to A4 inclusive is passed unaltered to Z1 to Z4.

When an interrupt occurs on one of the 8 interrupt lines of the 6828, the IRQ line is activated. The processor enters its maskable interrupt service routine and automatically reads the data from FFF8 and FFF9, the recovered data being interpreted as the address of the service routine.

The memory access to FFF8 and FFF9 selects the 6828 device which modifies address bits A1 - A4 so that the actual memory read is performed on a different location depending on which device caused the interrupt and according to the Table below.

Source of interrupt	Reference to FFF8 and FFF9 re-routed to		Z_4	Z_3	Z_2	Z_1
$\overline{IN7}$	FFF6	FFF7	1	0	1	1
$\overline{IN6}$	FFF4	FFF5	1	0	1	0
$\overline{IN5}$	FFF2	FFF3	1	0	0	1
$\overline{IN4}$	FFF0	FFF1	1	0	0	0
$\overline{IN3}$	FFEE	FFEF	0	1	1	1
$\overline{IN2}$	FFEC	FFED	0	1	1	0
$\overline{IN1}$	FFFA	FFEB	0	1	0	1
$\overline{IN0}$	FFE8	FFE9	0	1	0	0

DECREASING PRIORITY

Table 14.3: Operation of MC6828 Interrupt Controller

If two or more interrupt requests are received simultaneously, then the vector applicable to the highest priority device will be supplied to the processor.

It was stated above that the 6828 will only be selected on a read cycle. This is true in respect of the operations detailed above. However, any attempt to write to locations FFE8 through FFF9 will be intercepted and will cause the interrupt priority mask to be written to. In this way, it is possible to enable or disable all interrupts or to select a priority level below which all interrupts will be inhibited.

As shown in Figure 14.20, the MC6828 is inserted into the address bus. Its only effect, when not selected, will be to add a slight propagation delay to the A1 - A4 lines. This is the easiest way of using the 6828. However, it may be removed

writing to this address	will inhibit all interrupts from these levels
FFE0 or FFE1	NONE
FFE2 or FFE3	0
FFE4 or FFE5	1, 0
FFE6 or FFE7	2, 1, 0
FFE8 or FFE9	3, 2, 1, 0
FFEA or FFEB	4, 3, 2, 1, 0
FFEC or FFED	5, 4, 3, 2, 1, 0
FFEE or FFEF	6, 5, 4, 3, 2, 1, 0
FFE0 thru FFFF	ALL

Table 14.4: Interrupt Inhibit Control for MC6828

from the address lines along with its associated ROM and this arrangement permits the expansion of the number of vectored interrupt lines almost without limit, by permitting more than one MC6828 to be incorporated into the system.

14.7 Other Processors Related to the MC6800

The original 6800 has proved a popular microprocessor even though it required more support hardware than some of its competitors. As a result of this popularity, Motorola have issued other, related, processors which attempt to fit the MC6800 family into applications where the 6800 part itself could not readily be used. These variations include faster devices (6800A, 6800B); single chip processors (6801, 6803) and a 2-chip processor, the 6802. In addition, a new and powerful processor, the 6809 has been issued to plug the gap between the standard 8-bit processors and the 16-bit highly developed machines.

The relationships between these devices is shown in Figure 14.21.

14.7.1 THE 6800A AND 6800B

These two devices are identical to the basic 6800 except that they use 1.5 MHz and 2.0 MHz clocks respectively.

14.7.2 THE 6802

This enhancement of the 6800 incorporates the standard 6800 instruction set without the benefit of any additional commands. However, the clock circuitry which has to be provided separately in 6800 systems is integrated into the processor chip in the 6802. In addition, 128 bytes of read-

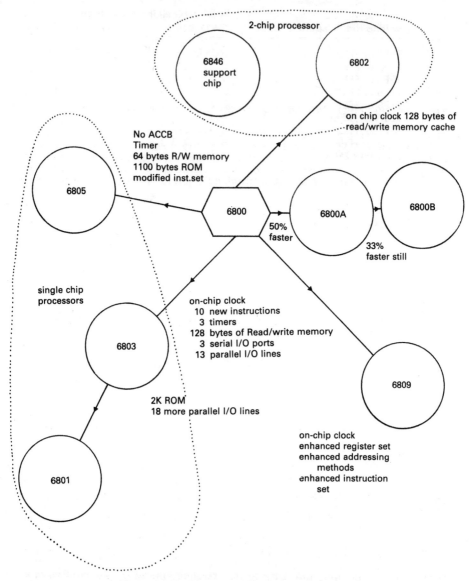

Figure 14.21: Processors Related to the MC6800

write memory are also provided and in many systems this
obviates the need for external read-write memory. An
interesting feature of the 6802 is the provision of 32 bytes
of the read-write memory in a form which can relax into a
low-power standby mode thus facilitating the provision of
battery back-up.

To fabricate a complete system with the 6802, ROM for program storage, I/O ports and possibly timers will be needed. These can be provided by the 6846 general purpose support chip which contains 2K bytes of ROM, 8 I/O lines and a timer. Thus the 6802 plus 6846 constitute a simple 2-chip processor suitable for many low cost applications.

14.7.3 THE 6801 AND 6803 SINGLE-CHIP PROCESSORS

These processors carry the philosophy of the 6802 one stage further by effectively integrating the facilities of the 6846 chip onto the 6802 processor chip. In this way a complete single chip processor is formed. However, the process has been taken a little further than this and some new instructions have been added.

Both the 6801 and 6803 obey the full instruction set of the 6800 but to these are added ten extra instructions. The major innovation is the use of the A and B accumulators as a single 16-bit accumulator referred to as accumulator D. (Note that accumulator D is not an extra piece of hardware, it is simply a different use of A and B.)

Six of the new instructions relate to this "new" accumulator.

    (i)   load ACCD from memory
    (ii)   store ACCD in memory
    (iii)   add a number to ACCD
    (iv)   subtract a number from ACCD
    (v)   shift ACCD left
    (vi)   shift ACCD right

Three of the new instructions are related to improved index and stack handling facilities:

    (vii)   add accumulator B to the Index Register
    (viii) push Index Register to stack
    (ix)   pop Index Register from stack

The final new instruction is an 8 x 8 bit hardware multiply. The operands are initially placed in the A and B accumulators and the 16-bit result is left in the D accumulator. The process takes about 10 usec.

The hardware facilities which the 6803/6801 have in excess of the 6800 include on-chip clock, read/write memory, ROM, parallel I/O and serial I/O. There are various versions of the 6801/6803 having different amounts of these facilities; these are summarised below.

Notice that the 68701 version is identical to the 6801 except that EPROM is used in place of mask programmed ROM. This makes the 6701 highly suitable for development work and low-to-medium volume production.

Another interesting feature of the 6801 is the way in which it may be expanded. As it stands, no address or data buses

Device	Timers	Clock	Memory		I/O		Instruction	Remarks
			ROM	Read-write	Parallel	Serial		
6800	None	Off-chip	External ... 64K max		External, part of address space		6800	Multi-chip system
6801	3×16 bit	On-chip	2K }MASK	128	31	3	6800+TEN }	
6801E	3×16 bit	Off-chip	2K	128	31	3	6800+TEN	16 bit 'accumulator D' available
68701	3×16 bit	On-chip	2K }EPROM	128	31	3	6800+TEN	
68701E	3×16 bit	Off-chip	2K	128	31	3	6800+TEN }	
6802	None	On-chip	NIL (external ... 64K max)	128	NIL	NIL	6800	intended as 2-chip set with 6846 support IC. R/W memory includes 32 byte low power standby cache
6803	3×16 bit	On-chip	NIL	128	13	3	6800+TEN }	16-bit 'accumulator D' available
6803E	3×16 bit	Off-chip	NIL	128	13	3	6800+TEN }	
6805	1×8 bit	On-chip	1152 MASK	64	20	NIL	6800 modified & enhanced for bit manipulation	mask options include: CMOS, TTL & LED compatible I/O, setting of on-chip prescaler for timer
6808	None	On-chip	External ... 64K max		NIL	NIL	6800	Same as 6802 except that 128 bytes of R-W memory are absent
6809	None	On-chip	External ... 64K max		NIL	NIL	New upward compatible with 6800 at the source code level	Enhanced register set, enhanced instruction set, new interrupt structure

Table 14.5: Summary of Hardware Facilities for MC6800-Related Processors

are brought out to the device pins and it is truly a single-chip device. By writing the appropriate bit pattern to an internal register, the 6801 can be switched from single-chip mode into expanded-non-multiplexed mode or into expanded-multiplexed mode.

Both modes switch one of the I/O ports into an address bus port. In addition, the non-multiplexed mode uses another I/O port as a Data Bus Port. This non-multiplexed mode thus provides an external address space of 256 bytes which is primarily intended for I/O expansion using 6800 family parts.

In the multiplexed mode, the address port provides the high-order addressing lines and the second port is used alternately as a data port and as the low-order address port.

This latter information has to be strobed into a suitable latch using a timing signal provided by the 6801. In this mode, the full 64K addressing space is made available externally.

14.7.4 THE 6809

The 6809 of the devices discussed in this section has the largest number of enhancements over the 6800, yet it remains a member of the 6800 family.

Certain hardware features have been added to the 6809, these include:

(i)   a second index register (Y)

(ii)   a second stack pointer (U)

(iii)   an 8-bit direct page register

(iv)   on-chip clock circuitry

(v)   the provision of a 16-bit accumulator D exactly as in the 6801

(vi)   a second maskable interrupt line FIRQ

The 8-bit direct page register may be loaded under program control and provides the most significant 8 bits of any memory reference mode using the Motorola 2-byte direct addressing method. Thus the advantages of this addressing method are now available throughout the full 64K addressing space.

The second maskable interrupt takes precedence over the IRQ interrupt and is vectored using locations FFF6 and FFF7. It Is fast because only the status register and program counter are stacked (unlike IRQ which stacks everything).

The two unused flags of the 6800 status word are used in connection with FIRQ. One of these bits is used as a mask bit and the other is used internally by the return-from-interrupt Instruction so that it pops the correct number of items from the stack.

In addition to the direct addressing enhancement mentioned above, the 6809 has many other improvements too numerous to mention here, to its addressing structure. Particularly to be noted are the extension of relative addressing, previously confined to branch instructions, to all memory reference instructions, and the further enhancement of this mode by the provision of the 'long relative' address which uses 16 bits Instead of the 6800's 8-bit offset. In this way, the full addressing space is brought within the capabilities of relative addressing. Likewise, it is possible to have a full 16-bit offset associated with indexed addressing and this overcomes the MC6800 problems noted in Section 9.2.4.

Many instructions have been made more general by the use of a "POST-BYTE" which serves to further refine and specify the instruction. This makes some instructions 4 bytes long but the increased flexibility is claimed to compensate for this. Included in the modes thus made available are auto-increment and auto-decrement addressing, indirect addressing etc. and various combinations of these modes.

Some new instructions have been added to the 6809 compared to the 6800. The 6809 contains those new instructions incorporated into the 6801 plus a number of new instructions associated with the manipulation of the newly provided registers. Additionally, instructions now exist to transfer the contents of any register to any other, or to exchange their contents and to extend an 8-bit number to its 16-bit 2s complement equivalent.

Two additional software vectored interrupt instructions SWI2 and SWI3 are provided.

Selective stack manipulation is now possible; any combination or all of the programmer's registers may be pushed or popped in a single instruction.

15. Program Development

In a microprocessor based system the development and testing of the programs is of paramount importance since this software replaces the hardware circuitry which would, in a "conventional" system, define the functions performed by the system. It is, therefore, of paramount importance that this software is reliably and accurately written so that it performs the desired functions effectively.

Much of the development cost of a microprocessor system will be expended on the preparation of software and much of the maintenance effort will be directed to ensuring that adequate performance is achieved throughout the lifetime of the product. This Chapter is therefore devoted to explaining some of the techniques which are employed in the preparation of software. In particular, attention will be given to the methods employed for production of reliable, maintainable software and to the tools which are used for its preparation.

The use of a systematic approach to software development is likely to lead to an end product which is relatively error-free and which is more likely to be produced on schedule and within the allocated budget. Such software is also likely to be well documented and thus provides for easier and cheaper maintenance.

15.1 Structured Programming

In the early days of computers, it was necessary to make use of all the various oddities of any given computer to ensure that the resulting program was fast to execute and occupied as little memory as possible. These considerations tended to result in highly disorganised programs that were conceived and written as a single entity. As such, they are very difficult to document and consequently very difficult to debug or modify once developed.

The current trend is towards very complex programs and increasing emphasis is being placed on the reliability and maintainability of software. This in its turn has led to the development of a "structured programming" philosophy which attempts to constrain the programmer to approach his tasks in a way that will tend to promote the generation of easily understood programs. Many of the recently developed computer languages such as Pascal incorporate language constructs which both promote this approach and discourage the programmer from the practices which lead to unstructured programs. In some instances, structured programs will be slightly less efficient than their unstructured equivalents but this is a small price to pay for being able to maintain the software at a later date.

A number of procedures should always be adopted when writing programs in order to make them easily understood at a later date.

(i)   The processing should be clearly and unabmiguously specified in a number of stages, each of increasing detail ("top down design").

(ii)   Each stage of the specification should be flowcharted using the rules of structured programming.

(iii)   When the program is actually written, it should be composed of modules corresponding to the processes defined in (i) and (ii).

(iv)   To enhance readability, attention should be paid to the layout of program code. Each module should be physically separated from its neighbours; it should be titled; all variables used should be given meaningful names; the program code itself should be comprehensively and meaningfully commented.

Considerable emphasis is given to the concept of a module of program and this deserves some further explanation. In a large development project, it is likely that many people will be involved in the preparation of software since it is only in this way that the task can be completed within a reasonable time span. In order to maximise efficiency, it is necessary to allow each programmer to proceed, as far as possible, independently of the other members of the team. If this is not done, much time will be spent in resolving the difficulties which will arise because of the dependence of one team member on another. It is, therefore, helpful to divide the problem into a number of relatively independent and well-defined tasks. Each programmer can then be given one or more such tasks and can proceed to implement it without further interaction with the other team members. Of course, considerable attention must be given to providing a full definition of the task including

(i)   How information is to be passed to the task from other tasks (the input interface).

(ii)   How the results are to be passed out of the task to subsequent processing modules (the output interface).

(iii) The exact processing to be carried out (task definition) including a set of test data, the successful processing of which will be taken as an assurance that the module is meeting its specification.

Items (i) and (ii) will include how the data is to be stored and the type of representation to be used. All of these points must be resolved before the module may be written and, if completed perfectly, they will greatly reduce the interactions required between individual programmers. Further, once these definitions are written down, they go a long way towards the documentation of the system.

Given this information and the appropriate programming tools (such as assemblers which produce relocatable code and the matching linkage editors - discussed later), it is possible for a programmer to write and fully test a module before submitting it for integration into the overall body of the system. This is a very great aid since, if each module functions correctly, then any malfunction of the system as a whole must be due to faulty or inadequate definition of the overall system.

In practice, a number of small modules will be combined together as building "bricks" in a larger module and a number of these will be combined to produce the overall system. The size of each module (whether that module consists solely of program code or an assembly of other modular building bricks) should be such that its function is readily understood. As a general guideline, it is commonly recommended that the flowchart describing a module should be capable of being drawn on a single A3-sized sheet of paper. At the lowest level of module, the blocks drawn on the flowchart will be implemented as one or more lines of program and the module is unlikely to consist of more than about 100 lines of code.

One advantage of the modular approach is that each function (or closely-related group of functions) is realised by a single module with a single entry and exit point and with well-defined input/output interfaces. Because the module interacts with the rest of the system only through these single entry/exit points, it is a simple task to modify or replace the module should this prove necessary and one can have considerable confidence that the change will not produce unexpected difficulties for other unrelated parts of the system. Figure 15.1a shows this situation and in Figure 15.1b it is contrasted with that which would apply in an unstructured system where a given section of code can be entered from many different places and can exit to many different destinations.

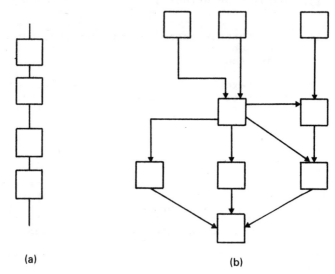

(a)   (b)

Figure 15.1: The Advantage of Single Entry/Exit Modules in Reducing Program Connectivity

Not only is it difficult to replace a module in 15.1b, it is also difficult to be sure that all possible paths through the flowchart are properly tested.

15.1.1 TOP DOWN DESIGN

Top down design involves a number of stages.

(i)   Goal specification: At this stage the broad purpose of the program is stated and the guidelines or limitations of its functions are defined.

(ii)   Specification: This is the second stage of top down design. In it the number of types of input and output will be defined along with the way in which the input and output is represented. Also included in the specification is the strategy to be adopted in processing the inputs to give the outputs.

(iii)   Pseudocode: By writing in plain words, a kind of
        pseudo-computer program can be constructed which
        clearly lays out the various processes that must
        ᵤe executed to achieve the goals using the
        strategy defined in the specification. As far as
        possible, the pseudocode is made independent of
        any particular computer language. Some of the
        processes specified at this stage may be simple
        single instructions in the final program while
        others may have to be decomposed into one, or
        more, subroutines.

(iv)   Code: The final stage of design. The pseudocode
        is converted into the chosen computer language.

EXAMPLE

Consider the design of a program to prevent a driver starting
his car if it is in a dangerous condition.

GOALS:

To ensure that a car is in a safe condition before it is
driven by checking that all doors are shut, lights on (if
required) and that all the occupants are wearing seat belts.
The driver will be warned if his fuel supply is low.

SPECIFICATION:

Inputs - Inputs will be of a binary nature indicating whether

(a) Ignition key on
(b) A seat is occupied
(c) A seat belt is fastened
(d) A door is closed
(e) The daylight is adequate
(f) The headlights are on
(g) The fuel level is adequate

The car is assumed to be equipped with four seats and four
doors.

Outputs - Three binary outputs are available:

(a) Ignition enable/disable
(b) Fuel low warning
(c) Car safety warning
(d) Starter motor control

Strategy - When the driver inserts his ignition key, the
program is automatically started. Those seats which are
occupied are detected using cushion switches and the
corresponding seat belts are checked to ensure that they are
fastened.

The daylight level is checked and if it is too low, the
headlights are checked to ensure that they are switched on.

Finally the doors are checked to see that they are shut.

If any of the above tests is not satisfied the "car safety" warning is illuminated and the condition re-checked after a delay.

If the tests are satisfied, the fuel level is checked and a "fuel warning" illuminated if it is below the required level.

Finally the car engine is started.

PSEUDOCODE:

BEGIN
     WHILE all occupied seats are not belted,
          issue safety warning and wait.
     WHILE light is low and headlights are not on,
          issue safety warning and wait.
     WHILE doors are not shut, issue safety warning and wait.
     IF fuel is ok proceed, ELSE issue warning and proceed.
     Start engine.
FINISH

PROGRAM: In this example the program itself will not be constructed.

In many cases, there will be a disparity between the complexity of tasks specified in one part of the pseudocode and the tasks specified in others. It is desirable that complex tasks should be broken down into smaller tasks, which might be subroutines, so that no single task is too large. Ideally all tasks should be of a similar length which is fairly well limited.

All tasks (program modules) should be designed, written and documented according to the axioms of structured programming.

15.1.2 PROGRAM STRUCTURES

Structured programming dictates that the program structures used should have a single input and a single output path. Two building blocks are used to produce these structures:

The process block

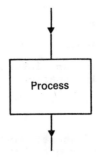

and the decision block

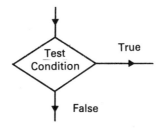

Notice that the decision block is "unstructured" because it has two outputs.

There are three types of structure defined.

SEQUENCE:

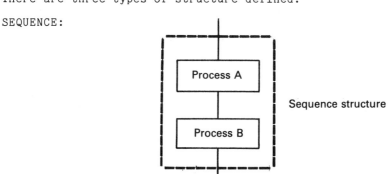

Sequence structure

IF-THEN-ELSE:

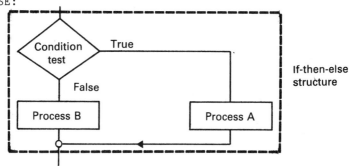

If-then-else structure

IF True THEN process A ELSE Process B

LOOP:

There are two types of looped structure

'DO-WHILE'

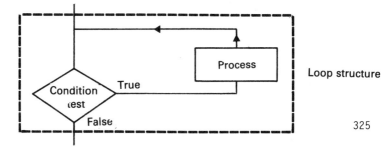

Loop structure

"DO-UNTIL"

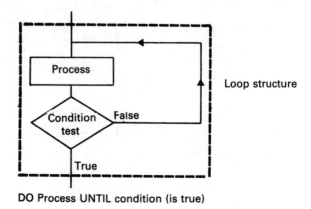

Loop structure

DO Process UNTIL condition (is true)

Note that the "Process" referred to in each of the structures is itself single-input/single-output and can be composed of any other structure or structures defined above.

Thus complex tasks are readily decomposed into other simpler tasks and so on until everything is reduced to a manageably simple level. This is the sequence of structured programming.

Furthermore, each of the tasks has a single input and a single output and can be readily documented, tested and understood.

15.1.3 STRUCTURED LANGUAGES

The writing of structured programs is greatly aided by the use of a suitable high-level language. Many of the older languages (e.g. FORTRAN) do not provide the necessary language constructs to write structured programs easily. The programmer has to use 'GOTO' type statements but he must be careful to do so only when it is permissible to do so within the constraints of structured programming. 'GOTOs' are notorious breakers of program structure.

An example from BASIC and CORAL will illustrate the difference between structured and unstructured languages. The example is an implementation of the 'IF-THEN-ELSE' structure shown above.

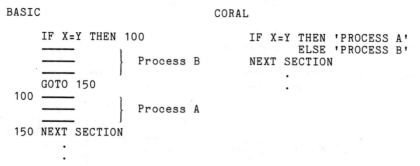

In BASIC, the ELSE part is implied and the "else" process follows the statement. Thus a GOTO is required to escape at the end of it. However, Coral has the 'ELSE' explicitly stated and control of the program passes to 'Process A' or 'Process B' depending on the result.

In both cases Coral returns control automatically to "next section" when the called process is finished.

'Process A' and 'Process B' would, in a Coral program, be the declared names of distinct blocks of code and the relevant code would not be written "in line" as in BASIC.

When drawing flowcharts, a convention should be adopted for the direction of data flow. This is normally from top to bottom and from left to right. If data flows in directions other than these standards, it must be indicated by arrowheads. Such instances should be minimised.

To conclude this discussion of structured programming, the car safety example will be flowcharted (Figure 15.2). Notice that the complete system consists only of permissible structures, that the outer structures completely include the inner structures and that no overlaps occur: structures are totally included in others or totally excluded by them. Undoubtedly, some of the single block processes shown would be decomposed into assemblies of simpler structures before being coded. The "delay" process occurs several times and it would almost certainly be realised as a subroutine.

In what has been written above, considerable emphasis has been placed on the rigorous use of program structures and on the use of well-defined input and output interfaces. Sometimes this involves a certain degree of inefficiency resulting in programs that require more storage space and execution time than their unstructured counterparts. Usually the difference is small and can be tolerated.

However, there are occasions when it is desirable to "shrink" the code. One example might be that a suite of modules occupies 2060 bytes (2K + 12). If this is to be placed in a read-only memory, there could be very worthwhile savings to be achieved by shrinking the code to 2K bytes. In such instances, one would be justified in taking the structured code and looking for redundant instructions which occur because of the requirements of program structure. These may then be eliminated. An example of such instructions would occur if, say, module 'A' assembles some data in the accumulator and then stores it. If module 'B' follows module 'A' and its first action is to access the data word, then an economy will be achieved by letting module 'A' leave the data in the accumulator instead of storing it.

It must, however, be emphasised that a structured version of the program should be written and tested first. This will provide the necessary documentation and will act as a point of reference should the unstructured version malfunction.

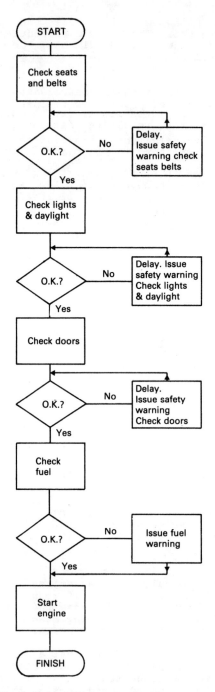

Figure 15.2: Flowchart for Example Program

15.2 Writing Programs

The purpose of writing a program is to prepare a sequence of (binary) machine-readable instructions which may be stored in the memory of the computer and subsequently executed in order to achieve the desired results. It is clearly impractical to prepare such a sequence of instructions directly by hand since the binary representation is very cumbersome for human manipulation and the resulting "machine code" program would be virtually uncheckable. Alternative methods which are more suitable for manual manipulation must therefore be used. These involve the use of programming languages which enable one to write readable programs. Programs written in such languages have to be translated into the equivalent machine-readable form before they can be loaded into the computer memory and executed. Fortunately, the translation process is readily automated and the user written "source code" is processed by a LANGUAGE PROCESSOR (an assembler or compiler) in order to produce the machine-readable "object code".

Programming languages may be broadly classified into those that are essentially "problem oriented" and those which are "machine oriented". Machine oriented languages maintain a close connection between the basic statements permitted and the operations which the hardware of the computer is capable of performing. Such languages are termed MNEMONIC ASSEMBLY LANGUAGES and the processor which converts the language statements into object code is called an assembler. Mnemonic assembly languages are naturally very closely linked to the architecture of the machine in question. In no way can they be described as problem oriented. As a result, considerable programming effort is required to solve any particular problem and the resulting code is not likely to be particularly easy to read. This makes program maintenance and debugging a tedious operation. Assembly language programs may only be executed on the processor for which they are written and cannot therefore be transferred to other machines. By contrast there are a number of so-called high-level languages in which it is possible to write programs using constructs which are very close to those used to express problems in everyday circumstances. Such languages are necessarily problem oriented rather than being machine oriented and they provide the user with a degree of machine independence, or PORTABILITY. This is a great advantage since the programs will run on any computer without modification. Also the programmer does not require a great deal of specific knowledge about how a computer operates.

In practice, the situation as regards portability is slightly less than perfect because each manufacturer tends to develop his own version of "language X" with some added features over and above the standard.

Provided that a suitable language has been chosen, then it usually takes far less time to write a program in a high-level language than it does in assembler-level. On the other hand, the code written in a high-level language has to be translated into machine code. This task is undertaken by a special program called a COMPILER. The writing of compilers is a complex task and their operation will only be touched upon a little later. At this point it is sufficient to say that each line of the high-level program code translates into many lines of machine code. Thus the penalty the programmer pays for using a high-level language is a loss of control over coding methods and storage allocation etc. and this will frequently lead to programs that are less efficient in memory requirements and execution time than the equivalent assembly-level programs when these are written by a good programmer. In real-time applications, it is frequently necessary to have certain processes carried out rapidly and for these it is desirable that assembler-level programming be used whereas for the rest of the program high-level languages may suffice, and even offer advantages in terms of ease of programming. Certain languages allow this mixing of high and low-level languages, others do not.

The compilation phase of a program development may be quite time-consuming. However, if a program is compiled only once and then run very many times, this compilation overhead becomes insignificant. The problem arises during the debugging phase when even a small error in one line of the program will require the whole program to be re-compiled. This means that development can be a very slow process.

An alternative approach is to use an INTERPRETER to convert from the high-level language to the machine code (BASIC often uses an interpreter). Using this system, the program is translated line-by-line and executed as it is translated. No complete copy of the translated program is ever generated; only one line. Thus if a minor change to a program is made during development, it does not slow the debugging process down unduly. However, this line-by-line translation has to be carried out every time the program is executed and this tends to reduce the efficiency of the program. Some versions of BASIC get over this problem by providing an interpreter for development and a compiler which can be used to translate permanently the developed program into machine code en-bloc so that translation is not required each time the program is run.

Programs written as a series of modules will only require the faulty module to be re-compiled and then all the modules to be re-linked. This latter process can, however, be quite time consuming.

It should be noted that some of the standard high-level languages such as COBOL (for business computing) and FORTRAN (for scientific work) are getting rather long in the tooth and their structure owes a great deal to the state-of-the-computer-art in the late '50s and early '60s. Languages such as RTL/2, CORAL, Algol, Pascal and Ada are newer and are structured languages which will promote good programming style. The problem in some cases, however, will be that these newer languages are not supported on all machines and that their features are not well enough standardised to make for easy portability.

To summarise therefore:

Use assembly-level programming when:

(i)   The operations require a very detailed use of specific machine instructions and features.

(ii)   When storage allocation and execution speed are of paramount importance.

(iii)   The problems of documentation and debugging can be adequately handled.

(iv)   Portability is not needed.

Use high-level languages when:

(v)   There is a language to suit the job in hand.

(vi)   Detailed interaction with the machine is not required.

(vii)   Execution speed is less important.

(viii) The self structuring and self documenting features of high-level languages will be useful.

(ix)   Portability is needed.

In connection with (viii) a suitable "structured" language should be chosen while in connection with (vi), and especially for real-time applications, a language which permits assembly-level code to be mixed in with the high-level language statements should be used (e.g. CORAL).

Lastly, if development time is important, an interpreter-translated language is desirable whereas, if run-time performance is important, a compiler-translated language should be used.

15.2.1 OPERATION OF ASSEMBLERS AND LOADERS

An assembly language is a method of representing actual machine instructions and operands in a way which is meaningful to read. Every binary machine code instruction contains information about the exact operation to be carried out and the location of the operand or operands. Depending on the particular processor and instruction, this machine code representation will occupy one or more words of computer memory. For instance, the instruction which enables the MC6800 to add the contents of memory location 1024 to the contents of Accumulator A is:

Word 1	1011 1011	Operation Code
Word 2	0000 0100	High Address
Word 3	0000 0000	Low Address

An assembly language permits this instruction to be written on one line using a self-evident mnemonic to make the whole more readable.

i.e.   ADD 1024

This is still a very elementary way of writing out instructions and it presupposes that the reader can remember the significance of the contents of location 1024.

A much more readable program results if the absolute location address '1024' is replaced by a name which is chosen to give some clue as to the significance of the contents of location 1024. For instance

ADD SUBTOTAL

As used in this context, the word "SUBTOTAL" is called a SYMBOLIC ADDRESS.

The assembler operates by maintaining lists of valid instruction codes with their binary equivalents, and lists of user-defined symbolic addresses with their numerical equivalents. The process of converting the assembly language statements into the binary machine code then becomes a simple matter of scanning tables.

The equivalence between mnemonics and instruction codes is, of course, constant. However, the relationship between the names of storage locations and the corresponding memory addresses is dependent on the program and so the symbolic address table must be reconstructed each time an assembly language program is processed by the assembler.

The programmer must ensure that the assembler has sufficient information in order to construct the symbolic address table. Any symbol, whether it has the significance of an address or not, may usually be allocated a value by a direct assignment statement such as

                SUBTOTAL   =   1024
or
                SUBTOTAL   EQ   1024

The exact form of such statements varies depending on the particular assembler in use. Alternatively, the symbolic address may be given a value implicitly by using it to LABEL a particular memory location.

This will be made clearer by the following piece of code which is intended to add together the two numbers stored in the locations labelled NUM1 and NUM2, and to store the result in the location labelled RESULT.

```
Label Field    Instruction Field   Operand Field   Comment Field

START:         LOAD                NUM1
               ADD                 NUM2
               STORE               RESULT
               HALT                                ; FINISH HERE
NUM1:
NUM2:
RESULT:
```

If we assume that the instructions LOAD, STORE and ADD all
occupy three words and that HALT requires only one, it is
possible to work out what actual locations will be used for
NUM1 etc.

Assuming that we start at location zero:

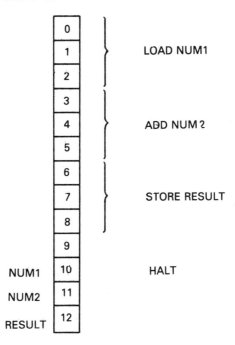

Thus NUM1 is location 10, NUM2 location 11 and RESULT
location 12.

Notice the way in which the assembly language statements are
laid out in fields. Most languages permit a variety of
characters to be used to delimit each field but the use of
tabulation characters is recommended since it produces a
well-spaced and easily read result.

In the above example, the semicolon indicates the start of a
comment (which will be ignored by the assembler). The
locations 0, 10, 11 and 12 are labelled implicitly by writing
the names in the label field (and terminating them with a

colon). When these names appear in the operand field of an instruction, they are used as symbolic addresses and specify where the data to be operated upon resides.

The same results could have been achieved using the direct assignment statements.

```
START     =   0
NUM1      =  10
NUM2      =  11
RESULT    =  12
```

but this has a number of disadvantages.

(i)   The programmer would have to laboriously work out exactly where each operand was located.

(ii)   Any change to the program means that the assignments have to be re-worked. Inevitably this process gets overlooked sometimes.

Usually the operand field also includes indicators to control which addressing method is to be used. For example, assume that

means "use immediate-mode"

@ means "use indirect mode"

and further assume that the assembler's symbolic address table has somehow been established such that

NUM = 100

Then the instruction

ADD NUM

would add the contents of location 100 to the accumulator while:

ADD @NUM

would treat the contents of location 100 as a POINTER to the data, and:

ADD #NUM

would add the number 100 to the accumulator.

This latter mode uses the contents of the operand field not as a symbolic address but as literal data. It is one example where 'NUM' would be likely to be given a value by direct assignment since, presumably, one is trying to add a fixed constant to the accumulator. (In such a case the name used should be 'HUNDRED' rather than 'NUM' so that the significance of the operation is more obvious.)

From the foregoing discussion, the reader should have a fairly good idea of what a program written in an assembly language will look like and why this layout is a considerable improvement over direct binary machine coding. It will be clear that the program which translates the assembly language statements into a machine-executable form must carry out two fundamental tasks:

(i)   It must construct a symbol table of all user defined symbols (whether defined implicitly or explicitly).

(ii) It must carry out a table-look-up operation on each statement to convert the contents of the instruction field and the contents of the operand field into a binary form which can be executed by the target computer.

These two requirements lead to the classic two-pass assembler. The next Section will examine in a little more detail how such assemblers actually achieve their objectives.

15.2.2   2-PASS ASSEMBLERS

It will be recalled that, for clarity, programs have been set out with clearly defined "Fields". The assembly process also requires these fields to be defined although delimiters other than spaces may be used.

During the "first pass", the assembly program sets an internal location counter to the start address of the program. It then scans the program incrementing the location counter to correspond with the number of storage locations that will be required by the instructions which it has encountered.

When a label is found in the label field the assembler inserts it in a table of "user-defined symbols" along with its corresponding location as determined by the location counter. When this is done, the table is also checked to see whether the symbol is already defined ·in the table. If it is, the definition is not unique and an error message "multiply defined label" is issued. A simplified flowchart illustrating the first pass is given in Figure 15.3.

Once the program has been scanned in this way, the "second pass" is started. This proceeds as shown in the flowchart below until all of the instructions have been translated. During the second pass, another important type of error is possible. When the assembler is trying to determine the operand address, it scans the table of user defined symbols to look for the symbolic address of the operand. If, by some mistake, no such label has been identified in the label field during the first pass, there will not be a table entry and the address cannot be determined. In such cases an error message, "undefined label", would be issued.

Once assembly is completed, the assembler will usually print out a complete listing of the mnemonic program and its

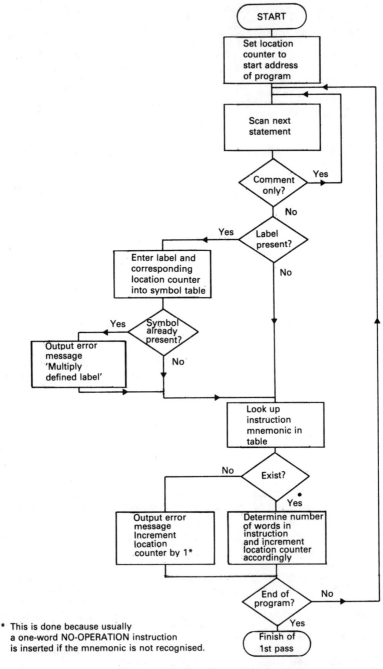

* This is done because usually
a one-word NO-OPERATION instruction
is inserted if the mnemonic is not recognised.

Figure 15.3: First Pass of Assembler

corresponding machine code translation. Most assemblers require information to help them complete their task. For instance, the programmer must tell the assembler what the first location of the program is. Such instructions are given in the form of ASSEMBLER DIRECTIVES. These are instructions to the assembler indicating how it is to operate. Typical of such directives are:

$ORGN: n

This tells the assembler that the following code is to be assembled from location n onwards.

$NOLIST

This tells the assembler not to produce a listing at the end of assembly.

$END

This indicates the end of the assembly language program.

The final products of an assembly operation are

(i)   a listing of the program

(ii)   a string of binary numbers (in memory or on disc or paper tape, etc.) representing the actual machine code program.

A simplified flowchart illustrating the second pass is given in Figure 15.4.

15.2.3 LINKAGE EDITORS AND MODULAR PROGRAMS

It is often convenient to write programs as a collection of small modules rather than as a single large entity. This approach is very much in line with the concept of structured programming; it can also result in considerable saving of time since it is frequently possible to re-use program modules in many different projects.

When programs are written in this modular form, it is not possible to determine where in memory they will finally reside and so it is not possible to issue an origin directive. Such programs have to be assembled in a relocatable form and this is achieved by assuming that the program will reside in memory starting at location zero. This is, of course, not true but a consistent assumption such as this enables a linkage-editor program to bring together all of the various modules and to re-locate those that require it.

The assembly of relocatable programs requires a number of modifications to the assembler. First, it must provide information for use by the linkage-editor. For instance, if a relocatable program is being linked so that its first address is 0200 instead of 0000, then the linkage-editor will have to add 0200 to all the addresses of operands within the program. However, it will NOT have to do this if an instruction

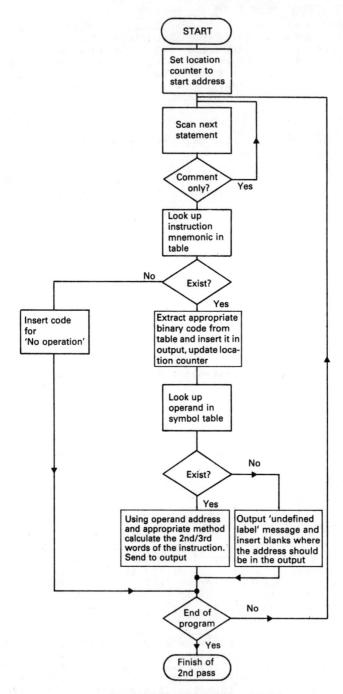

Figure 15.4: 2nd Pass of Assembler

addresses an operand WITHIN ITS OWN SECTION OF RELOCATABLE
CODE using the RELATIVE mode of addressing. This is because
the operand address information in such instructions is an
offset and offsets do not change if both of the items are
moved by the same amount. Those instructions which require
relocation adjustments will usually be indicated to the
programmer on the assembler listing. A second problem for the
assembler of relocatable programs is that of symbolic
addresses which are not defined within the section of program
that is being assembled but are defined within some other
section of relocatable code which will be linked to the
current section later. Such labels are called GLOBALS. It is
necessary for the programmer to issue a directive declaring
each globally valid label to the assembler. In some cases,
the assembler will also assume that a locally undefined
symbolic address is globally defined. Such globals are
indicated on the assembler listing and in the information
passed to the linkage-editor.

Because it requires no additional work during relocation,
relative addressing should be used whenever possible in
relocatable code.

The function of the linkage-editor is to produce a single
piece of relocatable code by linking together a number of
modules of relocatable code. This is done by extracting the
first module and assuming it to be loaded from location 0.
All labels which have occurred in that module and which have
been declared as globally valid are entered in a table along
with their addresses. The final location of the first module
is then calculated and the address of the next location is
used as the relocation constant for the second module. All
addresses in the symbol table of the second module have this
constant added to them and all instructions which reference
these addresses (except by relative addressing) have their
address part modified accordingly. The globals in this module
are added, with their relocated addresses, to the global
table. The third and subsequent modules are linked in a
similar manner.

Once this has been completed, the whole body of linked code
is scanned for symbolic addresses which have been flagged as
global. The absolute addresses for these instructions are now
extracted from the table of globally valid labels and the
corrected instructions assembled into the code.

On completion of this a complete single, relocatable program
has been constructed. In some systems it is possible to
include manufacturer-written library routines into user
programs automatically during the linking phase.

When it is required to run the program, the loader is invoked
and the linked program is loaded into memory at some defined
location, all relocatable instructions in the linked program
(except those using relative addressing) being modified again
by the load-time relocation constant to produce an absolute
binary program. Linkage-editors designed to process programs
for a single-user environment will often permit the load-time

relocation constant to be specified at link time, thus saving the loader this final relocation task and enabling a relatively simple binary loader to be used. This facility cannot be used by multi-user systems since, in such systems, the final destination has to be decided by the operating system at run-time. The load address of a program in such systems will change each time it is used depending upon what other jobs are being run.

15.2.4 ABSOLUTE LOADERS

These are very simple loaders whose function is to load into memory, starting at some defined location, a program which has been prepared in absolute binary form (probably, but not necessarily on paper tape). Such loaders are called absolute loaders and they are typically only 100 or so instructions long. Their sole function is to read binary words into sequential locations in memory with the bare minimum of error checking.

Such loaders have been widely used in minicomputers in the past but today they are confined to the very smallest machines or to the "bootstrap" function in larger machines. They are, however, still widely used in microcomputer systems. Often two such loaders will be available, the first being relatively sophisticated and including good error checking capabilities; the second is much simpler and is used primarily for the bootstrapping function.

This latter use is worthy of a little expansion. When a computer is first supplied, its memory is empty and it is necessary to load programs in order to make the system go. However, a loader program is required to do this! How can the loader be loaded? The traditional way of doing this is to use the switches on the front panel. Needless to say, this is a tiresome procedure and only a very short (typically 12 instruction) loader would be inserted in this way. Such a simple loader has no error checking capability so it is only used once, to load another loader program, and it is this (slightly) more sophisticated loader which is used to read in other programs.

This whole procedure is known as bootstrapping. In modern machines the first, very simple, program is physically wired into the computer (i.e. its memory isn't empty when supplied) and it is invoked simply by pressing a switch on the front panel of the machine. In a microprocessor-based system, this occurs when the reset line is asserted either during "power on" or subsequently when the reset button is pressed.

The data which is read into the computer may take one of a number of forms and the loader is designed to accept only one of the possible formats.

Usually the data is configured into three sections:

(i)   A LEADER which gives information to the loader.
        Usually this consists of a statement of the start
        address of the area to which the data is to be
        loaded and a count of the number of data
        characters.

(ii)   The BODY which contains the actual data to be
        loaded, encoded in a suitable form.

(iii)   A TERMINATOR which provides error-checking
        information.

There are three commonly used methods for encoding the data
in the body:

(i)   BINARY: Each byte of data is simply transmitted
        as it is.

(ii)   ASCII ENCODED HEXADECIMAL: Each byte is
        represented as two hexadecimal symbols which are
        then transmitted in their ASCII encoded form,
        i.e. the byte 1011 0010 would be encoded as 'B 2'
        and then transmitted as the two ASCII characters

        X100 0010   ASCII 'B'
        X011 0010   ASCII '2'
        ↑

        parity bits

(iii)   BNPF: Each byte is encoded as a "frame" of 10
        ASCII characters. The start of a frame is
        indicated by 'B' and the end by 'F'. The
        characters in between represent the 1s and 0s of
        the byte being transmitted with 'P' being
        equivalent to 1 and 'N' equivalent to 0. Thus the
        byte 1011 0010 would appear as

        X100 0010   B
        X101 0000   P
        X100 1110   N
        X101 0000   P
        X101 0000   P
        X100 1110   N
        X100 1110   N
        X101 0000   P
        X100 1110   N
        X100 0110   F
        ↑

        parity bits

15.2.5 MACRO ASSEMBLERS

Frequently used routines are often written as subroutines to
save both on memory space and also to save the programmer the
boredom of rewriting the same piece of code several times
with, perhaps, only a change of operands.

The problem with subroutines can be that they involve a considerable overhead of wasted time since the sequence control register has to be saved and, in many instances, a number of arguments are passed to the subroutine.

In such instances the macro facility, which is available with many assemblers, is most useful.

The programmer first has to define his "macro" using dummy arguments.

```
e.g.        .MACRO      SWAP     ALPHA,BETA

            LOAD        <ALPHA>
            STORE       TEMP
            LOAD        <BETA>
            STORE       <ALPHA>
            LOAD        TEMP
            STORE       <BETA>
            JMP         END
TEMP
END         NOP
            .ENDMACRO
```

The above code defines a macro called SWAP which exchanges the contents of two locations in memory, ALPHA and BETA.

The programmer then writes his program and when he wishes to exchange two variables in memory (say "first" and "second") he simply writes:

```
    ————————
    ———————— }    Preceding lines of code
    ————————

SWAP            First, Second

    ————————
    ———————— }    Following lines of code
    ————————
```

When this is processed by the assembler, it appears as if the programmer had written

```
    ————————
    ———————— }    Preceding lines of code
    ————————

    LOAD    FIRST
    STORE   TEMP
    LOAD    SECOND
    STORE   FIRST
    LOAD    TEMP
    STORE   SECOND
    JMP     END

TEMP
END     NOP

    ————————
    ———————— }    Following lines of code
    ————————
```

342

Thus the programmer is saved the trouble of writing the same code several times and yet he has not had to suffer the linkage overheads of a subroutine call.

15.2.6 CONDITIONAL ASSEMBLY

A number of assemblers (and some high-level language compilers) have the facility to include sections of program selectively.

This facility takes the form of a pair of assembler directives which instruct the assembler itself to test some parameter and to skip the code between the directives if the condition specified is satisfied. The parameter specified could be a constant used by the program during its normal operations (provided that it has a definite value at assembly time) or it might be a parameter specially inserted by the user as a means of customising his software. Either way, the result is the same - the assembled program is modified to suit the prevailing circumstances WITHOUT the programmer having to make any substantial alterations to the source code of the program.

This feature is particularly useful to software suppliers who have to tailor their programs to suit specific customer requirements. It is also of great help to manufacturers of equipment which can be supplied with a number of options since by re-defining just those parameters which control the assembly process, it is possible to produce a software package which conforms to the requirements of the selected options.

Two examples will serve to illustrate the process of and use of conditional assembly.

The directives used are

at the start of the code block $IF   XXXXX   .cnd

at the end of the code block $ENDIF

where XXXXX represents the parameter to be tested and 'cnd' represents the condition.

The condition could be

EQ	Equals
LT	Less than
GT	Greater than
GE	Greater than or equal to
LE	Less than or equal to
NE	Not equal

and the comparison is with zero.

Thus, in the section of code shown below, the block, B, is only included if 'DEFPAR' is greater than zero.

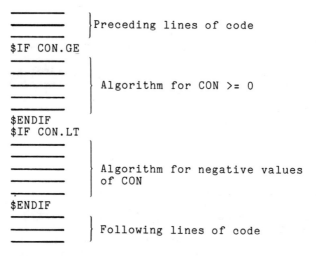

```
————————  }  Code block A
————————
$IF DEFPAR.GT
————————  }
————————     Code block B
————————  }
$ENDIF
————————  }  Code block C
————————
```

EXAMPLE 1

A particular process requires one algorithm to be used if a constant is positive or zero and a different algorithm to be used if the constant is negative. The excerpt of code shown below will achieve this. The parameter is labelled 'CON'.

```
————————  } Preceding lines of code
————————
$IF CON.GE
————————  }
————————     Algorithm for CON >= 0
————————  }
$ENDIF
$IF CON.LT
————————  }
————————     Algorithm for negative values
————————  } of CON
$ENDIF
————————  } Following lines of code
————————
```

Because GE and LT are inverses of each other one, and only one, of the alternative algorithms will be included.

EXAMPLE 2

A software supplier provides a signal processing package for a specific computer system. This system is available with or without a hardware floating-point arithmetic unit. In order to take advantage of the possible presence of the hardware unit, the supplier writes his package to include instructions for the hardware floating-point unit and a software floating-point package for those machines which do not include the hardware unit. Rather than keep separate copies for both

344

eventualities, conditional assembly is used to produce the appropriate object code for each customer. The assembly process is controlled by specifying certain parameters according to the hardware configuration possessed by the customer.

The parameter HFPU is set to zero before assembly if no floating-point is present and the signal processing package would appear thus

```
HFPU = 0        Only this line need be changed when a
                floating-point unit is available

————
————
————

$IF HFPU.EQ

————  ⎫
————  ⎪  This code included for systems with
————  ⎬  no floating-point hardware
————  ⎪
————  ⎭
$ENDIF
$IF   HFPU.NE

————  ⎫
————  ⎪  This included for systems with
————  ⎬  floating-point hardware
————  ⎪
————  ⎭
$ENDIF

————
————
```

The advantage to the supplier is particularly great if there are a large number of possible variations. For instance, if there were eight alternatives he would have to stock $2^8 = 256$ different versions of the package. Conditional assembly permits him simply to edit the defining statements (such as HFPU = 0) and then reassemble his package. Since, in this case, there will only be eight such defining statements, this will take very little time and the chance of error is small.

15.3 The Operation of a Compiler

Compiler design is a complex subject and, in this Section, no attempt will be made to detail the compilation process. The intention is merely to indicate the processes that must be completed.

A language is defined by the syntax rules which govern its construction and the semantics which are defined to correspond to each statement. The function of a compiler is to scan each program statement and to extract, using the rules of syntax, the semantically significant components. These components (e.g. the signs +, -, *, / etc.) are then processed so that a sequence of machine-level instructions is generated to perform the function. The tasks to be performed include allocation of storage, the setting up of loops (as a result of 'do-while' type statements, etc.) and the ordering of variables within arithmetic expressions so that they can be performed in the correct sequence.

For example

$$Y = (A + B)*C$$

is different from

$$Y = A + B * C$$

The compiler must detect this difference and implement the expression correctly.

The operation of a compiler will be illustrated by explaining how three typical statements would be converted into assembly code. Once the program is converted in this way it simply has to be assembled using the methods described in the previous sections.

15.3.1 COMPILATION OF A "GOTO" STATEMENT

The program takes the form

```
          ————————
          ————————
          ————————
          GO TO 10
          ————————
          ————————
   10  ———————
          ————————
          ————————
          ————————
```

The compiler will scan the program statements converting them into equivalent assembly-level code. At this stage (equivalent to the assembler first pass) it will not be possible to fill in any addresses. Thus at this stage the GOTO statement is simply translated as

                    JUMP ————

At the end of this pass the position of all labels will have been determined. Thus it will then be possible to determine what actual memory address corresponds to the label 10 (say 2014). During the next pass this address will be filled in and so the GOTO 10 finally becomes:

                    JUMP 2014

15.3.2 COMPILATION OF A "DO" LOOP

The program takes the form

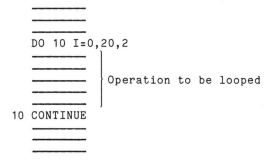

```
DO 10 I=0,20,2
                  } Operation to be looped
10 CONTINUE
```

The code included between "DO" and "10" is to be repeated for
various values of I (which may, or may not, be used by
calculations within the loop) ranging from 0 to 20 in steps
of 2. Thus the compiler has to set up some housekeeping
statements at the start and end of the loop. It will also
have to allocate storage for the loop counter I. Assume that
this location is labelled IX.

The code generated might look like:

```
        LOAD    #0      Set up initial value of loop counter
        STORE   IX
LIOS:   ─────
        ─────           } Operations to be looped
        ─────
        LOAD    IX      Retrieve loop counter
        ADD     #2      Update loop counter
        STORE   IX      Save it
        SUB     #20     Test whether loop counter > 20
        JUMPGE  LIOS    If not, go back and do the loop
                        again
```

The first two statements are inserted at the position
occupied by the 'DO' statement itself. Notice the immediate
mode (#) addressing is chosen to pre-load the counter and
that the start of the loop has had to be labelled by the
compiler (LIOS).

The intervening code is compiled as appropriate while, at the
same time, the compiler searches for a 'CONTINUE' statement
with the label 10 (which matches the 10 in the 'DO'
statement).

When this is found, the code shown is inserted in place of
the 'CONTINUE'. This consists of statements which update the
counter and statements which test to see whether the counter
has exceeded the limit indicated in the 'DO' statement.
Control is transferred to the statement labelled LIOS (by the

347

compiler) if the loop counter has not exceeded the limit (20 in the example).

Notice that immediate mode addressing is widely used. The parameters which originate from the 'DO' statement are underlined in the code shown above. A little thought will show that much of the processing carried out by the compiler involves parameter substitution into standard pieces of code.

15.3.3 COMPILATION OF ARITHMETIC STATEMENTS

There is a problem when organising a string of arithmetic statements since the order of the arithmetic signs and the operands is not sufficient.

For instance $\qquad$ y = a + b * c/d

is different from $\qquad$ y = (a + b)*c/d

The difficulty was overcome by a Polish logician, Jan Lukasiewicz (Jan Wookashayveech), when he derived the "reverse Polish" notation (as used in certain calculators).

Using this scheme the operation:

$$y = a + b$$

is written as $\qquad$ yab+=

and the rule for executing it is: "Scan the reverse Polish string from left to right until an arithmetic operator is found. Use this on the two preceding variables and then continue the scan" (Rule I).

Thus $\qquad$ abc*d/+
becomes $\qquad$ a(b*c)d/+
then $\qquad$ a((b*c)/d)+
and finally $\qquad$ (a+((b*c/d)))

whereas $\qquad$ ab + c*d/
becomes $\qquad$ (((a + b)*c)/d)

Thus, given a reverse Polish string, the compiler can easily generate the correct order of operands. Fortunately, the conversion to reverse Polish from a normal transcription of a formula is also governed by a simple rule:- "Scan original string from left to right ignoring left parentheses '('. As each operand is encountered, push it onto an operand-stack and push each operator onto an operator-stack. Continue until a right parenthesis ')' is found.

When a ')' is found, pop all items on the operator-stack in turn and push them onto the operand-stack. Continue scan until string is exhausted" (Rule II).

The contents of the operand-stack is now a reverse Polish string when read from the bottom of the stack to the top.

stage	operand stack	operator stack	formula
0	null	null	(((a+b)*c)/d)
1	null	null	((a+b)*c)/d)
2	null	null	(a+b)*c)/d)
3	null	null	a+b)*c)/d)
4	a	null	+b)*c)/d)
5	a	+	b)*c)/d)
6	b a	+	)*c)/d)
7	+ b a	null	*c)/d)
8	+ b a	*	c)/d)
9	c + b a	*	)/d)
10	* c + b a	null	/d)
11	* c + b a	/	d)
12	d * c + b a	/	)
13	/ d * c + b a	null	

Figure 15.5: Generation of a Reverse Polish String for (((a+b)*c)/d)

Once the compiler has constructed the reverse Polish string using Rule II, it is a simple process for it to scan the string as instructed by Rule I to produce a correctly ordered sequence of operations on two variables.

This procedure is illustrated in Figure 15.5 by showing how the statement

$$y = (((a + b)*c)/d)$$

can be decomposed.

The reverse Polish string can now be scanned with Rule I using variable T (for TEMP) to represent the partially calculated result.

Stage	String at end of stage	Operation performed
0	ab+c*d/	—————
1	Tc*d/	T = a + b
2	Td/	T = T*c
3	T	T = T/d

This would appear in assembler mnemonics as

```
LOAD    a
ADD     b
MPY     c
DIV     d
STORE   y
```

Notice that, in this case, the accumulator has been used as the temporary storage location.

The above problem was posed in a fully parenthesised form. This is unusual since most programmers will put in only the essential brackets. Thus the compiler has to pre-process the formula and insert the parentheses before it can convert to reverse Polish form. That is, it has to convert the programmer's statement

$$y = (a + b)*c/d$$

into

$$y = (((a + b)*c)/d)$$

15.4 Debugging Programs

Once a program has been successfully assembled and loaded, there still remains the considerable task of verifying that it operates correctly and, if it fails, of finding out why. Such faults usually arise because the programmer has not understood fully the subtleties of the computer he is using or because he has not defined adequately the processes which have to be performed. Such errors are logical errors rather than syntactical or semantic errors as these latter are normally detected by the assembler or linking loader. Occasionally a syntactically and semantically correct statement can be written but not be what the programmer intended due to typing errors and the like.

As part of the program design, the programmer should have specified a set of test data which will fully exercise all modules of and paths through the program, including both valid data and various types of invalid data too. If invalid data is expected to be a problem then suitable DATA VETTING routines must be written into the program.

Debugging a program consists of allowing a program to process various items of data and, if the program fails to produce the expected output, identifying the area of the program where the divergence from the intended processing procedure occurs. To do this adequately requires the programmer to be able to examine the contents of any memory location or register· at every step of the process. By doing this and comparing the results with those expected, it is usually possible to locate and correct the problem.

It is clearly impossible for a programmer to interact with the computer program while it is running because of the high speeds involved. To achieve this interaction, another computer program must be invoked - the debugging program.

To use a debugging program, it is loaded into the memory along with the development program. When the combination is run, it is the debugging program that takes control. The programmer interacts with the debugging program and using it can examine or modify any memory location.

One of the most useful features of such programs is the BREAKPOINT facility. Using the debugging program the programmer can specify any location in the development program as a breakpoint. If he then executes the development program, the debugging routine will monitor the execution and, when the designated breakpoint location is reached, it will halt the execution of the development program. The programmer is now free to inspect any memory location he wishes and in this way he can check whether the processing so far is correct. If it is then he has to set a breakpoint lower down in the program and repeat the operation. If, however, the processed data is not as it should be he can change the contents of memory etc. to the correct values and proceed with the rest of the program to check that out. Then he has to re-start the development program and set a breakpoint nearer to the start of the program so as to identify the exact place at which processing goes wrong. Intelligent use of this technique can rapidly isolate the fault.

Sometimes the problem with a program is that it never reaches a conclusion because it gets "hung up" in an endless program loop. When this happens, the programmer must set a breakpoint inside the loop. Sometimes the fault can be diagnosed immediately the breakpoint is reached, but more often it is necessary to examine conditions in the program just before it should break out of the loop. To get to this situation by continually "proceeding from the breakpoint" can be very time-consuming if the loop is intended to execute very many times. In some situations it is possible to change certain memory locations to fool the program into thinking that it is ready to break out but often it must be left to work its own way out. A modification of the breakpoint feature can make this a great deal easier.

Some debugging routines have the facility to set a breakpoint but not to activate it until it has been passed a defined number of times. In this way a large number of iterations can be executed at high speed and without manual intervention.

Interrupt driven routines are notoriously difficult to debug because the occurrence of significant program events is random and not under the control of the programmer. Only persistence and a great deal of careful thought will solve this kind of problem. Indeed, faults in this type of system sometimes only make themselves apparent on very isolated occasions.

Debugging programs written in a high-level language is rather a different proposition to doing this job with assembler-level programs. There is not a one-to-one correspondence between the program as written and the code loaded into the machine. Even if a listing of the compiled code is available, it may not be very helpful to the programmer since he will no longer be in direct contact with the machine instructions.

Debugging, therefore, has to take place at the level of the programming language used. FORTRAN, for instance, has the facility to include special debugging statements in the program. These are specially 'tagged' and are included in the compiled code only if the programmer asks for 'Debug' mode during compilation, otherwise they are ignored. Normally, the extra lines of program are used to print out the values of key variables at each stage of the program execution thus permitting logical errors to be corrected.

CORAL has a slightly more flexible and powerful debugging feature called Trace. Using this, different parts of the program can be monitored selectively. Trace will monitor procedures executed, assignment statements (i.e. a = b+c), the control variables of 'FOR' loops at each iteration, and labels encountered. The exact amount of data traced during any given execution of the program is governed by certain "steering" data supplied to the system. To gather this amount of data in FORTRAN would require the programmer to insert many 'debug' statements in his program and then to change them each time different data was required.

In addition to the facilities mentioned above as being included within the capabilities of particular high-level languages themselves, there are also debugging programs which are oriented towards high-level languages, though separate from them. These operate in broadly the same way as those described above for assembly language programs, but interaction is at the level of the source language rather than at the level of the object code generated by the compiler.

15.5 Special Programming Techniques

There are a number of special programming techniques which result in the generation of programs that are particularly useful.

It is frequently necessary to provide in a complete system certain 'utilities' which are used by many different programs. Many examples could be cited but probably the most common of such utilities would be a program to implement certain mathematical functions (such as matrix multiplication) which do not form part of the basic capabilities of the processor. One approach would be to provide every user program with its own copy of the relevant utility but this is rather wasteful. An alternative, better, approach is to maintain a single copy of the utility and to share it between all the users. In a system in which one program can interrupt another (i.e. all real-time applications) there is clearly a problem because if the interrupting program requires use of the same utility as the interrupted program, there will be a conflict which could only be resolved by forcing the interrupting program to wait. This would, in many instances, be unacceptable. The alternative is to write the utility program in such a way that it is completely unchanged at any stage in its execution. A program written in this way is said to be REENTRANT and can be shared by any number of users. Reentrant programs can even call themselves!

As was pointed out earlier, it is advantageous to produce programs in a modular form so that they may be easily maintained. Such programs have to be linked together before they may be used and this process of linking can be very time-consuming. It is clearly advantageous to use whatever means are available to reduce the effort required at link time. If certain techniques are adopted, it is possible to reduce this effort to nil, the resulting code is then said to be POSITION INDEPENDENT CODE (PIC) and will function correctly irrespective of where it is located in memory.

Such code is very useful in multi-user systems where the relocation of programs is a common occurrence; it can however also be put to use in dedicated microprocessor-based systems. Many such manufacturers will re-use the same routines (for mathematics, control of CRTs, scanning of input channels, data conversion, etc.) throughout their range of products. Clearly the routines may be expected to reside at different locations in different products. If such routines are written using position independent coding techniques, they may be committed to read-only-memory and the construction of the software for any given application is much simplified. All that the designers have to do is to select the appropriate ROMs and to allocate them suitable addresses in memory. The variable part of the program (which is characteristic of the particular application) is then written, calling on the necessary standard routines as required. Since the bulk of the application may well consist of standard routines which are already written, there may be a considerable reduction in the cost of the software writing process. An additional advantage may be that, because the standard routines are absolutely unchanged and used in a wide variety of products, the number of copies used may be large enough to warrant the use of cheap mask programmed ROMs even though the production run for each individual product is short and would imply the use of relatively expensive EPROMs.

Position independent code also enables software manufacturers to sell their products ready programmed into ROM (in object-code format) rather than having to sell it as source code for subsequent modification by the end user, with the consequent risk of copyright infringement.

15.5.1 REENTRANT CODING

When reentrant code is being used, the assumption is that the execution of the code may be interrupted and a new task, which may require to use the interrupted code, initiated. This process is termed a CONTEXT SWITCH and will invariably be accomplished by saving the contents of all of the general-purpose registers of the processor. These will be restored when the interrupted task resumes. The context switch will be supervised by the operating system (see section 15.7) which may be user-written or, more frequently, bought-in from a specialist supplier.

If a program is to be reentrant, the coding of which it is comprised must not be changed in any way by its execution. It must be PURE CODE consisting solely of instructions and constants. All variable data must be stored elsewhere. Typically operating data will be stored in the general-purpose registers or in what is termed an impure area of memory (clearly the impure area is read-write memory). If a large amount of data is involved, it cannot be accommodated just in registers but will have to be stored in the impure area. To access data in the impure area, indirect references are needed and the pointers cannot be stored with the pure code because they change along with the user program. Such pointers must, therefore, be kept in the general-purpose registers. Clearly it is a requirement that the processor must support register-indirect addressing (i.e. pointer-in-register addressing). Stack manipulation is a special case of this form of addressing as is indexed addressing. Since registers are saved during a context switch, the system automatically keeps track of the impure data. Each instance of the task must have its own impure area, perhaps organised onto the stack.

Since pure code is, by definition, never changed, it may be stored in read-only memory.

15.5.2 POSITION INDEPENDENT CODE

By definition, position independent code does not require any modification when it is relocated. The only way in which this may be achieved is if

(i)   The location being referenced is absolutely fixed in memory. Clearly such addresses cannot be themselves within a piece of relocatable code (including PIC).

(ii)   The location being referenced is calculable from a knowledge of the actual position of the referencing instruction. Such addresses must be within the same piece of relocatable code as the referencing instruction and must be referenced using an addressing method which calculates the actual address at run time (methods which calculate the address at assembly-time or link-time will not do since they tie the code to a specific start address).

From the foregoing it will be seen that no direct communication between modules of position independent code is possible. All such communication must be channelled through a "communications area" which must occupy an absolutely fixed position in memory.

If program execution is to jump from one piece of position independent code to another, this must be accomplished by using pointers located in the communications area. In a fixed configuration microprocessor system, these pointers would form part of a 'configuration data block' set up by the system designer. In a complex multi-user disc system where program locations are liable to change, the pointers would be maintained by the operating system.

Figure 15.6 illustrates a system with two PIC modules and a communication area.

A reference to location y by an instruction at x would be made using relative addressing since the address information carried in the instruction will then represent the offset of y from x. This is constant irrespective of the actual location of PIC1.

Communication between the two modules is most easily achieved by defining a fixed location in the communications area to hold the shared data. This may be referenced by either module using absolute addressing since the communications area is absolutely located. This method, however, presupposes that the designers of PIC1 and PIC2 have agreed in advance about this. This may be possible within one company but is unlikely to pertain if bought-in modules are used.

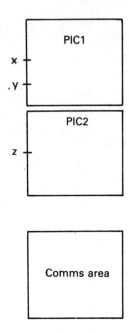

Figure 15.6: Communications between PIC modules

In this latter case, the data area will be defined by the
designer of each code module. This is likely to be expressed
as an offset from the start address of the module. The
designer of the overall system will have to arrange for his
program to pick up data from one module and to transfer it to
the next. This can be done by computing the absolute
addresses of the data items (given that the designer knows
where he is going to locate each PIC module). If the location
of each module can change at run time, then the addresses of
each data item will have to be calculated, as it is needed,
at run time by picking up the pointer to the base address of
the module, adding the defined offset and then using the
result as a pointer to the data item.

15.6 The Use of 'Editors' to Write Programs

Although it is possible to prepare programs "off-line" by
using a teletype in local mode to prepare a punched paper
tape containing the program text, this method is not
recommended.

Before time-sharing computer services were available, this
approach was the only possibility and the completed paper
tape was used as the source of data for the assembler or

compiler program. Any errors in the program had to be traced
to the appropriate section of paper tape and a new section
spliced in. In some instances, punched cards were used as an
alternative and this eased somewhat the problem of editing
the program.

A much more satisfactory approach is now possible using the
multi-access facilities of most computer systems. The user
simply enters a request to create a new program "file". The
operating system then reserves space for this "file" on a
disc and invokes the editor program which then supervises the
entry of data and text from the user's teletype or VDU into
this file. Once the input is complete, the user exits from
the editor program by using the appropriate commands and the
operating system tidies up after him, "closing" the file he
has just written.

The user can then obtain a permanent copy of his program by
requesting that it be listed on his teletype or on a line
printer.

As a result of reading the text, or possibly as a result of
error messages during assembly/compilation, the programmer
will wish to correct his program. This can be achieved by re-
entering the editor, but this time using the "edit" mode
rather than the "create" mode. This permits him to modify
sections of program to correct any errors that have been
found. It is, of course, possible to make a program worse
during editing and so it is wise to keep a backup copy of the
unedited program until the changes have been made
satisfactorily.

Some editors do this automatically in the "edit" mode while
in other systems the programmer has to make his own backup
arrangements.

There are two distinct types of editor. The simplest to use,
but the least flexible, is a line editor. These usually
provide numbers for each line of a text entered and
subsequently the lines are identified by these numbers. Lines
may usually be deleted, inserted, changed or appended to the
program, but only whole lines can be manipulated so that even
a single error in a line necessitates the whole line being
retyped.

In contrast, a text editor does not usually employ line
numbers. The user merely identifies a piece of text by typing
it and the editor searches the program until an exact match
is found. The user does, therefore, have to be careful to
ensure that his text specification is unique. Text editors
can replace just single characters if required or they can be
programmed so that all references to 'JMP I' in a program can
be automatically changed to 'JMP', if required, thus saving
the programmer a great deal of time. Often instructions for
re-positioning whole segments of text are included too.

The whole process of using a text editor is made a great deal
simpler if a copy of the text being edited is displayed on

357

the screen of a VDU. The position at which text is to be inserted or deleted is indicated by a cursor (often an underscore) which can be positioned using special cursor control keys. Editors providing this facility are usually termed SCREEN EDITORS.

Once a correct version of a program is available on a disc, it must be compiled or assembled. It is very common to carry out this task on a different machine from the target machine. For example, a program for an Intel 8080 microprocessor might well be assembled on the time-sharing computer which was used to edit the program. This process is known as CROSS-ASSEMBLY (or "cross compilation"). The object code produced by the assembler is written into a "file" on the disc. This object code must, of course, be transferred to the target machine (the 8080 in the example) and this can be done by punching it out onto paper tape for loading into the target machine or it may be loaded directly over one of the time-sharing computer's data links. This latter process is known as DOWNLINE LOADING.

15.7 Operating Systems

Any attempt to define what an operating system is is likely to degenerate into a mere catalogue of its capabilities and sub-divisions. For this reason, this section will simply give a brief resume of how operating systems have evolved.

In the early days of computers, programs were run by reading in a set of program cards which had been loaded by the operator. The program then ran and, from time to time, the operator would have to mount magnetic tapes and other such items while the program waited.

Each program occupied the computer and had total control of it for the duration of the job including any necessary printing of output etc. It was soon realised that valuable computer time was being wasted because the output printing and the inputting of data was limited by the speed of the peripherals and did not fully use the computer (the computer was "I/O bound").

A different approach was then adopted. All input was transcribed from cards or paper tape onto a fast medium such as magnetic tape, and in a similar fashion, all output was directed to a magnetic tape. In this way, the computer spent very little time processing I/O, a task that was delegated to a relatively simple I/O processor.

This situation remained satisfactory while computers were relatively slow so that the time taken manually mounting and dismounting tapes etc. was insignificant. However, improvements in electronic technology soon meant that the manual handling system was causing bottlenecks. One improvement from the programmer's point of view was the provision of subroutines to handle the peripherals thus saving each programmer from this chore. Such input-output control systems formed the first step towards an operating system. The programmer had delegated some routine tasks to the computer itself.

The bottleneck problem was overcome by collecting several jobs on to one tape so that the number of mount/dismount pauses was reduced and time saved. It was, of course, necessary to separate the jobs and so job control cards were placed between the various "card decks" that constituted each job before they were read onto tape by the I/O processor. It was now necessary to have some simple supervisor within the computer to recognise the job control cards and to take the appropriate action to separate each job, its input and its output. This was the first real instance of a computer supervising its own operations - an operating system. This type of system is known as a BATCH OPERATING SYSTEM.

The next step forward was to make use of any spare capacity by having two or more programs ready to run in the computer at the same time. As soon as one job is suspended pending completion of an I/O transaction, the next job is started. This clearly needs a scheduling program within the computer to keep track of the various jobs, their state of completion, the reason for them not running pending I/O etc. This is yet another component of the operating system as it is known today. Additional tasks that would be required are the protection of the storage area allocated for one program from being accessed by another and especially the protection of the memory allocated for the operating system itself.

The system evolved so far is known as a MULTI-PROGRAMMING, TIME-SHARED SYSTEM. The best use of the computer in these circumstances is achieved if the mix of jobs is fairly well spread between CPU-bound and peripheral-bound tasks. Thus at this point it became logical to consolidate the I/O processor into the main machine since the I/O processor is, by definition, peripheral-bound.

Once this state of development is reached there is little problem in doing away with the magnetic-tape-transcribed job stream and, instead, letting each user communicate with the computer via his own teletype or VDU. Such a system is known as a MULTI-ACCESS TIME-SHARED SYSTEM. To support this system there have to be additional modules attached to the operating system. There needs to be a program to control access to the machine and also to prepare accounts for the users (if it is a commercial system). The problem of scheduling the jobs becomes more difficult as does the problem of protecting users from each other. Users will require more commands than a batch system.

They will wish to write and edit programs, to store them, to compile them and to copy them. Thus a command interpreter will be required to recognise the commands input by each user, and a large number of other "utility" programs will also have to be provided.

The operating system which has now been arrived at is a typical multi-access system. It is not, however, a "real-time" system since there is no need to respond to teletype users in a fixed period. There is, however, no reason why the "jobs" in question should not arise as a result of some events on, say, a chemical plant and consequently require results to be produced within a defined and strictly limited period of time. Such systems are termed REAL-TIME SYSTEMS. They too require operating systems for the same reasons as outlined above but the various compromises that will have to be made in order to achieve the necessary real-time response will mean that there will be subtle differences between real-time operating systems and the others.

To summarise: operating systems exist to make the use of a computer as efficient as possible and to provide a helpful interface to the user. The primary functions of operating systems are to:

    (i)   allocate time and resources (scheduler)

    (ii)   operate peripherals (peripheral drivers)

    (iii)   communicate with the user (command interpreter)

Such systems will provide utilities to help the user:

    (i)   create files

    (ii)   copy files

    (iii)   edit files

    (iv)   to link and load jobs

    (v)   to store files

    (vi)   debug programs

and, in addition, language processors will be available to assemble and to compile a variety of computer languages.

16. Microprocessor System Development Techniques

The user of traditional computer-based equipment usually only has to worry about the development of his custom software. He can rely on the hardware being operational and can usually run diagnostic programs to verify this. In addition there will normally be a comprehensive range of user support software such as editors and compilers available to help in the writing of the special purpose software.

In contrast, the user of microprocessors is normally embedding the computing unit within the system so that it will replace electromechanical and random electronic logic. This will be done with a view to improving reliability, reducing hardware and assembly costs (through the use of fewer integrated circuits) and often with the intention of adding additional features which can only be achieved by computing machinery. The completed system will usually be more flexible than that which it replaces, requiring only a change in software to vary or upgrade its performance. In very many instances, the completed equipment will not have traditional computer peripherals, such as keyboards etc., and will be set in motion simply by the operation of a key-switch. All of these factors combine to make the development of a working microprocessor system a considerable task.

Methods of tackling the problem of ensuring that the completed system is maintainable, will be examined a little later in the Chapter. However, it is appropriate to point out at this stage that the cost of developing a custom designed circuit board along with its supporting software may be considerable. Furthermore, if the production run for the finished equipment is too short, the cost of this development may completely eliminate the previously mentioned cost savings of a microprocessor solution.

16.1 The 'Single-Board Computer' Approach

Before proceeding further, therefore, it is sensible to examine an alternative approach which can offer the advantages of a microprocessor-based design while easing the development problems associated with designing such systems ab initio. It is possible to buy microprocessor systems on a single circuit card from specialist manufacturers. Most manufacturers of such products offer a large range of such cards including:

(i) CPU cards with various facilities including a range of memory sizes and types.

(ii) peripheral cards including analogue-digital and digital-analogue converters, floppy disc controllers, additional memory, VDU controllers, etc.

All such cards from a given range will be compatible and capable of interconnection via some standard bus structure. The manufacturer will also usually supply a range of chassis units, often including power supplies. The user simply picks the modules he needs in order to meet his requirements and plugs them into a chassis unit which will then be incorporated into the final product. The electronic unit thus formed is virtually a made-to-measure microcomputer, the hardware of which is fully proven.

The advantages of this approach are that the hardware development phase is much simplified and the equipment manufacturer does not have to set up a large maintenance facility. Any faulty cards can simply be returned to the single-board computer (SBC) manufacturer for repair. This will be a quick and fairly cheap procedure because the SBC manufacturer will be producing a large volume of units and will, therefore, be well set up for trouble-shooting.

The disadvantage, of course, is that it will not be possible to tailor the hardware to the application as closely as if a special-purpose system had been designed. Thus some hardware which is not required will have to be purchased and, of course, the SBC manufacturer will be reaping the profit from the electronic assembly business.

Nevertheless, for short production runs, and for manufacturers with little electronic expertise, the single-board computer approach can be the best. In addition, it is quite likely that the SBC manufacturer will also supply a range of generally useful software.

Having pointed out this alternative approach, it is now time to examine how a fully customised product may be developed.

16.2 The Problems of Microprocessor System Development

The use of microprocessors in a project brings with it a whole host of new problems for both field service and development personnel. The traditional tools such as oscilloscopes, meters, etc. are only of limited value when troubleshooting microprocessor equipment and, as a consequence, a completely new range of test equipment has had to be developed.

Traditional equipment fails because it is frequently necessary to monitor more than 24 different logic signals (address, data, control lines, etc.) in order to obtain significant information. Such a vast amount of information is difficult to display and even more difficult to interpret since it is the conjunction of many binary "events" that corresponds to a significant event in the system sense (e.g. an access to location FFFE to WRITE 00 is a constraint on at least 25 binary variables, hence in this instance, 25 variables constitute a "significant event"). Secondly, "significant" events may occupy only a few microseconds but will occur at intervals of many milliseconds thus making their display on a conventional non-storage oscilloscope very difficult. Finally, it may be impossible to find a single waveform with the necessary discrimination to provide adequate triggering.

The difficulties encountered with hardware troubleshooting are made even worse by the fact that the software will also need debugging. In a traditional piece of electronic apparatus, there is no software to debug; in a conventional computer project one normally assumes that the hardware is functioning properly, and there is adequate diagnostic software available to prove the point. None of these statements applies in most microprocessor development situations.

The problem is further complicated by the fact that in many microprocessor systems the hardware and software are so interdependent that it is impossible to test one properly without having the other available. This may be illustrated by a simple example, an analogue-digital converter (Figure 16.1).

In a purely hardware realisation of this device, the logic changes the code nnnn until the output of the digital-

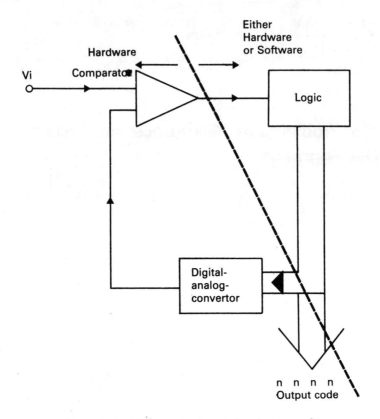

Figure 16.1: A Typical Analog-Digital Convertor System

analogue convertor is equal to the input voltage V(i). Then the code nnnn is the digital equivalent of the voltage. Such devices are fairly easy to troubleshoot since all of the electronics is accessible. However, in many modern microprocessor systems, the hardware logic is replaced by sequential program logic steps within the processor (to save money) and getting the device to work involves debugging the software and the hardware together.

The stages in the production of a working microprocessor system may be illustrated by a flowchart such as that in Figure 16.2.

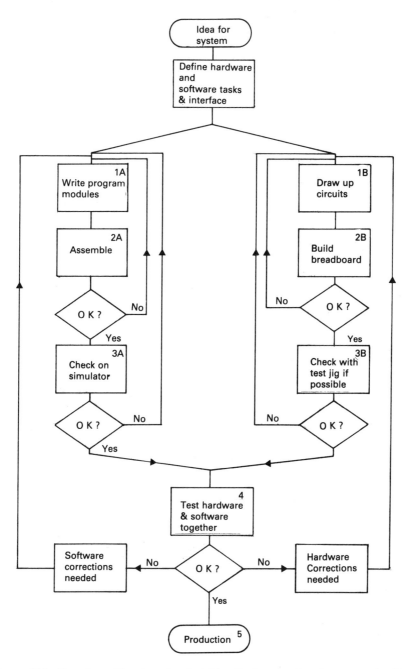

Figure 16.2: Flowchart Showing the Activities During the Development of a Typical Microprocessor-based Product

16.3 Systems Development Using a Micro-processor Development System

A typical development system is illustrated in Figure 16.3.

The heart of the system is the "development system processor" which, with the development system memory, users' terminal and discs, forms a microcomputer which may be used to input and edit source-code programs. Communication with an EXTERNAL COMPUTER is also handled by the system processor via a serial I/O port. Under the control of the development processor, it is possible to transfer the contents of a selected area in the user program memory into a PROM via the PROM programmer module.

The assembler processor is dedicated to two functions: the conversion of source code into executable object code and, when the target processor is in use, to monitoring the

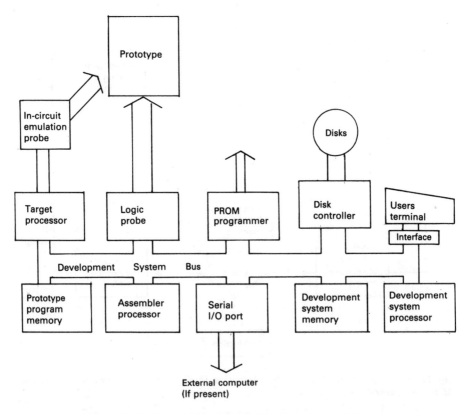

Figure 16.3: Arrangement of a Typical Development System

function of the target processor and converting its bus transactions back into mnemonics.

The above-mentioned hardware is permanently installed in the development system irrespective of the type of microprocessor being supported.

The target processor is a microprocessor of the type being used in the development. The target processor module is, therefore, exchangeable.

Development systems of the sort illustrated in Figure 16.3 are manufactured by several firms and are capable of supporting all of the development phases shown in Figure 16.2. They are not to be confused with processor evaluation kits which are very much cheaper (£ 100 - £ 500) and which sometimes are wrongly called development systems.

Following the development chart shown in Figure 16.2, it may be assumed that the system conception and definition have been completed as a paper exercise and the time has come to actively start developing the project. We will concentrate on the software development initially (Boxes 1A - 3A).

16.3.1 SOFTWARE DEVELOPMENT

Using the text editor and file manipulation functions of the development system processor (just like any minicomputer or mainframe) the source code is entered and corrected using the VDU. Once entered, it is assembled by the assembler processor (under the control of the user terminal).

When this process is complete the user will have, in addition to his original source file, an object file containing the binary program code. It is also likely that he will have a listing of errors found by the assembler.

These errors are corrected using the edit facility of the development system processor and then the new source code is re-assembled. Eventually a syntactically correct program is produced. It remains, however, to verify that the program actually processes data in the way that the user intended. This can only be proved by executing the program using test data to exercise each of the many paths through the program.

The process of program testing is made much simpler if the program is well structured and is composed of many small modules. The testing is carried out in the development system by the target processor. The object code is loaded from disc into user program memory and executed under the control of the development system processor. Break points may be inserted and all of the usual debugging techniques employed by the user via the user's terminal.

Inevitably errors will be found and these are corrected by editing the source code and then re-assembling it. Eventually all of the software modules will have been proven both individually and jointly, and the programmer will have considerable confidence that the programs are correct, but this cannot be guaranteed until the programs are able to interact with the hardware. The only remaining problems at this stage should be hardware/software interaction problems and these cannot be eliminated until the hardware is complete.

16.3.2 HARDWARE DEVELOPMENT

Once the specification has been agreed, the hardware will be designed and built. Limited testing will be carried out using lights, switches, testmeters, oscilloscopes, etc. in an attempt to prove the hardware.

All analogue hardware and some digital hardware can be tested in this way. Much of the hardware will however remain untested because

(i)   its operation is dependent on software stimulus

(ii) it consists of interface adaptors (PIA/ACIA) which cannot be tested until their internal registers are set, and this requires software control.

16.3.3 HARDWARE-SOFTWARE INTEGRATION

This is the stage at which the partially-tested hardware and software modules are brought together for final testing. Faults will be found and corrected by changing either the hardware or the software. At the completion of this phase there will exist a fully operationl prototype system.

The integration process starts with a partially tested hardware system and a fairly well tested software system. In order that the remaining faults can be eliminated from the system, the hardware and software must be permitted to interact. However, it is necessary that this interaction be monitored so that faulty operations can be detected and their cause isolated. Probably the most powerful technique for undertaking this task is IN-CIRCUIT EMULATION (ICE) which is available with most development systems.

The details vary from one development system to another but typically a connector is plugged into the vacant microprocessor socket in the prototype system (Figure 16.4). A "target microprocessor" (which is actually identical to the microprocessor to be used in the final piece of hardware) is mounted in a probe and effectively substitutes for the missing microprocessor in the prototype.

The one difference is that this "emulator processor" runs under the supervision of the system processor in the development system. Most systems also have the facility to monitor digital signals within the prototype (such as flags, etc.) so that the relationship between external hardware "events" and software can be seen.

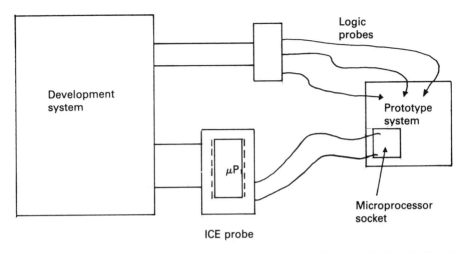

Figure 16.4: Connection of the Development System to the Prototype During 'In Circuit Emulation'

In this initial stage of integration the program is resident within the development system user program memory and executes on the target processor. No use is made of the memory etc. within the prototype and only I/O transactions are sent to the prototype. In this way the minimum of unproven hardware is used.

Once this stage is passed, the programs may be progressively transferred into the memory of the prototype. Since programs in the prototype will be held in PROM, this transfer involves the "burning" of PROMs. This process may usually be undertaken by a PROM-programmer unit fitted to the development system. Using such equipment, specified areas of memory are programmed into a PROM which is subsequently plugged into the prototype, thus transferring the programs. The relevant area of memory in the development system user program memory being disabled.

The transfer process may be done in easy stages so that only one device is unproven at any given time. This greatly simplifies the location of faults. Thus at any given time, the prototype hardware may be obeying some programs residing in its own memory and some programs resident in the development system user program memory. Eventually, all of the programs are transferred to the prototype and the development system is operating in a purely supervisory role.

The process of fault finding during the integration phase warrants discussion. The techniques used follow very much those of software development, using break points to halt operations at critical points in program execution. The difficulties of fault finding on a microprocessor system at this stage of development are, however, somewhat greater

369

since the faults that remain are likely to be in the interaction of hardware and software and the servicing of asynchronous events such as interrupts.

The significant events associated with these occurrences are not simply memory addresses (as is the case with software alone) but may also include the state of the external hardware of the prototype. For this reason it is necessary to have a set of logic probes, as shown in Figure 16.4, which may be connected to strategic points in the circuitry. Thus the setting of a break point can be made dependent not only on the instruction being obeyed, but also on the state of the external circuit. Additionally, some faults are data dependent and so it is usually possible to include the state of the data bus in the break point specification.

In summary, therefore, the development system enables execution of the program until a break point is encountered. The break point being specified as

Address bus = m m m m

and

Data bus = n n

and

External probes = y y

The activation of break point may be delayed until its n th occurrence (useful for looped programs) or constrained to occur only during read, write or I/O type operations.

Once the processor is halted, the user is left to study the state of the circuit, accumulators etc. and to decide what caused the fault. In practice, such a simple approach can be difficult because it is the events which lead up to or follow from a specific break point which give the clues. Unfortunately, these sequences of events occur very rapidly but usually with a low repetition rate making them difficult to capture on an oscilloscope. The answer to this problem is provided by the TRACE facility offered by microprocessor development systems.

When using the trace facility, the development system places the information which it acquires (address, data, external probe, etc.) into a "trace memory" the contents of which may be examined at leisure once the processor has stopped. Trace memories are typically 64 to 128 words long. If the processor is stopped immediately the contents of the trace memory represent the events leading up to the break; if the halt occurs 128 cycles later (for a 128 word memory) the stored information gives the consequences which followed from the break event whereas if the halt occurs n (< 128) cycles after the break, the stored information shows . the events surrounding the break (pre, post and variable centre triggering Figure 16.5).

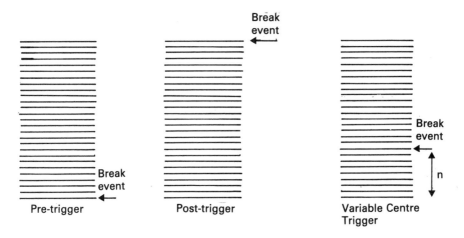

Figure 16.5: Data Capture in a Trace Memory

The interpretation of a large number of 1s and 0s from the trace memory can be rather difficult. The problem is usually eased by the fact that where the data is in fact an instruction, the binary code is disassembled and the mnemonic is displayed instead. Data bus and address bus information are normally displayed in either octal or hexadecimal format (Figure 16.6).

ADRESS	OPCODE/DATA		EXTERNAL
0B9B	ADD	2000	0000 0101
2000	F0	Read	0000 0101
0B9E	CP	FF	0000 0101
0BA0	TZ	1000	0000 0101
0BA3	LDA	F220	0001 0101
F220	08	Read	0001 0101
0BA6	CP	00	0001 0101

(Break point   ADD=0BA6
DATA="don't care"
EXTERNAL=0001 0101)

Figure 16.6: A Typical Trace Display

Using these tools, it is possible to find and cure most faults. Once completed, the ICE probe is removed and a microprocessor mounted in its place. The prototype should now be fully functional.

16.4 System Development Without a Micro-processor Development System

There is no doubt that it is easier to develop a prototype using the methods described above than to do so without these facilities. However, it must be recognised that microprocessor development systems are expensive and may be beyond the reach of some companies just entering the microprocessor equipment scene.

How then may these enterprises proceed? Referring to Figure 16.2, the first few stages of system development remain unchanged. The hardware and software tasks still have to be defined along with their interface and this phase remains the same.

The hardware development phases 1B, 2B and 3B also remain the same (but see below for comments on how a slightly different approach may aid integration of hardware and software).

The writing and assembly of the programs requires a computing facility and this is where the newcomer with little capital to spend runs into trouble; two approaches are possible.

(i)   If there is a minicomputer available in-house then this can be used. If the machine is set up for time-sharing or is available for dedicated use, then it is merely a matter of getting clearance to use the machine. It will almost certainly have editing and file management utilities. If it is normally used for some dedicated purpose, then these utilities may not be available in which case they will have to be purchased from a software house or from the computer manufacturer. Once the program is written, it must be assembled, and this will entail the purchase of a cross assembler for the available minicomputer. It is important to ascertain before proceeding with development that adequate support facilities, such as an assembler, are compatible with the in-house computing facility.

(ii) Where no in-house computing is possible, the only alternative is to use one of the national time-sharing bureaux. This will entail an outlay in terms of capital cost or rental for terminal equipment such as a terminal and modem, as well as charges for computer usage. Again one must ensure that the bureaux supports the chosen microprocessor with the necessary assembly facilities etc. This approach may be appealing because of its low capital cost, but rental and connection charges may be very high· and the time taken to obtain computer print-out may slow up development significantly.

Using the above described facilities, it is possible to proceed through stages 1A and 2A. It is, of course, not possible to try out the object code generated by the assembler on a real, proven microprocessor since the user does not have access to a development system. An alternative software technique is, however, available.

The technique is known as simulation, and the necessary software can usually be purchased for use on in-house minicomputers and is frequently available on those bureaux machines which support microprocessor development software.

A simulator is a piece of software which has as its input the object code produced by the assembler. The simulator reads this code and interprets it just as the hardware microprocessor would. It calculates the contents of registers, condition code flags, memory etc. and produces all of this information as an output listing. In this way the user can, on receipt of the listing, trace through the various stages of program execution in much the same way as he would when using the development system.

By using a comprehensive set of test data and a simulator, it is possible to exercise all paths through the program and to detect and correct most software errors. On completion of a software simulation, stage 3A (Figure 16.2) of the development is completed and integration can start.

It is in the area of system integration that the user without a full development system is at the greatest disadvantage. The basic operations that have to be carried out are:

(i)   Transferring the object code to the hardware.

(ii)   Monitoring the execution of the program to detect the remaining faults.

16.4.1 TRANSFERRING OBJECT CODE

The simplest approach to this problem is to transfer all of the object code from the minicomputer or bureaux machine to PROMs and then to install these in the developed hardware. To achieve this, a PROM programmer must be purchased. Some of these devices allow the user to program each location in the PROM by hand using switches or a keyboard. This approach is not to be recommended for any but the simplest programs since it takes too long and is very error prone. An alternative which is far more efficient is to obtain the object code on paper tape. Many modern PROM programmers have the facility to allow the connection of a tape reader so that the object code once obtained on paper tape, may be read in and the PROM programmed automatically.

Both of the above methods suffer the disadvantage that, once an error is found in the program, the only way of correcting it is by blowing a new PROM with the corrected code. This can be time consuming since it requires the correction of the source code, the generation of a new paper tape and the programming of a new memory device.

On the very best PROM programmers, this approach can be "short-circuited" because they operate on a slightly different principle. The original paper tape is not read directly into the PROM but is instead read into a local read/write memory and then transferred into a PROM. Since these devices are provided with keyboards, it is possible to edit the object code directly (in hexadecimal) and then to blow a new PROM. Care must be taken with this approach to ensure that the source code is brought up to date at the end of each session and that all changes are carefully documented.

A related approach to the problem is the use of a PROM simulator. These devices are, in fact, an assembly of read-write memory. This memory can be written to via a keyboard thus enabling its contents to be defined. Attached to the unit via a suitable cable is (typically) a 24-pin connector which may be plugged into the PROM sockets in the prototype hardware. The electronics is so designed that the prototype can gain READ ONLY access to the read-write memory via this connection and the device is made, both logically and electrically, to appear as if it were the type of ROM being simulated. Since the device is, in fact, read-write memory, editing is simple. In some cases the memory may be loaded from a paper tape reader, thus avoiding the tedious keyboard input. The use of a simulator can thus save time by avoiding the PROM erasure/blowing cycle. Once the program is correct, the ROM simulator may be used as a PROM programmer to produce a permanent copy.

In many of the above mentioned cases, the use of paper tape may be avoided by connecting the programmer or simulator directly to the host computer system via a serial data link.

16.4.2 MONITORING PROGRAM EXECUTION

As discussed in Section 16.3.3, the monitoring and debugging of program execution follows a similar philosophy to software debugging except that the significant events may include hardware and data conditions. Equipment (other than a microprocessor development system) is available to perform this function. Such equipment is termed a logic state analyser and is able, via 24 or more logic probes, to monitor the data, address and other lines within a microprocessor system. There exist specially adapted logic state analysers designed to monitor microprocessor (as opposed to general logic) systems. An example of such a device is the Hewlett-Packard 1611A equipment. These devices are frequently referred to as microprocessor analysers and may be adapted to cope with specific microprocessors by the addition of a plug-in "personality" module.

Because the analysers are configured for a specific processor, they provide especially useful facilities such as disassembling of instruction codes etc.

The microprocessor analyser is connected to the prototype as shown in Figure 16.7. The microprocessor is unplugged from the prototype and inserted into the microprocessor probe. This probe is then inserted into the vacant socket on the prototype and the extra logic probes connected into the rest of the circuit as required.

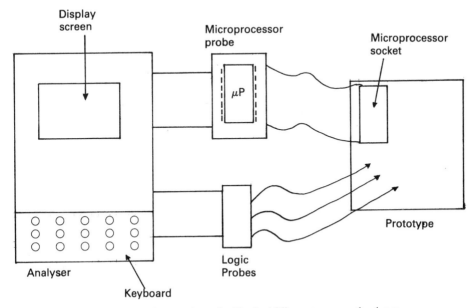

Figure 16.7: Connection of a Typical Microprocessor Analyser

Data entry to such machines is usually by a simple keyboard by which the user specifies the "Trigger" event such as a combination of data, address and external information. Once the Trigger occurs, the user can inspect the events surrouding the trigger by having selected pre, post or variable centre triggering. In some machines, it is possible to defer post-tracing until some time after the specified trigger, as shown in Figure 16.8.

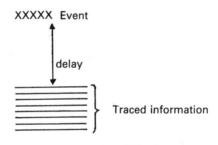

Figure 16.8: Delayed Tracing

16.5 Other Techniques for Testing Microprocessor Systems

Many development systems and microprocessor analysers have facilities in excess of those described above. It is the purpose of this section to briefly outline how some of these additional features may be used.

In many systems there exists the facility to enable and disable the trigger selectively. If a trigger event occurs when the trigger is disabled, it is not recognised. The events which enable or disable the trigger may be specified in a manner similar to that used to specify the trigger event itself. To see how this facility may be used, consider for example a situation where the interrupt handler is causing problems. It apparently works well sometimes and then fails. It is suspected that it only fails when it is invoked as a particularly critical area of the main program (Figure 16.9).

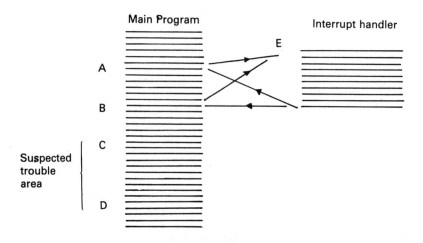

Figure 16.9: Using a Selective Enable Feature to Restrict Trace Operation

It is no good triggering on address E in the program since the handler will then be traced every time it is entered. Similarly, by their very nature, it is not possible to know how many interrupts will occur before address 'C', so triggering on the n th occurrence of E will not work. However, if the tracing mechanism is only enabled between addresses C and D, and the trigger event is set at E, then only those entries to the interrupt handler which occur in the suspected trouble area will be traced.

It is sometimes possible to specify that triggering should occur on any address outside a specified range. This can be useful if the program suddenly goes wild. Unless the user has some idea which instructions are reached, it is difficult to set up a conventional trigger specification. However, he may well know that, when operating correctly, the program obeys instructions in the range 1000 to 2000. Thus if the trigger is set up as

$$\text{Trigger} = \left\{ \begin{array}{l} \text{Address} \geqslant 2001 \\ \text{Address} \leqslant 0FFF \end{array} \right\} \text{ and INSTRUCTION READ}$$

any excursion outside of the permitted range will cause a trace to be initiated and the resulting display will show clearly where program control was transferred to.

Conventional microprocessor analysers and development systems sample all the waveforms at some specified time in the processor cycle. The information obtained is then displayed as a pattern of 1s and 0s which are assumed to be constant throughout the cycle. However, many logic faults are caused by short-duration "glitches" in the waveforms. These can only be seen on high quality oscilloscopes, or some special types of logic analysers. The problem with using oscilloscopes is to obtain a steady display at the appropriate timebase speed to show up the fault. This may be achieved with some types of analyser because they provide a "trigger output". This output is usually a TTL logic compatible pulse which is generated by a trigger event in the analyser. Thus the oscilloscope may be triggered by this output and used as a waveform analysis tool in conjunction with the microprocessor analyser or development system.

In some systems it is possible to time the interval between enabling and disabling the trigger. This can be most useful in time-critical systems and especially in control systems. For instance, it may be used to determine the execution time of a program loop or the time between an interrupt occurring (trigger enable) and the service routine being entered (trigger disable).

One problem with all microprocessor systems is determining the exact contents of the internal registers. Unlike a minicomputer with a console, there is no means of gaining direct access to these registers. One method of obtaining the required information is to insert extra instructions into the program. These will write the contents of the relevant registers to some unused memory location thus making the data visible on the bus. If several registers require monitoring regularly, the simplest solution is probably to write a subroutine which makes the contents of all registers visible on the bus. It is then only necessary to insert a simple 'jump to display subroutine' instruction in the program at those points where this information is needed.

A normal trace includes a number of instructions preceding and following the trigger event. As an alternative, it is often possible to capture just the triggering event itself. This facility is used when the trigger event occurs many times. Each occurrence is recorded in the trace memory and

377

the complete record of triggering events displayed once the memory is full. This "trace triggers" mode can be very useful in studying the changes which take place each time a loop is executed, for instance during an iterative computation such as a multiplication subroutine. The user first works out on paper how the computation should proceed and inserts the necessary instructions to make the relevant data visible on the bus. The trigger is then established in such a way that the "captured" event includes this data bus transaction. When the system is run, the data at successive iterations is captured and then displayed, and the user can compare his pencil-and-paper results with those obtained by the actual system. In this way, programming errors etc. can be quickly identified and eliminated.

16.6 Techniques for Simplifying the Maintenance of Microprocessor Equipment

The techniques discussed above are perfectly suitable for fault finding on development equipment. The main drawback of these methods, though, is the high cost of the test equipment and the very high level of skill required to use it. A knowledge of both the hardware and the software is required for effective use.

In order to reduce investment in fault finding, a board exchange system is often used. This is satisfactory where each board contains few circuits and is mounted in a convenient card cage but is untenable for very large boards or those made integral with the equipment. The inventory cost of board exchange schemes may be very high.

Traditional equipment servicing techniques involve monitoring all nodes in a circuit and tracing through until the measurements made change from 'healthy' to 'faulty' conditions. When this has been done, the faulty component has been traversed and can usually be fairly quickly isolated, although feedback loops can sometimes complicate matters. It is usual to indicate on circuit diagrams the values of voltages and the shapes of waveforms to be expected at significant points in the circuit.

Problems arise in digital circuitry because the significant features at each node will be fairly long bit streams which are usually impossible to display usefully on an oscilloscope or to recognise once they are there. Some means of compressing this information is required.

All methods of fault finding require that repetitive and reproducible conditions be set up in the system. This may be done in microprocessor-based systems by executing a suitable test program or, as will be shown later, by letting the microprocessor "free run".

16.6.1 TRANSITION COUNTING

This method counts the number of times the data on a node changes from one clock period to the next, the clock being that of the system. This system is very simple and can pick up many errors. There is, however, something approaching a 50% chance that a single-bit error will not be detected. In particular, a '1' or '0' which is misplaced in time will not be found. With transition counting, the data stream is compressed into a single number.

16.6.2 SIGNATURE ANALYSIS

Signature analysis is a technique developed and marketed by Hewlett-Packard. The data stream at any given node is applied to a shift register with feedback applied. The technique is reminiscent of PRBS generation and, in the proprietary instrument, the shift register is 16-bits long and feedback is taken from stages 7, 9, 12 and 16 (to achieve a maximal-length sequence) (Figure 16.10).

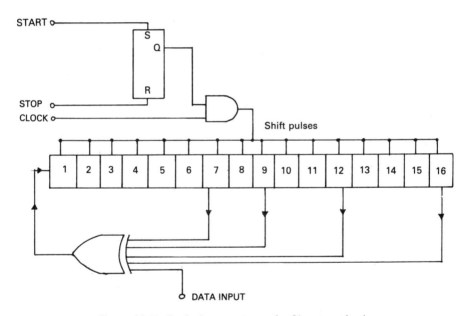

Figure 16.10: Basic Arrangement of a Signature Analyser

The data stream from the node is fed to the input during a "data acquisition window" defined by a 'start' and a 'stop' input to the instrument. The instrument is clocked by a clock input which is derived from the system under test as are the other two inputs. The final contents of the shift register are displayed as four hexadecimal digits - the so-called signature of the node. The power of the method arises from

379

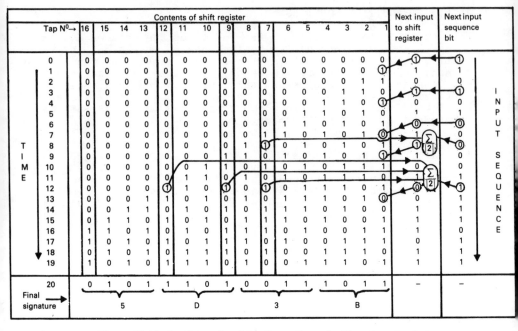

Figure 16.11: An Example of the Operation of a Signature Analyser

the fact that the influence of a '1' or a '0' entering the register is not confined to the first 16 shifts following its appearance but is perpetuated via the feedback connections (Figure 16.11).

The only way in which its influence can be cancelled is by fortuitous occurrence of other errors at just the right time. It can be shown that all single-bit errors will be found and 99.998% of all multi-bit errors will be found in sequences longer than 16 bits. All errors will be found in sequences 16 bits long or less.

The signature of a node is, therefore, a very distinctive feature of that node. The procedure for using signatures is to specify a test procedure and to determine the signatures of all nodes using the test procedure and a known good system. Once this is done, the faulty components can be isolated using traditional tracing techniques as outlined above. A signature different from that on the circuit diagram, or an 'unstable' signature, will indicate the presence of a fault.

To be sure of finding faults, the test regime must exercise every node by producing at least one transition on it.

16.6.2.1 AN EXAMPLE OF A SIGNATURE ANALYSIS PROCEDURE

Consider the simple microprocessor system shown in Figure 16.12.

380

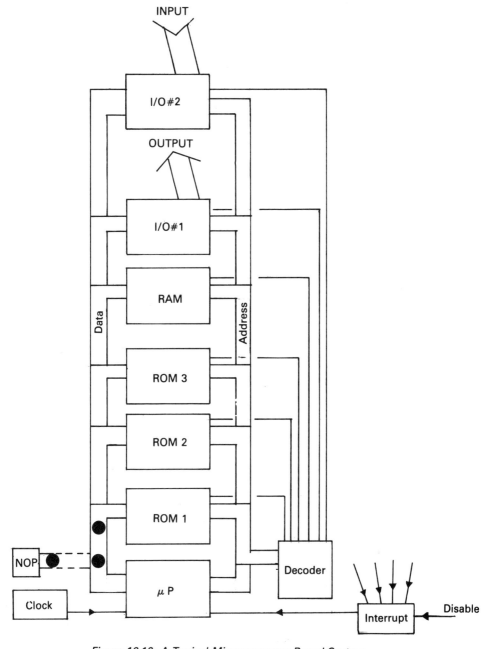

Figure 16.12: A Typical Microprocessor-Based System

The initial assumption is that nothing is working and so it is necessary to check out the KERNEL of the system. This comprises the clock, power supply, microprocessor and each ROM. The clock and power supply are checked using conventional techniques.

The processor board is then put in the "free run" mode which does not require any program in ROM. To do this, the interrupt system is disabled and a jumper in the data bus is moved so that the op-code for some simple single byte instruction is forced onto it (e.g. no-operation (NOP)). When the processor is powered up, it will automatically enter a "fetch" cycle and then obey the NOP. The address will be incremented and another fetch executed (NOP being a single byte instruction). Thus the processor cycles round every possible address and reads from it. The contents of each ROM will, therefore, be placed on the now disconnected part of the data bus at some time.

Using these facts, a signature analysis scheme can be worked out which tests the whole of the kernel of the system.

(i)   Connect Analyser clock to system clock, Start to address bit 15, Stop to address bit 15.

(ii)   Measure signatures on all lines A0 - A15. If this succeeds, there is a high probability that the processor itself is OK and that all of the address bus is functional.

(iii)   Measure signature on all the decoder outputs. Correct results indicate that the decoder is functioning correctly.

(iv)   Move start to the decoder output and likewise the stop to the decoder output for ROM 1 (ensuring that positive and negative transition switching are correctly selected to open a window for the analyser when ROM 1 is being addressed).

(v)   Using this set up the signatures on the data lines are read. Correct signatures indicate a functioning ROM with the correct contents.

(vi)   Repeat with ROM 2 and ROM 3.

(vii)   RAM cannot be tested in this way without first initialising it. This requires that a self test program be executed. To achieve this, the data bus jumper is returned to its normal position. The self test program will be located in one of the already-tested ROMs and the use of simple jumpers can force it to execute. A typical RAM test would involve writing a checkerboard pattern to RAM then reading it back, perhaps repeating with an inverse checkerboard.

(viii) Connect the start and stop on the RAM enable line

and monitor the data line signatures. Correct signatures indicate a working RAM.

(ix) The I/O ports also have to be tested under program control since they usually have to be initialised. Once this is done, the self test program will enter a loop which writes a known sequence of data to each output port in turn (I/O 1 in this case). The start and stop will usually be connected to the chip enable inputs (from the decoder). The signatures on the output lines of I/O 1 can be taken and correct values indicate that I/O 1 is working.

(x) The input port (I/O 2 in this case) can be checked by connecting I/O 1 to I/O 2 via a test fixture and repeating test (ix) but including a "read from I/O 2" in each loop. Monitoring the data line signatures will confirm correct operation of I/O 2. The start and stop controls will be connected to the enable line for I/O 2.

(xi) Everything except the interrupt system has now been tested. Interrupts are difficult to test because they are asynchronous and random events. Signature analysis requires repeatable sequences. Sometimes this can be arranged by synchronising the interrupts with a test fixture, perhaps connecting all of the interrupt lines to one of the I/O ports.

Thus by using a carefully graded set of signature measurements, it is possible to verify that the system is working and to localise any faults.

More complex systems will require a more comprehensive set of tests, perhaps involving other simple test jigs. If there is other logic circuitry associated with the system, this may also be tested. It is only asynchronous circuits (such as UARTS) which give problems for signature analysis and these can often be overcome by providing simple temporary sychronising circuitry during the test.

The pre-requisites for a successful test are that the connections of the clock, start gate and stop gate shall be correct and that the self test program (where appropriate) is correct. The latter is checked during free run tests while the former may be checked before each test by signature analysing the +5 line. This will give a characteristic signature for the test set up which is also characteristic of a "stuck at one" condition on a node. "Stuck at zero" always gives a 0000 signature irrespective of the test set up.

Faulty signatures may be caused by faulty integrated circuits but they may also be the result of short or open circuits. The former are particularly troublesome on bussed structures, or indeed at any point in a circuit which several devices may drive. This is illustrated in Figure 16.13.

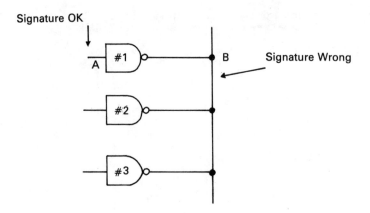

Figure 16.13: A Fault Condition on a Bus

The most obvious conclusion would be that device #1 is faulty. However, the fault could occur for at least five other reasons:

(i)   2 or 3 has its output driver burnt out with a short circuit to ground.

(ii)   2 or 3 has its output driver burnt out with a short circuit to +5v.

(iii) There is a "solder splash" causing a short circuit to ground.

(iv)   There is a "solder splash" to +5v.

(v)   Either or both of the devices 2 and 3 are driving the bus with data when only device 1 should be.

Faults (i) and (iii) will produce an all zero signature while (ii) and (iv) will produce the characteristic 'stuck at 1' signature.

The exact cause of the fault will take some time to isolate. This will probably be done by removing all other devices from the bus and then re-inserting them one-by-one until the fault reappears. This task is particularly onerous if, as is likely, most of the devices are soldered into the board. Figure 16.14 shows a possible situation with a short circuit to ground between devices 2 and 3. The current flows resulting are shown and if these were visible to the service technician, they would immediately indicate the position of the fault.

Clearly an ordinary multimeter is of no value in these circumstances since voltage measurements are not · helpful and it would be necessary to cut the circuit track to make current measurements.

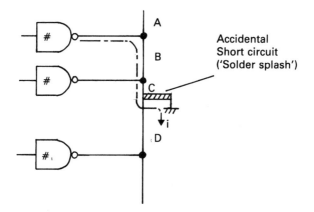

Figure 16.14: The Principle of 'Current Tracing'

There exist, however, a class of test equipment called
'CURRENT TRACERS'. These operate by sensing the magnetic
field surrounding a current-carrying conductor and do not
have to make electrical contact with the conductor in
question. The use of such an instrument to diagnose the fault
shown in Figure 16.14 is simple. The current tracer is simply
used to monitor the current on the bus at positions A, B, C
and D. The fact that there is no current at A, but current at
B and in the track between device #1 and the bus indicates
that device #1 is sourcing the current. Following along the
bus, current is found to be absent in the connecting tracks
for devices #2 and #3 thus eliminating them. The current
disappears at some point on the bus between devices #2 and #3
and this indicates the exact position of the "solder splash".

385

17. Single-Chip and Special-Purpose Microprocessors

One of the main uses for microprocessors is in the field of logic replacement and other "embedded" applications. This use is distinct from their use in microcomputers and often requires quite different characteristics to be emphasised in the architecture.

Frequently such dedicated applications require less computing power than is provided by general purpose microprocessors. They are also often very cost sensitive. For this reason most manufacturers offer one or more "single-chip" microprocessors geared to a particular applications area. A number of consequences result from the decision to produce all the necessary computing facilities on a single chip.

(i)   The assembly cost and power consumption of the computing system is reduced since there is only one integrated circuit and a few discrete components to assemble.

(ii) Because of the reduced parts count, reliability is likely to be higher.

(iii) Because the amount of computing power is being reduced, the processor section can be made to occupy less silicon area and, although memory etc. is incorporated to produce the complete single-chip computer, there may be an overall reduction in the area of silicon used. This reduction in area will lead to improved device yields and a consequently reduced price for the processor.

(iv)   Because the instruction set has been modified to suit a specific class of application, the actual performance of the single-chip processor may equal or even exceed that which could be obtained by using a comparable general-purpose microprocessor.

Many of the applications to which single-chip processors can be applied require the ability to sense binary conditions (switch position on/off etc.) and to manipulate binary outputs to activate contactors, lights etc. Clearly it is a great advantage if processors designed for this kind of application include instructions which can read from memory, process, output and store in memory the basic unit of binary information, the bit. Most general purpose microprocessors do not incorporate this "bit twiddling" capability and binary quantities have to be manipulated in 8-bit groups for the most part. By contrast, single-chip microprocessors usually have excellent bit manipulation capabilities.

Another specialised area for the application of microprocessors is the field of signal processing. One manufacturer has produced a specialised "analogue" microprocessor which has an architecture which is specifically designed for this purpose and which is quite unlike that found in more conventional processors. Here again, the need to enhance performance in one particular area and to reduce circuit size, cost and power consumption has resulted in a specialised single-chip product optimised for the application area.

An important application area for embedded microprocessor systems is that of peripheral control. As peripherals become more complex, it becomes necessary to delegate the responsibility for their detailed handling from the main processor to units of intelligence within the peripherals themselves. Special-purpose controllers for devices like floppy discs and CRTs have existed for some time. However, such specialised devices can only be produced to control peripherals which are expected to be used in bulk. For other types of peripheral, it is necessary to program a more general-purpose device. Thus there exists a class of special-purpose single-chip microprocessors designed to perform well in the peripheral control environment. Typical requirements might be the manipulation of 4-bit quantities (BCD characters), implementation of code conversions via look-up tables and the efficient implementation of handshaking protocols.

Typically, single-chip microprocessors include ROM (or EPROM), read/write memory, I/O ports and timing facilities. Table 17.1 summarises the features of a number of popular products.

Manufac-turer	Processor	On-chip clock	R/W memory (bytes)	ROM/EPROM (bytes)	Counter/ Timers	Serial I/O lines	Parallel I/O lines	Expand-able	Purpose
MOTOR-OLA	6801	Yes	128	2K ROM	3×16 bit	3	31	Yes	
	6801E	No	128	2K ROM	3×16 bit	3	31	Yes	
	68701	Yes	128	2K EPROM	3×16 bit	3	31	Yes	
	68701E	No	128	2K EPROM	3×16 bit	3	31	Yes	
	6803	Yes	128	NIL	3×16 bit	3	13	Yes	
	6803E	No	128	NIL	3×16 bit	3	13	Yes	
ZILOG	Z8	Yes	144	2K ROM	2×16 bit	2	32	Yes	
MOSTEK	3870	Yes	64	2K ROM	1× 8 bit	No	32	No	General
INTEL	8051	Yes	128	4K ROM	2×16 bit	2	32	Yes	
	8751	Yes	128	4K EPROM	2×16 bit	2	32	Yes	
	8031	Yes	128	NIL	2×16 bit	2	32	Yes	
	8049	Yes	128	2K ROM	1× 8 bit	No	24	Yes	
	8039	Yes	128	NIL	1× 8 bit	No	24	Yes	
	8048	Yes	64	1K ROM	1× 8 bit	No	24	Yes	
	8748	Yes	64	1K EPROM	1× 8 bit	No	24	Yes	
	8035	Yes	64	NIL	1× 8 bit	No	24	Yes	
	8021	Yes	64	1K ROM	1× 8 bit	No	20	No+	
	8022	Yes	64	2K ROM	1× 8 bit	No	24*	No+	
	2920–16	Yes	40×25 bit words	582++ EPROM	No	No	12**	No	Signal Pro-cessing
	8041A	Yes	64	1K ROM	1× 8 bit	No	24+++	No	I/O Control
	8741A	Yes	64	1K EPROM	1× 8 bit	No	24+++	No	

*   Plus an on-chip A–D convertor
\+   I/O only is expandable with 8243 I/O expander
\++   Organised as 194 × 24 bits

**   4 analog inputs, 8 analog outputs
\+++ 16 I/O plus 8 dedicated to bus interfacing

Table 17.1: Single-Chip Microprocessors

17.1 The Facilities of a Typical Single-Chip Processor

Single-chip microprocessors are virtually complete computing units designed to be embedded in systems. Virtually all the products available include on-chip clock oscillator circuitry so that it is simply necessary to connect an appropriate crystal directly to the pins of the package.

Because many of these devices find application in "real-time" computing environments, it is essential that they contain a means of producing precise time delays. To achieve this, the processors contain one or more timers. These count upwards from some pre-determined value (loaded under program control) and set a flag, possibly causing an interrupt, when the counter overflows. Some processors are able to organise their counters to operate in other modes, perhaps to cause repeated interrupts at fixed intervals or to generate output waveforms. The source of input to the timers is the internal clock of the processor (possibly pre-scaled by some factor) but many microprocessors also permit the selection of an external source. This enables event counting and other functions to be undertaken easily.

The greatest limitation in a single-chip processor is likely to be the number of I/O lines provided. Since these devices are aimed at the low cost market, the packages used are typically 28 or 40-pin ones and this imposes a very obvious limit on the I/O functions. Most manufacturers have recognised this possible limitation and provided a means whereby additional I/O lines may be added. This process must involve very little hardware and be easy to program. A typical example is the INTEL 8048 which may be expanded using the special-purpose I/O expander, the 8243. Using this device it is feasible to expand the 8048 system to a massive 16,777,216 lines!

The intended application area of single-chip microprocessors is clearly shown by the memory provision included on-chip. A typical value would be 2K bytes of program memory plus 128 bytes of read-write memory. Clearly these devices are intended to operate fairly simple programs with very limited amounts of data. On occasions it will be necessary to expand the amount of program memory or data memory. This option is catered for by permitting some of the I/O pins to be re-assigned as bus pins. The method of switching from purely single-chip operations to the expanded mode varies between individual products. Some require mode-select pins to be wired to the appropriate logic levels (e.g. MC6801); others achieve the same result by setting up an internal mode register (e.g. Z8) and yet others assume that certain addresses and addressing modes will be used to access the expanded facilities (e.g. 8048). It is clearly possible to also expand I/O provision in this way.

The instruction sets of single-chip processors are also a reflection of their intended application areas. The facilities required for carrying out complex arithmetic functions and data management will often be lacking. However, facilities for carrying out logic, for manipulating single BCD characters ("nibbles") and for performing table look-up functions will be strong. Typically the instruction set will also support the easy manipulation of single-bit quantities thus making these devices ideal for logic replacement purposes.

17.2 Development of Single-Chip Processor Based Systems

In principle, the development methods for single-chip processor systems are no different from those employed when using general purpose microprocessors. However, the fact that the system bus is totally internal to the integrated circuit makes it impossible to use development systems in the usual way.

One approach is to use special development oriented chips which make the bus visible. The additional connections to the important signals are brought out to additional pins and these development circuits (bond-out chips) are usually housed in 64-pin chip packages. In cases where the on-chip memory is not provided by the development chip, conventional memory devices will be connected to the development bus as substitutes.

An alternative, but similar, approach is to use the bus expansion capabilities of the chip itself. A small circuit board is constructed containing EPROM memory and read-write memory interfaced to the processor along the expansion bus. Because this necessitates the sacrificing of some of the on-chip I/O lines, these are replced by I/O expansion circuits on the board. In this way the EMULATION BOARD so constructed contains all the bus signals necessary for monitoring the system. The emulation board is connected into the system under development via a suitable dual-in-line plug. This plug carries signals from the emulator board and distributes them to the identical pins which would be used by the target single-chip processor. In this way the system under development can be physically identical to the production models, a situation that cannot pertain when special enlarged development chips are used.

Since emulation boards are electrically identical to the target processor, they can be used for field service work, the single-chip processor merely being unplugged and replaced by the connector to the emulator (see Figure 17.1).

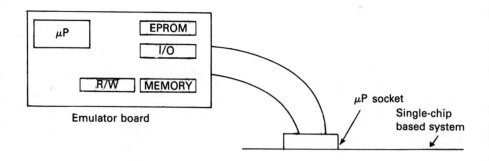

Figure 17.1: Use of an Emulator Board

For field service work, the EPROMs on the emulator board may be replaced with ones containing special diagnostic "exerciser" programs. In this way all the usual techniques, including signature analysis, may be used.

Where emulator boards are not used, field service becomes more difficult. If the on-chip memory is sufficiently large it may be equipped with diagnostic software to exercise the external logic. If not, then some alternative means of inserting diagnostic software must be found. The supply of special single-chip processors specially equipped with the diagnostics only is one solution. Alternatively, with some processors, it is possible to force them to fetch their instructions from external memory.

It is very important in all microprocessor systems that the problems of development, and in particular field service, are taken account of. In the case of products based on single-chip processors, this requirement is many times more important because of the very limited information about system operation that may be obtained by monitoring their external connections.

18. Bit Slice Processors

The processors described so far have been fairly complete containing arithmetic units, control units and registers plus (in some cases) memory, timers and interface adaptors. In order to pack all of this circuitry into one integrated circuit, a relatively slow type of transistor has to be used, the MOS transistor. Thus the complete microprocessor is relatively slow with a fixed instruction set. Recent developments in semiconductor technology have resulted in increased circuit speed and complexity thus allowing greater sophistication in instruction sets and faster execution speeds; nevertheless, these processors are still too slow for some applications. This situation is exacerbated if the instructions available are not well suited to the proposed task.

In such situations the Bit Slice microprocessor may be an appropriate device to use. These devices are best thought of as computer building blocks rather than complete processors. They are constructed, as a rule, using bipolar transistors and as such provide for high switching speeds. Bipolar technology occupies a significantly greater area of silicon than MOS and so it is not usually feasible to produce bipolar microprocessors with the completeness of those fabricated with MOS technology. This problem is solved by removing some of the necessary circuitry out of the main processor chip into subsidiary units. In particular, the control unit is removed.

As will be shown later, the way in which this is done enables the end user to specify his own instruction set. This permits the construction of processors which are oriented to specific application areas. Examples of the use of bit-slice processors include:

(i)   special purpose calculating circuitry for instruments

(ii) controllers for disc stores etc.

(iii) special purpose arithmetic units such as floating point processors

(iv) computers themselves; a particular application might be to construct a high speed emulator of the 6800 microprocessor. This would obey all of the 6800 microprocessor's instructions but at perhaps five times the speed. The penalty for this would be increased size, weight, cost and power consumption when compared with the single-chip MOS version.

(v)   special purpose signal processors.

In order to achieve the maximum flexibility, the processor chip in a bit-slice product family is designed so that several may be connected together to produce a system capable of handling any word length of data that the designer requires. Typically, each processor "slice" contains the facilities to manipulate 4 bits of data and these slices are cascaded to build up the desired processing capability. Figure 18.1 shows an assembly of 3 bit-slice processors being used to fabricate a 12-bit arithmetic unit. Each "slice" contains a 4-bit ALU, a 4-bit shifter and a selection of 4-bit registers. Connections between the circuits permit the "carry out" of one slice to be propagated into the next higher unit. In addition to the functional units shown in Figure 18.1, each slice will contain status monitoring circuits to detect, for instance, when the result of an operation is zero.

It will be clear from the above discussion that a processor designed with bit-slice components will contain significantly more integrated circuits than a typical MOS microprocessor system and will be more difficult to design. A comparison between these two types of system is given in Table 18.1.

	bit slice	convertional
Number of packages in a typical design	10→ 40	1→ 10
Design effort required	High	Low, especially hardware design
Speed of resulting processor	High	Moderate
Flexibility	Good	Low

Table 18.1: Comparision of Bit Slice and Conventional Processors

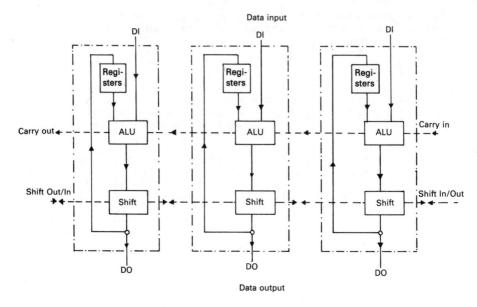

Figure 18.1: Cascading Three 4-Bit Slices to Produce a 12-Bit ALU

One of the difficulties encountered with bit-slice systems is the design of the control unit. The technique used for this is called microprogramming and the support device for control unit fabrication included in bit-slice component families is termed a microprogram sequencer. A number of bit-slice microprocessors are currently available, each with its complement of support circuitry. The fabrication techniques used are varied but are drawn from the high speed semiconductor technologies. The characteristics of some of these devices are summarised in Table 18.2.

It was mentioned earlier that the operation carried out by a bit-slice processor at any given time is determined by the signals supplied by the control unit to the various control inputs on the device. Typically these inputs will cause a simple arithmetic or data transfer operation to occur and it requires many such simple operations to be executed in a coordinated sequence for a complete computer instruction to be carried out. The process of designing such a sequence is termed MICROPROGRAMMING and each elementary set of inputs at the control pins of the bit-slice is termed a MICROINSTRUCTION. The overall 'computer instruction' (e.g. INDIRECT ADD) which is achieved by the sequence of microinstructions, is termed a MACRO INSTRUCTION. The sequence of microinstructions themselves is called a MICROPROGRAM.

Manufacturer	Fairchild	Texas Instruments		Motorola	Fairchild	Advanced Micro Devices	
Family	8 bit	74S481	SBP400A	10800	Macrologic	2900	*Bit slice arithmetic units*
Technology*	e.c.l., s.t.t.l.	s.t.t.l.	i.i.l.	e.c.l.	s.t.t.l.	t.t.l.	
ALU word bits	8	4	4	4	4	4	
Part number	ADIL, 74LS481	74S481	SBP400	10800	9405	2903, 2901A	
Number of basic operations provided in ALU	27	24780	512	100+	64	25, 16	
Max. ALU clock rate MHz	20	10	5	20	10	10	
Package size (No of pins)	·	48DIP	40DIP	48DIP	24DIP	40DIP	
General-purpose regs in ALU	1	0	10	0	8, 16	16	
Microprogram sequencer part no.	·	74S481, 74S482		10801	9406	2910, 2909/11	*Microprogram Sequencers*
Number of address bits	·	4	4	4	12	4	
Sequencer file size	·	4x4	4x4	4x4	16x4	5x12, 4x4	
Package size (No of pins)	·	48, 20		20	24	40, 28/20	
Voltages required	-4, -5, -2	5	5	-5.2, -2	5	5	

* TTL – Transistor-transistor logic
STTL – Schottky TTL
ECL – Emitter-coupled logic
IIL – Integrated-injection logic (I²L)

Table 18.2: Some Typical Bit Slice Processors

18.1 Computer Sequencing and Microprogramming

The operation of a computer is controlled by a "control unit", the function of which is to set up data paths in the appropriate sequence and to pass data along these paths. Such control units may be designed using random logic but this approach is not very flexible and does not readily permit the control unit to be easily tested during design or to be modified. An alternative approach is to use a technique called MICROPROGRAMMING which is much more flexible. Because bit-slice processors are used in widely differing applications, it is advantageous to be able to buy support circuits which simplify the complex process of designing a control unit without needlessly constraining that design. The microprogramming approach to control unit design enables this objective to be realised. The primary support chip for control unit design is the microprogram sequencer and a typical one will be described later in this chapter. However, it is first necessary to explain what is meant by microprogramming.

Figure 18.2 shows the simple computer architecture which was derived in Chapter 2 while Table 18.3 is the sequence table of a 2-word LOAD instruction using this architecture. (First word is op-code, second word is address, SCR points to first word initially.)

The sequencing in Table 18.3 is carried out by the control unit. The first eight steps are carried out at the start of every instruction (the instruction fetch), the remainder being dependent on the particular operation code then in the instruction register. As stated earlier, the control unit may be constructed from logic elements arranged specifically to implement the actions specified (and no others). Because certain assumptions will be implicit in the design (in order to simplify the logic) it is usually very difficult to modify such a control unit.

An alternative approach may, however, be used. This is most easily shown by re-writing the sequence table in a slightly different form. A column in the new table is allocated for every possible control action in the machine

e.g.   enable Driver A

strobe ACC

read memory

Each step in the conventional sequence table is then written into the new one with a '1' present when actions are required on a particular control line. Thus the LOAD instruction sequence table would appear as shown in Table 18.4.

There is a short time delay between each line of the table above. If two actions are not dependent on each other then they can appear in the same line, but if two actions are dependent (e.g. signal ALU to ADD then strobe the AC) they must appear one after the other to ensure that the result of the preceding line is available before it is used. Notice that data paths are set up, then used, for this reason. Also note that the data path controls are maintained during the usage of the path (e.g. lines 1, 2). In some cases the same data path is used twice in succession and if the uses made of the path are not mutually exclusive then the lines in the

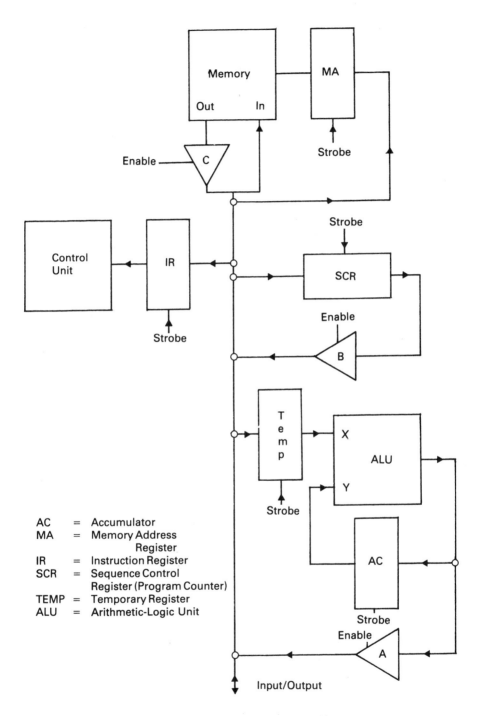

AC   = Accumulator
MA   = Memory Address
         Register
IR   = Instruction Register
SCR = Sequence Control
         Register (Program Counter)
TEMP = Temporary Register
ALU = Arithmetic-Logic Unit

Figure 18.2: Architecture of a Simple Processor

Step	Actions Taken		Data flow
1	Enable driver B		
2	Strobe MA		(SCR)→MA
3	Enable driver B		
4	Strobe 'Temp'		(SCR)→Temp
5	Open X I/P, Signal ALU 'Increment' Enable driver A	Instruction	
6	Strobe SCR		(Temp)+1→SCR
7	Read memory, enable driver C	Fetch	
8	Strobe IR		(Mem)→IR
9	Enable driver B		
10	Strobe MA		(SCR)→MA
11	Enable driver B	Address	
12	Strobe temp		(SCR)→Temp
13	Open X I/P, Signal ALU 'increment' Enable driverA	Operand	
14	Strobe SCR		(Temp)+1→SCR
15	Read memory, enable driver C	Obtain	
16	Strobe temp		(Mem)→Temp
17	Open X I/P, Signal ALU 'ADD', Enable driver A		
18	Strobe MA		(Temp)+0→MA
19	Read memory, enable driver C	Execute	
20	Strobe temp		(Mem)→Temp
21	Open X I/P, Signal ALU 'ADD',		
22	Strobe ACC		(Temp)+0→ACC

Table 18.3: Sequence Table For the 2-word Instruction 'LOAD'

STEP	ENABLE DRIVER A	ENABLE DRIVER B	ENABLE DRIVER C	STROBE MA	STROBE IR	STROBE SCR	STROBE TEMP	STROBE ACC	OPEN X i/p	OPEN Y i/p	SIGNAL ALU INCREMENT	SIGNAL ALU ADD	SIGNAL ALU COMPLEMENT	SIGNAL ALU SUBTRACT	Other ALU operations	MEMORY READ	MEMORY WRITE
1	0	1	0	0	0	0	0	0	0	0	0	0	0	0		0	0
2	0	1	0	1	0	0	0	0	0	0	0	0	0	0		0	0
3	0	1	0	0	0	0	0	0	0	0	0	0	0	0		0	0
4	0	1	0	0	0	0	1	0	0	0	0	0	0	0		0	0
5	1	0	0	0	0	0	0	0	1	0	1	0	0	0		0	0
6	1	0	0	0	0	1	0	0	1	0	1	0	0	0		0	0
7	0	0	1	0	0	0	0	0	0	0	0	0	0	0		1	0
8	0	0	1	0	1	0	0	0	0	0	0	0	0	0		1	0
9	0	1	0	0	0	0	0	0	0	0	0	0	0	0		0	0
10	0	1	0	1	0	0	0	0	0	0	0	0	0	0		0	0
11	0	1	0	0	0	0	0	0	0	0	0	0	0	0		0	0
12	0	1	0	0	0	0	1	0	0	0	0	0	0	0		0	0
13	1	0	0	0	0	0	0	0	1	0	1	0	0	0		0	0
14	1	0	0	0	0	1	0	0	1	0	1	0	0	0		0	0
15	0	0	1	0	0	0	0	0	0	0	0	0	0	0		1	0
16	0	0	1	0	0	0	1	0	0	0	0	0	0	0		1	0
17	1	0	0	0	0	0	0	0	1	0	0	1	0	0		0	0
18	1	0	0	1	0	0	0	0	1	0	0	1	0	0		0	0
19	0	0	1	0	0	0	0	0	0	0	0	0	0	0		1	0
20	0	0	1	0	0	0	1	0	0	0	0	0	0	0		1	0
21	0	0	0	0	0	0	0	0	1	0	0	1	0	0		0	0
22	0	0	0	0	0	0	0	1	1	0	0	1	0	0		0	0

Table 18.4: Modified Form of Sequence Table

table may be combined. For instance, line 1 above sets up and then uses the same data path as line 3. In one case the MA register is strobed and in the other the TEMP register. Thus lines 2, 3 and 4 could have been combined to give a single entry in line 2, eliminating lines 3 and 4.

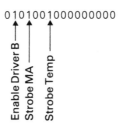

399

A similar simplification could have been made in lines 10, 11 and 12.

The contents of this table appear to be very similar to an ordinary computer instruction when the latter is written in binary form. Indeed each line of the table is a type of instruction. Each of the table entries is called a MICROINSTRUCTION to avoid confusion with the ordinarily understood computer instructions (MACROINSTRUCTIONS). By using the same reasoning, the assembly of these microinstructions as shown in the table constitutes a MICROPROGRAM. Indeed the table above contains the microprogram for the 'LOAD' instruction.

It is possible to conceive of a computer, the control unit of which is simply a memory unit (microprogram memory) and a microprogram sequence control register (MSCR). As an instruction is obeyed, the MSCR steps through the microprogram extracting each microinstruction in turn and loading it into a suitable microinstruction register each bit of which is connected to the appropriate register or other piece of hardware (Figure 18.3).

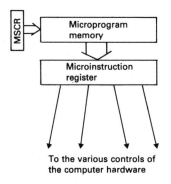

Figure 18.3: Implementation of a Microprogrammed Control Unit

The layout of the microprogram would be as shown in Figure 18.4.

Each instruction is obeyed by first executing the fetch microprogram and then jumping to some other location in microprogram memory to obey the appropriate execute microprogram. The contents of the IR at the end of the fetch microprogram would dictate which location in microprogram memory was reached.

It will be clear from the above discussion that it must be possible to change the contents of the MSCR so that different portions of microprogram can be reached. This facility is needed at the end of the 'FETCH' microprogram so that the appropriate execution microprogram can be obeyed.

400

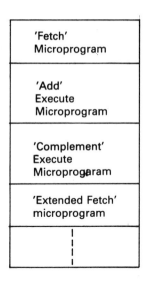

| 'Fetch'
Microprogram |
| 'Add'
Execute
Microprogram |
| 'Complement'
Execute
Microprogaram |
| 'Extended Fetch'
microprogram |
| ¦
¦
¦ |

Figure 18.4: Typical Layout of Microprogram Memory

Additionally, this facility will be needed in all
instructions which carry out conditional branching

e.g. Jump to XXX if result = 0.

Clearly such an instruction will have two sections of
microprogram, one being obeyed if Result is equal to 0, and
the other if Result is not equal to 0. From this it will be
seen that some hardware in addition to the MSCR will be
required. There will have to be some means of calculating the
address of the next microinstruction other than simply
incrementing the MSCR and, where appropriate, a method of
selecting the required condition-code flag must be provided.

Additionally, it is helpful if there is a 'jump-and-return'
(microsubroutine jump) facility. This facility could be put
to use, for instance, by all two-word macroinstructions.

In the absence of any micro-subroutine facility, the execute
microprogram of all two-word macroinstructions would have to
incorporate the necessary microinstructions to fetch the
second operand. Thus many copies of the same piece of
microcode would be contained in the microprogram memory; this
is wasteful.

The availability of the micro-subroutine facility means that
a single copy of the extended fetch can be used and be jumped
to when needed. These concepts are illustrated below (Figure
18.5).

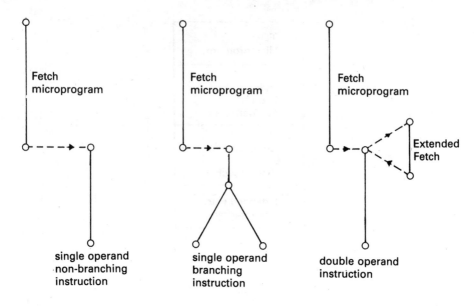

Figure 18.5: Possible Microprogram Execution Paths

The situation may be summarised thus: the microprogram sequence control register governs the order of execution of microinstructions. It must have the facility for

(i)   being incremented

(ii)   being changed (jumps)

(iii)   being changed but keeping track of the next sequential microinstruction.

This latter facility is usually implemented by storing the contents of the MSCR prior to the jump on a stack.

While the arithmetic, logical and register facilities are provided for by the bit-slice microprocessor, the MSCR and its associated facilities are usually provided in a separate package called a microprogram sequencer. A simplified block diagram of a typical bit-slice sequencer is shown in Figure 18.6. Particular examples of these devices will be discussed later but it is appropriate at this stage to examine the structure briefly.

As may be seen in Figure 18.6, the sequencer has a single output which carries the address of the microinstruction to be accessed. This microinstruction address can typically be obtained from one of three sources determined by the control input.

One possible source is the incrementer in which case the current address will be (previous address + 1). In this way it is possible to step sequentially through a microprogram.

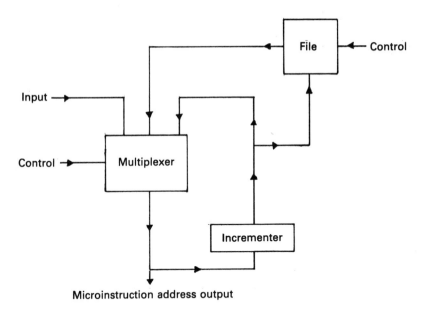

Figure 18.6: A Typical Microprogram Sequencer

Alternatively, the address may be provided from an external source via the input. A typical instance of this usage would be after the fetch sequence when the next executed microinstruction must be determined by contents of the macroinstruction register. This is just one example of a microprogram jump.

This use of the input lines extends to the micro-subroutine jump (i.e. an extended fetch phase). However, in these circumstances it is also necessary to preserve the address of the next sequential microinstruction so that a return may be made at the end of the micro-subroutine. This is the purpose of the register file shown in Figure 18.6. This file is organised as a hardware stack and when the controls are set for a micro-subroutine jump, the return address (which is available at the output of the incrementer) is pushed onto the stack. When, subsequently, a 'return from micro-subroutine' is required, the controls select the file input to the multiplexer and pop the return address from the stack.

The number of bits in any particular microprocessor sequence control register is governed by the total number of microinstructions that are stored in the microprogram ROM. IT IS IN NO WAY CONNECTED WITH THE WIDTH OF THE MICROINSTRUCTION, the latter being governed by the complexity of the machine and the number of data paths that need controlling, whereas the number of microinstructions is dependent on the number of microinstructions implemented and the complexity of those macroinstructions. This will be made clear by the following example:

A computer is realised using bit-slice microprocessors and has a macroinstruction format as shown below. Estimate the size of the microprogram ROM and the number of 4-bit microprogram sequencers required. The width of each microinstruction is 48 bits, and the average length of each microprogram is 10 microinstructions.

MACROINSTRUCTION

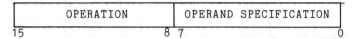

OPERATION	OPERAND SPECIFICATION
15 8	7 0

The operation code occupies bits 8-15, i.e. 8 bits. Thus there are 256 (2^8) possible macroinstructions. Thus the expected number of microinstructions is 10 x 256 = 2560.

Thus the microprogram ROM must have at least 2560 locations each capable of holding 48 bits.

NOW 2^{11} = 2048
           2^{12} = 4096

so the microprogram SCR will have to be 12 bits wide and will therefore require

        12/4 = 3 4-bit microprogram sequencers

The system would appear as:

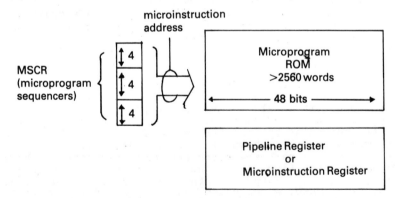

Figure 18.7: Control Unit Designed in Example

Notice that the microinstruction is loaded into a register before it is obeyed. In this way the next microinstruction can be fetched from the microprogram ROM while the current one is being obeyed. This saves considerable time and is called pipelining (Figure 18.8).

Once the design is complete, the contents of the microprogram ROM may be specified and the start address of each microprogram can be listed. In the example given above this might be:

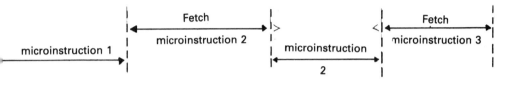

(a) No Pipelining

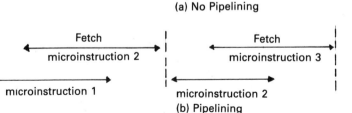

(b) Pipelining

Figure 18.8: Effect of Pipelining on Execution Time

Microprogram Title (Macroinstruction)	Decimal Value of op. code	Start address in microprogram ROM
add	0	0000_{10}
add immediate	1	0005_{10}
' '	' '	
shift left	50	0300_{10}
shift right	51	0302_{10}
' '	' '	' '
complement	240	2100_{10}
' '	' '	' '

Clearly, when the "shift right" macroinstruction is to be obeyed, the address 0302 must be supplied to the sequencer which will then step through the requisite microinstructions.

One obvious way to specify to the sequencer where to start is to use the operation code of the macroinstruction as the start address of the requisite microprogram. One problem with this method is immediately apparent in the above example. The 8 bits of the (example) macroinstruction operation code field will only permit the specification of an address in the range

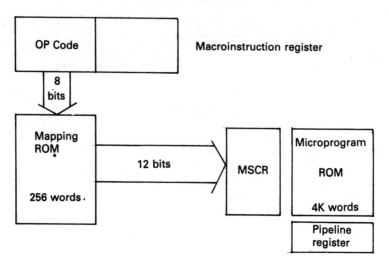

Figure 18.9: Use of a Mapping ROM

0 to 255. The 8 bits could be "packed out" with four zeros in the least significant places to give microprogram start addresses of 0, 16, 32, 48 etc. However, microprograms vary greatly in their length and this approach would inevitably lead to many available locations being wasted.

One (inefficient) solution is to expand the operation code field to 12 bits which will then be able to cover the full range of microprogram ROM addresses. A much more efficient and flexible method is to use a MAPPING ROM consisting of 256 12-bit words. The macroinstruction operation code is used to specify one of the 256 locations in the mapping ROM and the contents of this location are arranged to be the start address of the appropriate microprogram in the microprogram ROM (Figure 18.9).

The contents of the mapping ROM in the example would then be

Location	Contents
0	0
1	5
,	,
50	300
51	302
,	,
240	2100
,	,
,	,
,	,

Microinstructions are typically 30 to 90 bits wide, each bit being used to perform one particular function. These functions include

(i)   setting up data paths within the bit-slice processor (typically 10 bits)

(ii)   selection of source and destination registers (typically 8 bits)

(iii)   control of external data paths (typically 15 bits)

(iv)   control of sequencer operation (typically 6 bits)

(v)   memory control (typically 2 bits).

(vi)   externally supplied microprogram address (typically 12 bits)

The above totals 53 bits which would be distributed throughout the computer.

In this Chapter so far, the general motivation for using bit-slice processors has been presented along with the general principles of microprogrammed systems. Because of the flexibility of bit-slice processor approach to system design, it is difficult to show how these devices are used in the design of sequential machines without discussing a particular example. The following sections will address this problem by showing how a simple computer may be constructed using bit-slice devices. Rather than invent a hypothetical family of components for this purpose, use will be made of one of the most popular groups of bit-slice devices, the AMD 2900 series. These will be described first before proceeding with the design example.

18.2 A Typical Family of Bit Slice Components

In this Section, some members of the Advanced Micro Devices AMD 2900 family of bit-slice microprocessor devices will be discussed with the objective of illustrating the principles which have been put forward in the previous Sections.

The primary component in this family is the 2901 bit-slice microprocessor ALU slice. This device is available in the standard, /A and /B versions which differ only in their operating speeds (10.5, 12.5 and 16 MHz clock speed respectively). Each 2901 bit-slice ALU contains a 4-bit section of a complete processor and these may be stacked together to produce processors of 8, 12, 16, 32 etc. bits width as shown below (Figure 18.10).

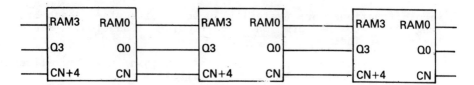

Figure 18.10: A Cascade of 2901 Bit Slice ALU Units

18.2.1 CASCADING ALU SLICES

Figure 18.11 shows a block diagram of a single 4-bit-slice.

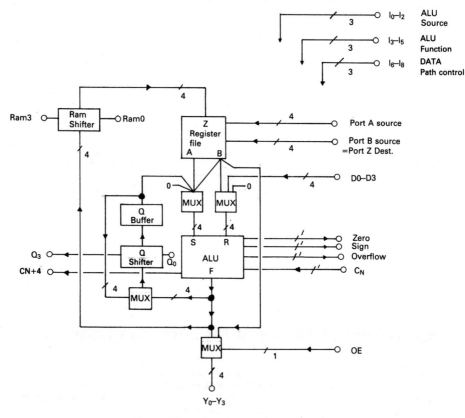

Figure 18.11: The 2901 Bit Slice ALU

The system is equipped with 6 pins which enable the shift
registers and the ALU to be cascaded into a multi-slice
assembly (RAM0, RAM3; CN, CN+4; Q(0), Q(3)) and with three
pins which enable the status of the result in each ALU to be
established (carry, overflow and sign). Data enters the slice

from the outer system via the data input lines (D0 to D3) and may be extracted via the output lines (Y0 to Y3). This latter output is controlled by an output enable line (OE). The data which is made available at the output comes from either of two sources, the ALU or the A-port of the register file; this is a file of 16 registers which may be randomly addressed. These are typically used to implement the programmers' registers and the machine's private scratchpad registers. In some types of bit-slice ALU, registers may be implemented by external hardware. These may be in addition to any internal registers or in replacement of them.

The register file has two output ports, A and B, plus a single input port, Z. Strictly speaking, four bits are required to define which register is read to port A, four bits for port B and another four bits to define which register will be written to. In order to save on the number of connections, the B source and the destination address are constrained to be identical by the use of the same four pins for both.

The control of the slice is completed by nine lines (I0 to I8) which determine the source of the operands to the ALU, the function of the ALU and the use of the remaining data paths. The S input to the ALU can be provided by the Q

Inputs R S	Implemented	Reason for non-implementation
A A	No	This implies that the same register is used for both ALU operands. This is achievable by using the combination R=A, S=B and giving the same address for both A and B.
A B	Yes	
A Q	Yes	
A O	No	This is identical to S=A, R=O except for subtraction. However, both S−R and R−S are available so this restriction is of no consequence.
O A	Yes	
O B	Yes	
O Q	Yes	
O O	No	Clearly any operation with both operands zero can be replaced by a known constant.
D A	Yes	
D B	No	Since registers may be passed to the S input from either the A or the B output of the file, the allocation R=D, S=A will achieve the same end.
D Q	Yes	
D O	Yes	

Figure 18.12: Possible Combinations of Input Data Source for the 2901 ALU

register, the B port, the A port or it may be set to zero. Likewise, the R input to the ALU can be obtained from the data lines, port A, or it may be set to zero. This gives rise to twelve possible combinations of operand (Figure 18.12). However, since some are either duplicates or unhelpful, only the eight combination shown in Table 18.5 and controlled by I0 to I2 are used.

Microcode			Octal	Source	
I_2	I_1	I_0		R	S
0	0	0	0	A	Q
0	0	1	1	A	B
0	1	0	2	0	Q
0	1	1	3	0	B
1	0	0	4	0	A
1	0	1	5	D	A
1	1	0	6	D	Q
1	1	1	7	D	0

Table 18.5: Use of Control Lines to Select ALU Input Data

The ALU is provided with three arithmetic operations and five logical operations as summarised below. These are controlled by I3 to I5.

Microcode			Octal	ALU Function	Symbol
I_5	I_4	I_3			
0	0	0	0	R Plus S	R+S
0	0	1	1	S Minus R	S−R
0	1	0	2	R Minus S	R−S
0	1	1	3	R OR S	R∨S
1	0	0	4	R AND S	R∧S
1	0	1	5	R̄ AND S	R̄∧S
1	1	0	6	R EX−OR S	R⊕S
1	1	1	7	R EX−NOR S	$\overline{R⊕S}$

Table 18.6: Use of Control Lines to Select ALU Operation

The range of arithmetic operations is considerably increased by the fact that one of the operations may be zero and because the "carry in" (Cn), if present, effectively adds one to the result during addition and subtracts one during subtraction. Thus, in addition to the above listed operations, the following may be achieved by careful use of the operand source controls (I0 to I2).

Incrementation
Decrementation
Negation (2s complement)
1s complementation (inversion)

410

For instance, incrementation of a register addressed by port A of the register file may be achieved by selecting port A as the S input with 0 as the R input, thus forming A+0 but at the same time forcing the carry in (Cn) to be '1', thus giving A+0+1 = A+1 at the ALU output.

If Cn had been set to zero, the contents of the register addressed by port A would have emerged unchanged (A+0) at the ALU output. This is known as a "pass" condition and provides the means by which register contents can be made available to the external hardware.

The complete repertoire of available instructions is given in Table 18.7.

The final three control bits (I6 to I8) are used to control the flow of operands back to the register file and the Q register. In addition, the operands may be shifted left or right during transit and this feature is also controlled by I6 to I8. The usefulness of some of these data paths will not be immediately apparent. However, some will be demonstrated in the examples. The various paths available are shown in Figure 18.13.

In addition to the 2901 ALU slice described above, there is a slightly different and more recent ALU slice in the range, the 2903. This device has rather more flexibility in terms of data input and output and also provides additional ALU operations. A non-cascadable 16-bit ALU, the 29116, has been announced.

18.2.2 THE SEQUENCER SLICE

The 2900 family of devices contains three sequencers which may be used to control the execution of the microprogram. Each sequencer realises some of the bits of the microprogram sequence control register and they may be stacked together to produce the desired addressing range.

The 2909 and 2911 sequencers are cascadable 4-bit slices and are very similar, the 2911 being the simpler of the two. In addition to these, there is the 2910, a non-cascadable sequencer which is 12 bits wide and which incorporates more powerful address generation and micro-subroutine calling facilities. For the purpose of the example, only the 2911 will be described.

A simplified block diagram of the 2911 sequencer is shown in Figure 18.14.

The Y output of the multiplexer provides the address information to the microprogram ROM and thus enables any particular microinstruction to be selected. The source of this information is selected by the multiplexer and may be any one of the following:

Octal I_{543}, I_{210}	Group	Function
4 0	AND	A ∧ Q
4 1		A ∧ B
4 5		D ∧ A
4 6		D ∧ Q
3 0	OR	A V Q
3 1		A V B
3 5		D V A
3 6		D V Q
6 0	EX-OR	A ⊕ Q
6 1		A ⊕ B
6 5		D ⊕ A
6 6		D ⊕ Q
7 0	EX-NOR	$\overline{A \oplus Q}$
7 1		$\overline{A \oplus B}$
7 5		$\overline{D \oplus A}$
7 6		$\overline{D \oplus Q}$
7 2	INVERT	$\overline{Q}$
7 3		$\overline{B}$
7 4		$\overline{A}$
7 7		$\overline{D}$
6 2	PASS	Q
6 3		B
6 4		A
6 7		D
3 2	PASS	Q
3 3		B
3 4		A
3 7		D
4 2	ZERO	0
4 3		0
4 4		0
4 7		0
5 0	MASK	$\overline{A}$ ∧ Q
5 1		$\overline{A}$ ∧ B
5 5		$\overline{D}$ ∧ A
5 6		$\overline{D}$ ∧ Q

Octal I_{543}, I_{210}	$I_9=CN=0$ (low)		$I_9=CN=1$ (High)	
	Group	Function	Group	Function
0 0	ADD	A+Q	ADD plus one	A+Q+1
0 1		A+B		A+B+1
0 5		D+A		D+A+1
0 6		D+Q		D+Q+1
0 2	PASS	Q	Increm.	Q+1
0 3		B		B+1
0 4		A		A+1
0 7		D		D+1
1 2	Decrem.	Q−1	PASS	Q
1 3		B−1		B
1 4		A−1		A
2 7		D−1		D
2 2	1s Comp	−Q−1	2s Comp (Negate)	−Q
2 3		−B−1		−B
2 4		−A−1		−A
1 7		−D−1		−D
1 0	Subtract (1s comp)	Q−A−1	Subtract (2s comp)	Q−A
1 1		B−A−1		B−A
1 5		A−D−1		A−D
1 6		Q−D−1		Q−D
2 0		A−Q−1		A−Q
2 1		A−B−1		A−B
2 5		D−A−1		D−A
2 6		D−Q−1		D−Q

Table 18.7: Complete Repertoire of 2901 ALU Operations

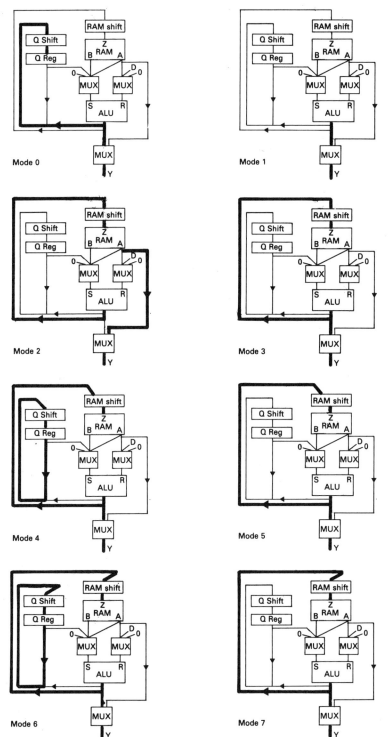

Figure 18.13: Data Paths in the 2901 ALU

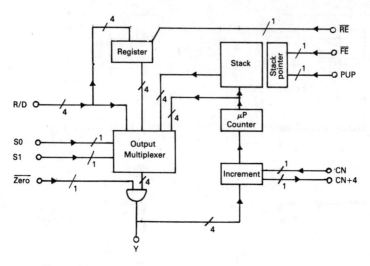

Figure 18.14: Layout of the 2911 Microprogram Sequencer

(i)   data input lines

(ii)   address register

(iii)   stack

(iv)   microprogram counter

If the data input lines are selected, then the microinstruction addressed will be that determined by the data on the input lines. This data will typically be obtained either from the output of the mapping ROM (for example, at the start of the macroinstruction execution) or from the JUMP FIELD of the microinstruction currently being obeyed (to permit branching of a microprogram). The selection of the source of data will be under the control of one or more bits in the current microinstruction and will often also be conditional on the status of the ALU (overflow, carry etc.).

The current output of the multiplexer, in addition to being passed to the microprogram ROM, is also passed through the incrementer to the microprogram counter. Thus, if the microprogram counter is continually selected by the multiplexer, sequential microinstructions will be accessed. The Cn and Cn+4 connections on the incrementer permit several sequencers to be cascaded. Under normal circumstances, the lowest order sequencer will have '1' supplied to its Cn terminal. However, under the control of the current microinstruction, this input can be forced to zero thus permitting repeated execution of the same microinstruction perhaps until some particular condition is satisfied.

If a micro-subroutine jump is required, this may be achieved by the coordinated use of the data input lines and the internal stack. In this mode of operation, the target address

414

of the jump is applied to the data input and the current
contents of the microprogram counter are pushed onto the
internal stack (up to four jumps may be nested). The
multiplexer is set to select the data input lines.

To return from the micro-subroutine, the multiplexer is set
to select the stack and the latest entry is then popped.

Addresses may be stored temporarily in the address register
by applying the required address to the data lines and
enabling $\overline{RE}$.

To force an all-zero microinstruction address (for instance,
during a reset operation) the $\overline{ZERO}$ control is enabled. The
operation of the stack is controlled by PUP and $\overline{FE}$ while the
multiplexer is controlled by S0 and S1. The operation of
these controls is summarised below.

S_1	S_Q	
0	0	Microprogram counter
0	1	Address register
1	0	Stack
1	1	Data inputs

$\overline{FE}$	PUP		
0	0	POP Stack	
0	1	PUSH Stack	$\overline{RE}=1$
1	0	No change	
1	1	in stack	

Table 18.8: Use of 2911 Sequencer Control Lines

Thus, the simpler operations of the sequencer may be
summarised as follows (A = microprogram address on data
input).

$\overline{FE}$	PUP	$\overline{RE}$	S_1	S_0	Least significant CN	
1	X	1	1	1	1	Jump to new address A and put A+1 in micro-program counter
0	1	1	1	1	1	Microsubroutine jump to Address A and then step on
0	0	1	1	0	1	Return from microsubroutine and step on from there
1	X	1	0	0	1	Step through microprogram
1	X	1	0	0	0	Repeat current microinstruction

Table 18.9: Simple Operations for 2911 Sequencer

18.2.3 OTHER 2900 FAMILY CIRCUITS

The 2900 family includes various other useful circuits including data and address bus drivers, and multiplexers specially designed to help in the construction of the ALU shift logic (see later).

One particular circuit worthy of mention is the 2902 "carry-look-ahead" generator. When several 2901 ALU slices are cascaded, the result of an arithmetic operation is not available until the carry signal into the highest order slice is available. With large word lengths, this may take a considerable time and limit the speed of operation. However, fairly simple logic may be employed to predict the value of the carry in advance of the "ripple through". Details of this logic may be found in any elementary treatise on computer logic.

The 2902 circuit contains the necessary logic and may be connected to the 2901 using the special P and G (carry propagate and carry generate) signals provided by that chip.

Figure 18.15 is a modification of Figure 18.10 and shows how the 2902 is used.

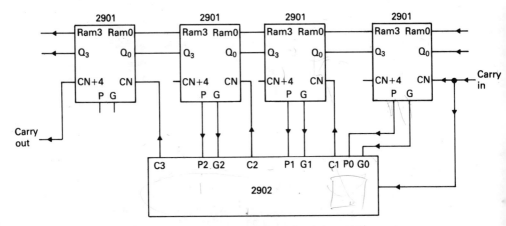

Figure 18.15 Use of the 2902 Carry-Look Anead Generator

18.3 Design Example – A Simple Computer

In this Section, the use of bit-slice components will be examined in the context of the design of simple computers. It should, however, be understood that this is only one possible use for these components. They may be used to design special purpose sequential equipment as well as more general purpose items such as computers. Nor need the equipment be basically complex. The 2911 sequencer may be used with just a few additional components to fabricate a simple, but effective, sequence controller for machinery, perhaps replacing electro-mechanical equipment.

The computer to be designed will use a 16-bit word length and instructions will consist of either one, two or three words. The first word will have the following layout:

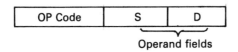

Operand fields

The operation code consists of 8 bits which will be used to select the appropriate microprogram via a mapping ROM. The two operand fields (S/D) each consist of 4 bits. If the most significant bit in each field is zero, then the remaining 3 bits specify which of the 8 general purpose registers is to be used as a source of operands. If the most significant bit is 1, this will indicate that the operand is to be found in memory at a location specified by the second or third words of the instruction.

The operations take the form

Where the operation requires only one operand, the second operand specification is taken as the destination of the result only.

Examples

(i)

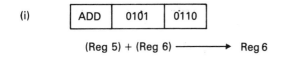

(Reg 5) + (Reg 6) ⟶ Reg 6

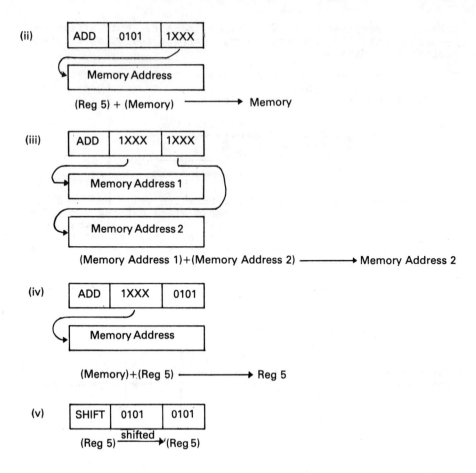

(ii)

| ADD | 0101 | 1XXX |

Memory Address

(Reg 5) + (Memory) ⟶ Memory

(iii)

| ADD | 1XXX | 1XXX |

Memory Address 1

Memory Address 2

(Memory Address 1)+(Memory Address 2) ⟶ Memory Address 2

(iv)

| ADD | 1XXX | 0101 |

Memory Address

(Memory)+(Reg 5) ⟶ Reg 5

(v)

| SHIFT | 0101 | 0101 |

(Reg 5) $\xrightarrow{\text{shifted}}$ (Reg 5)

In the above examples, where a memory location is indicated by a '1' in the most significant place of the source/destination fields, the exact values of the bits marked XXX will determine the addressing method to be used (Table 18.10).

X X X	Addressing Method
0 0 0	Absolute
0 0 1	Relative
0 1 0	Indirect
0 1 1	Auto increment
1 0 0	Auto decrement
1 0 1	Indexed
1 1 0	−
1 1 1	−

Table 18.10: Allocation of Codes to Specify Addressing Method

Eight of the 16 registers within the 2901 will be used to implement the 8 general purpose registers available to the programmer, the remaining 8 registers will be used for internal machine purposes. These are allocated as follows:

Register	Usage
0→7	Programmer's own
8	Stack pointer
9	Index register
A	Sequence control register
B	T_1
C	T_2
D	T_3 'Private'
E	T_4 temporary registers
F	T_5

Table 18.11: Register Allocation

Since the machine registers 8, 9 and A are outside the range directly available to the programmer using the above scheme of addressing, special machine control instructions will have to be provided to allow these registers to be manipulated.

The general structure of the computer will be as shown in Figure 18.16.

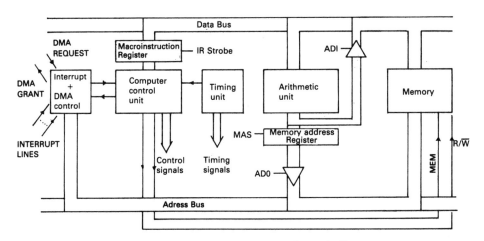

Figure 18.16: Hardware Layout of the Example Computer

From the above diagram, it will be seen that there are five main modules, namely:

                interrupt and DMA
                computer control unit
                timing unit
                arithmetic unit
                memory

Both the data bus and address bus will be 16 bits wide and, in addition, there will be a control bus carrying timing, interrupt, DMA and other signals. Only two of these signals are explicitly shown, namely

R/$\overline{\text{W}}$ - a '1' indicates a memory read
MEM - a synchronisation signal indicating when a memory transfer is expected.

The details of the memory system will not be discussed further (see Chapter 6) except to say that the MEM signal will be established when address and (for a write) data signals are stable and the R/$\overline{\text{W}}$ line indicates the direction of transfer. It is assumed that the memory system will be designed to respond to these signals.

The arithmetic unit contains a memory address register which can be loaded by taking the control signal MAS to logic '1'.

Clock signals will be needed to operate the 2901-based arithmetic unit and the 2911-based computer control unit. In addition, various other components will need to be clocked in the appropriate sequence in order to ensure the proper distribution of data around the system. The design of the timing unit, therefore, is very important. However, the design is very tedious and not a particularly rewarding study if the objective is to understand how bit-slice components may be used to form a complete system. For this reason and to avoid introducing undue complexity and detail, the timing unit will not be further considered.

Likewise, the control of DMA and interrupt requests can involve considerable complexity. In essence, interrupt requests are received and the logical 'OR' of these requests is interrogated by the computer control unit on completion of each instruction microprogram. If a request is found, the computer control unit will carry out a micro-subroutine jump to the interrupt handler microprogram. This will cause the interrupt control logic to be interrogated, the machine status to be stacked, and an interrupt vector to be read along the address bus. When the handling of the interrupt is completed, the macroinstruction, 'RETURN', will cause this procedure to be reversed.

DMA operation will be established in a similar way except that the DMA request line(s) will be interrogated at the end of every bus cycle rather than at the end of every macroinstruction. The DMA microprogram which is executed could consist of a single microinstruction which is obeyed repeatedly until the DMA request is removed. This microinstruction would have have the effect of turning off all bus drivers.

It will be noticed that there is no macroprogram sequence control register. Instead, the sequence control register is realised as one of the internal registers of the 2901 ALU and all address computations (e.g. for indexed addressing) are carried out by the ALU hardware. This is a simple and

economical choice but is not particularly efficient. A better
choice (from a performance point of view) would have been to
design a dedicated address computation unit. Such a unit
could be designed using a set of four 2930 program control
unit slices. Four sequencers would be needed since the
"address" bus is 16 bits wide and each 2930 includes only 4
bits. The logic contained within the 2930 includes facilities
both for arithmetic processing and also sequencing.

No special I/O interface is shown for our example computer in
Figure 18.14. It is assumed that all I/O will be memory-
mapped and that the peripherals may all be designed to
respond like memory units.

This just leaves the two main units of the computer to be
discussed, namely the arithmetic unit and the computer
control unit.

The logic of these will be discussed in some detail in the
next two sub-sections.

18.3.1 THE ARITHMETIC UNIT

The arithmetic unit will be constructed from four 2901 4-bit
slices to make up the 16-bit word length required. In order
to speed up operations, a 2902 carry-look-ahead unit will
also be used to support the four 2901s, the overall
connections being as shown in Figure 18.15.

The arithmetic unit will be controlled by the signals I0 $\longrightarrow$
I9 which carry out the functions listed in Tables 18.5, 18.6
and 18.7. From Table 18.7, it will be observed that the
"carry-in" to the least significant slice is also required to
specify fully the arithmetic operations. For convenience this
will be termed I9 in all future tables etc.

In order to control the flow of data out of the 2901, an
"output enable" (OE) control is provided. When OE is logic
'0', the output is inactive. It will be observed in Figure
18.16 that the output of the arithmetic unit is directed to
either the data bus or the address bus via two sets of tri-
state drivers. This is necessary since, in the current
example, the arithmetic unit is used for both address
calculation and data manipulation. The OE control is,
therefore, redundant and is replaced by the two "arithmetic
destination" signals AD1 and AD2.

The 2901 circuit provides virtually all of the logic
necessary for an arithmetic unit. However, two additional
sets of logic must be provided to complete the unit. First,
the status outputs of each 2901 must be combined
appropriately to produce the status flags for the machine as
a whole. These will be stored in a separate condition code
register rather than making use of one of the internal
registers of the 2901 since this does not involve much
additional complexity or hardware and will make the machine
easier to microprogram and faster in execution. Secondly,

some additional external logic will be needed to complete the data shifting paths. It will be recalled that there are several types of shift and rotate operation possible and the source of data entering the ends of the shift register and the "carry-out" bit will need to be selected appropriately for each type of shift.

18.3.1.1 STATUS REGISTER LOGIC

Each 2901 slice provides four status outputs. Their use depends on where within the computer word the slice in question is located. The four status outputs are:

Cn+4   Carry out from the high order bit of the slice.

F3   The most significant bit in the slice.

OV   Overflow (in a 2s complement sense). This is the exclusive-OR of the carry into the most significant bit and the carry out from it (Cn+4) (See Chapter 4).

F=0   This signal is the logic NOR of all the bits in the slice. It is '1' if, and only if, all the bits in the slice are zero.

Clearly the first three signals are only meaningful in a machine-status sense when they are extracted from the most significant slice in the arithmetic unit. The machine 'zero' flag, however, must be the logical AND of all the F=0 outputs.

Figure 18.17 shows the derivation of the machine status.

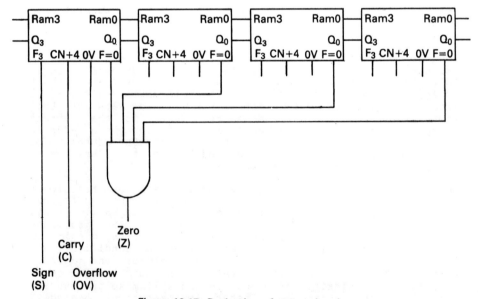

Figure 18.17: Derivation of status signals

422

These signals are routed to a 4-bit status register. Provision is also made for the status register to be written to under macroprogram control so the input to the status register is routed via a two-way multiplexer (MUX) controlled by CS0 & CS1.

```
CS0 = 0 input from arithmetic unit
CS0 = 1 input from data bus
CS1 = 1 output to data bus enabled
```

Both the true and false values of each condition will be available at the Q and $\overline{Q}$ outputs of each position of the status register, giving eight outputs altogether. The true outputs may be stored in memory (for instance during interrupt service). The contents of the status register will be used to influence the flow of both the macroprogram and the microprogram, hence one of the eight possible outputs must be selectable. This selection is achieved by an 8-way multiplexer, the multiplexer being operated by three control lines derived from the microinstruction (CCS0 to CCS2). The codes selected are shown in Table 18.12.

CCS2	CCS1	CCS0	Code Selected
0	0	0	SIGN (S)
0	0	1	Carry (C)
0	1	0	Overflow (OV)
0	1	1	Zero (Z)
1	0	0	$\overline{S}$
1	0	1	$\overline{C}$
1	1	0	$\overline{OV}$
1	1	1	$\overline{Z}$

Table 18.12: Condition Code Selection

The complete logic of the condition-code system is given in Figure 18.18. It will be noted there that the input to the carry is passed through a 2-way multiplexer. This is necessary because the carry flag is often involved in shift operations as well as arithmetic operations. The control of the multiplexer is via CS2:

```
CS2 = 0 carry from arithmetic status
CS2 = 1 carry from shift operation
```

Note that if CS3 = 1, updating of the status register is inhibited.

18.3.1.2 SHIFT CONTROL LOGIC

The discussion of the 2901 data paths showed that data may be shifted left or right in either the Q-shifter or the RAM-shifter. For the purposes of this example computer, it will

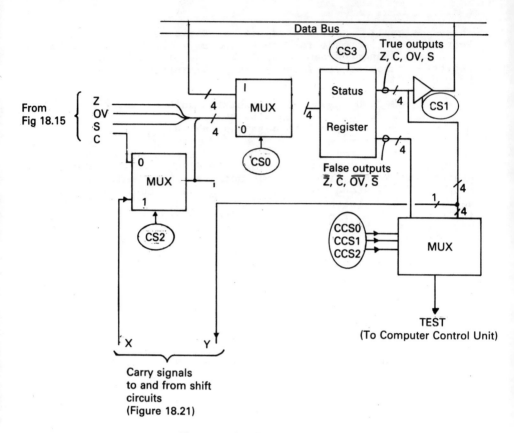

Fig 18.18: Condition Code Logic

be assumed that only one set of shift logic will be used and this will be associated with the RAM-shifter. Similar logic could be associated with the Q-shifter if desired.

As it stands, the 2901 implements only linear shifts. By placing additional logic at each end of the shift register it is possible to 'catch' the bits that fall out of the end of the shifter and to recirculate them appropriately. In this way, rotate and arithmetic shifts are possible. Figure 18.19 shows the range of shift operations that will be incorporated into the example computer.

It will be clear from Figure 18.19 that the only differences between the types of shift are:

(i)   the source of data being shifted into the register

(ii)   the source of data going into the carry.

The difference between "left" and "right" operations is clearly that the data is shifted into the least significant

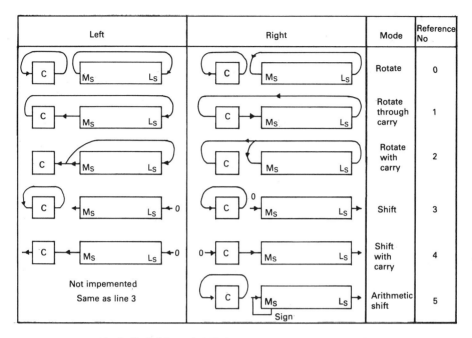

Figure 18.19: Definition of shift Operation for the Example Computer

position in the first case and into the most significant place in the second case.

In order to implement these shift operations correctly, all that is needed is a multiplexer which will select the source of data to be shifted into the register and the carry. Table 18.13 summarises the source of operands applied to the most significant end of the shift register, the least significant end of the shift register, and the carry. The order is identical to that of Figure 18.19:

Ref	LEFT			RIGHT			Operation
No	C	Ms	Ls	C	Ms	Ls	
0	C	X	Ms	C	Ls	X	Rotate
1	Ms	X	C	Ls	C	X	Rotate through carry
2	Ms	X	Ms	Ls	Ls	X	Rotate with carry
3	C	X	0	C	0	X	Shift
4	Ms	X	0	0	C	X	Shift with carry
5	X	X	X	C	SIGN	X	Aritmetic shift

Table 18.13: Specification of shift linkages

425

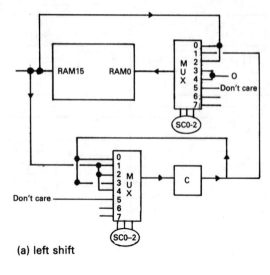

(a) left shift

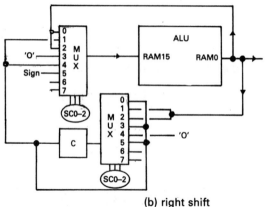

(b) right shift

Figure 18.20: Shift Logic for Example Computer

Figure 18.20(a) shows the circuitry necessary for left shifts while 18.20(b) shows that applicable for right shifts. The multiplexer is controlled by three lines, SC0 to SC2, and is so arranged that the binary number on SC0 to SC2 implements the shift linkage in the appropriately numbered line in table 18.13 (i.e. if SC0=0 SC1=1 SC2=0 a "rotate with carry" operation - Ref No 2 - will be implemented).

Inspection of the two diagrams reveals that both circuits are very similar, the principal differences being

(i)   the input to the carry multiplexer for SC2 $\longrightarrow$ SC0 = 100

(ii)   the interchange of the roles of the most and least significant bits.

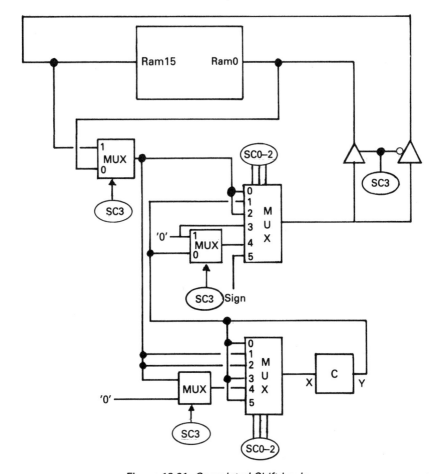

Figure 18.21: Completed Shift Logic

The two circuits can be combined, with the addition of a direction control (SC3), as shown in Figure 18.21. Note that the previously undefined arithmetic left shift (reference Figure 18.19) now becomes defined as a rather odd left shift in order to simplify the logic.

It will be noted that

$$SC3 = 1 \text{ for left shift}$$
$$= 0 \text{ for right shift}$$

The carry flag shown in Figures 18.20 and 18.21 is, of course, part of the condition codes register previously discussed and the markings x, y on Figure 18.21 correspond to similar ones in Figure 18.18. Note that, for the shift logic to operate correctly, control signal CS2 in Figure 18.18 must be set to '1'.

The complete logic of the arithmetic unit has now been
discussed and is shown in Figure 18.23 which is a combination
of Figures 18.15, 18.17, 18.18 and 18.21. The arithmetic unit
is controlled by 31 separate lines which will be derived from
the microprogrammed computer control unit. These are
summarised below.

Shift logic Control		Status register Source/Dest.	Condition Code	External ALU Destination	ALU inc.	ALU Destination	ALU Function	Source Operands	Port B Register	Port A Register
SC3	SC2 SC1 SC0	CS3 CS2 CS1 CS0	CCS2 CCS1 CCS0	AD1 AD0	I_9	I_8 I_7 I_6	I_5 I_4 I_3	I_2 I_1 I_0	B3 B2 B1 B0	A3 A2 A1 A0
1=Left shift See Fig 18.21		See Fig 18.18	See Table 18.12	See Fig 18.16	Equivalent to CN in Table 18.7	See Fig 18.11	See Table 18.6	See Table 18.5 See Table 18.7		

Figure 18.22 Arithmetic Unit Control Word

18.3.2 COMPUTER CONTROL UNIT

The control unit will be basically similar to that shown in
Figure 18.9 and will use 2911 microprogram sequencers.
Assuming that between 2K and 4K microinstructions are
required, then three 2911 sequencers will be required as
explained in the example in Section 18.1. The number of bits
required in each microinstruction has yet to be determined,
but it will be well in excess of the 31 required to control
the arithmetic unit.

The mapping ROM will have $2^8 = 256$ words in it since the
operation code is 8 bits wide. Each word will have to be 12
bits wide to provide the necessary 4K addressing ($2^{12} = 4K$)
for the microprogram ROM.

It is the function of the microprogram sequencer to select
the next microinstruction. As discussed in Section 18.2.2,
this selection is controlled by the state of the sequencer
control signals (FE, PUP, RE, S0, S1 and Cn to the least
significant 2911 slice). It will frequently be necessary to
make the selection of the next microinstruction conditional
upon some event which may be tested. Thus two distinct sets
of control signals must be made available, one to be used if
the test succeeds and another to be used if it fails.

The conditions tested will include the main machine status
conditions available on the 'TEST' line (see Figure 18.23).
In addition, the control unit will have to know whether
either, or both, the source and destination operands are to
be found in memory. This can be determined by testing the
most significant bits of the source and destination fields in

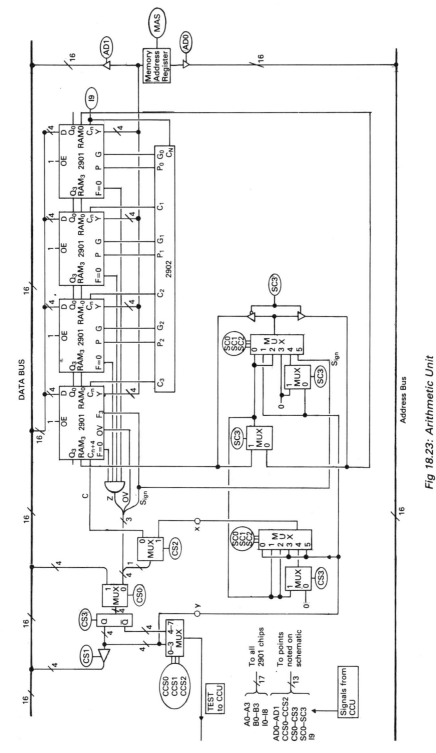

Fig 18.23: Arithmetic Unit

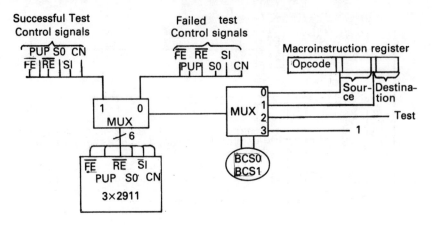

Figure 18.24: Microprogram Branch Control

the instruction and so these must also be made available as
testable conditions. This is shown in Figure 18.24 and the
operation of the control signals BCS0 and BCS1 is shown in
Table 18.14.

BCS1	BCS0	Action
0	0	Test for Source Operand in Memory
0	1	Test for Destination Operand in Memory
1	0	Test Arithmetic unit Condition
1	1	Select 'Successful' Control Signals

Table 18.14: Allocation of Control Signals to Test Selection Multiplexer

The final entry in Table 18.14 enables one set of control
signals to be unconditionally selected.

When a microprogram jump is required, the address of the new
microprogram or micro-subroutine must be supplied to the data
inputs of the 2911 sequencer. There are a number of sources
for this address.

(i)   The mapping ROM. This will be selected when it is
      required to execute an instruction.

(ii) The "Jump Field" of the microinstruction. The
      jump field is a 12-bit field which contains a
      target microinstruction address. This will be the
      usual source of addresses for conditional and
      unconditional microprogram jumps.

(iii) The address mode fields of the instruction
      register. Once the macroinstruction is fetched,
      the sequencer must determine the source and
      destination addresses of the operands. This will

be done by executing an appropriate micro-subroutine. Just which subroutine will depend on the addressing mode code, XXX, which is contained in the three least significant bits of the source and destination fields (Table 18.10).

Somehow these three bits must be expanded to form a 12-bit address field. One method would be to have a second mapping ROM (8 x 12-bit words) to specify the target addresses. However, although this is elegant and flexible, it does impose a significant extra delay on the execution (ROM access time). Since address calculation is a very frequent occurrence, this will be avoided by defining the start address of each address calculation subroutine as

$$111 \ 111 \ XXX \ 000$$

That is by arbitrarily adding six leading ones and three trailing zeros.

Thus the absolute addressing micro-subroutine is located in microprogram ROM at

$$111 \ 111 \ 101 \ 000$$

This, of course, makes the assumption that none of the subroutines is longer than eight microinstructions. If this proves not to be true, the system could easily be modified by moving the XXX bits one place to the left and adding an extra zero on the right. Further, with the scheme outlined above, it is possible that space will be wasted in the microprogram ROM if the address calculation routines are much shorter than eight microinstructions. This is the penalty which must be paid for the simplicity of the scheme.

Making these assumptions, the external data input to the sequencer may be controlled by SDS0 and SDS1, as shown in Figure 18.25 and Table 18.15.

When operands are fetched from memory they will have to be placed in a temporary storage location for future use. It will be arbitrarily assumed that register T1 (address B - Table 18.11) will be used for source operands coming from memory and that T2 (address C - Table 18.11) will be used for destination operands coming from memory. Register T3 (address D - Table 18.11) will be used by the address calculating subroutines as the place where they leave the calculated address. All of these assumptions are purely arbitrary and not necessarily the best in terms of efficiency. However, they lead to a particularly convenient situation in which the execution microprogram for each instruction is the same irrespective of the original location of the operands.

431

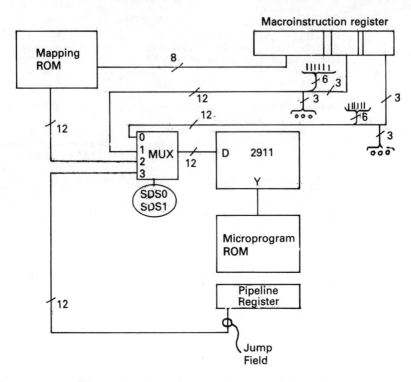

Figure 18.25: Control Unit of the Example Computer

SDS1	SDS0	Address Selected
0	0	Source Addressing Microsubroutine
0	1	Destination Addressing Microsubroutine
1	0	Mapping ROM
1	1	Jump Field of Microinstruction

Table 18.15: Operation of Address Selection Multiplexer

The execution microprograms will fetch the source operand from port A of the ALU register stack and the destination from port B. The result will then overwrite the destination as implied by the general specification of the operations:

    (source) .op. (destination) ⟶ destination

The arithmetic unit may be told which registers to use, for register addressing by simply applying the source field of the macroinstruction register to control lines A0 – A3 and the destination field to lines B0 – B3.

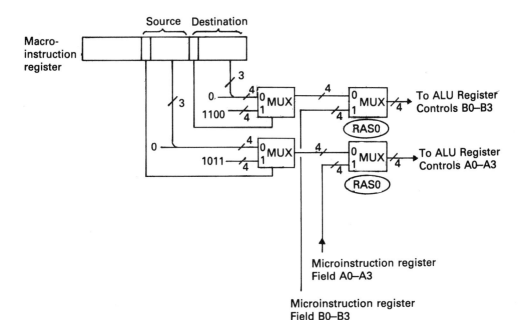

Figure 18.26: ALU Register Selection Logic

However, when memory resident operands are specified
addresses B (1011) and C (1100) respectively must be applied
to specify the temporary locations of these operands, this
can be done by the microinstruction register field or by
being switched to the appropriate code by the
source/destination fields. The mechanism for achieving this
is shown in Figure 18.26 where the additional control signal
RASO is shown. This serves to control whether the register
selection is carried out by the macroinstruction register
(RASO = 0) or by the register addressing fields of the
arithmetic unit control word (Figure 18.22).

The complete circuit diagram of the computer control unit is
composed of Figures 18.24, 18.25, 18.26 and is shown in
Figure 18.27.

The sequencer operation therefore is controlled by 18 bits in
the microinstruction register. These are shown in Figure
18.28.

The complete microinstruction will consist of the following
items:

(i)   Arithmetic unit control word (31 bits) Figure 18.22
(ii) CCU control word   (18 bits) Figure 18.28
(iii) Memory control (MEM)   (3 bits)
                     (R/$\overline{W}$)
                     (MAS)
(iv) Jump field   (12 bits)

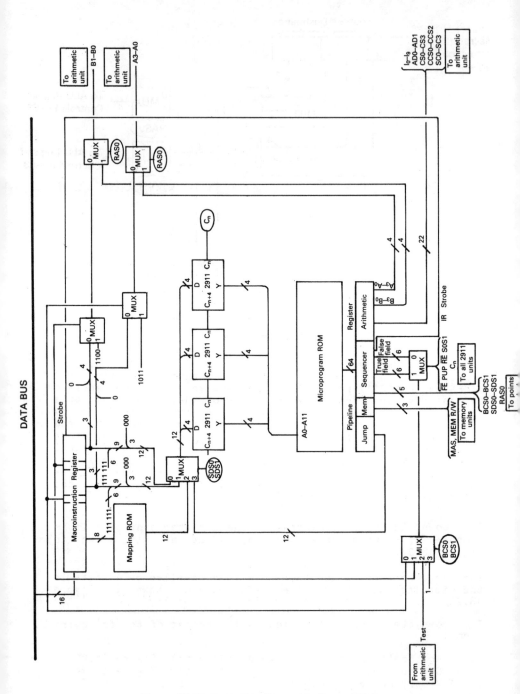

Figure 18.27: Complete Computer Control Unit

Register Address Select	Source Data Select	Branch Condition	Successful Test Control	Failed Test Control	
RAS0	SDS1 SDS0	BCS1 BCS0	$\overline{FE}$ PUP $\overline{RE}$ S1 S0 C_N	$\overline{FE}$ PUP $\overline{RE}$ S1 S0 C_N	
1 = Microinstruction 0 = Macroinstruction	See Table 18.15	See Table 18.14	See Table 18.9	See Table 18.9	1 = Strobe Macroinstruction Register

Figure 18.28: Sequencer Control Word

Thus the microinstruction width is 64 bits and will be arranged as shown in Figure 18.29.

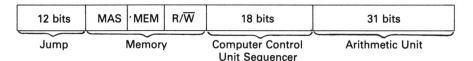

12 bits	MAS	·MEM	R/$\overline{W}$	18 bits	31 bits
Jump		Memory		Computer Control Unit Sequencer	Arithmetic Unit

Figure 18.29: Layout of Microinstuction

18.3.3 SOME EXAMPLE MICROPROGRAMS

To conclude this design study, a number of microinstructions and microprograms will be derived. Before going into the detail of this, however, it is worthwhile recalling that the operation of the computer has been designed so that the execution cycle of each macroinstruction is unaffected by the exact source of the operands. It will always operate on the basis that the source operand is available from port A and the destination from port B. Port A and B register addresses are obtained from the appropriate fields of the macroinstruction (RAS0 = 0). Furthermore, if memory is specified as the source or destination, private registers T1 and T2 will be assumed to have been pre-loaded with the specified source and destination operands respectively. The general procedure for executing a macroinstruction is shown in Figure 18.30. From this, it will be seen that the same general flowchart will suffice for all instructions, the differences occurring

    (i)   as a result of the micro-subroutines used to calculate the operand addresses

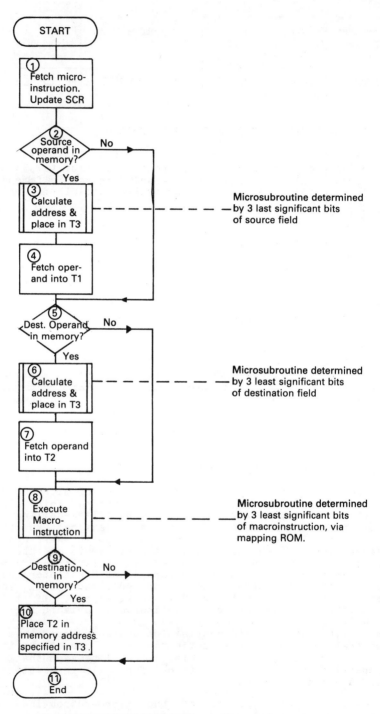

Figure 18.30: General Microprogram Flowchart

(ii) as a result of the micro-subroutine used to process the operand(s).

The first task, therefore is to determine the microinstructions which make up the flowchart in Figure 18.30. After this the structure of the specific addressing and execution micro-subroutines may be examined.

1) FETCH MACROINSTRUCTION, UPDATE SCR

The SCR is located in register A of the 2901. Two tasks must be carried out; first the current value must be placed on the address bus and the memory enabled to read. Secondly, the current value must be incremented and then replaced in register A.

Referring to Figure 18.13, it will be seen that both these functions can be achieved in one step using mode 2, provided that register A is output at both ports A and B.

Thus the specification for the microinstruction is

```
Register A field                 = 1010     (A)
Register B field                 = 1010     (A)
ALU Source                       = 011      (S=B R=0)
ALU Function                     = 000      (Add)
ALU Destination                  = 010      (Mode 2)
Increment Control                = 1        (Increment)
External ALU destination         = 01       (Address bus)
Condition Code Select            = XXX      (Don't care)
Status Register Control          = 1X0X     (Inhibit)
Shift Logic Control              = XXXX     (Don't care)
Macroinstruction Register
            Strobe               = 1        (Strobe)
Sequencer Failed Test Control    = XXXXXX   (Don't care)
Sequencer Pass Test Control      = 1X1001   (Step on)
Microprogram Branch Control      = 11       (Select pass conditions)
External Microprogram Address
            Select               = XX       (Don't care)
Register Select                  = 1        (From microinstruction)
Memory Control                   = 111      (Enable read, strobe
                                             memory address
                                             register)
Microprogram Jump Address        = XXXXXXXXXXX
                                            (Don't care)
```

This microinstruction is shown on line 1 of Figure 18.31 where it is assumed to be located at ROM address 100(HEX).

2) TEST FOR SOURCE OPERAND IN MEMORY

This microinstruction must cause a microprogram jump if the most significant bit of the source field in the macroinstruction register is 1, otherwise it must simply step on. The target address of the microprogram jump is the next test "diamond" in Figure 18.30. This address will be held in the jump field of the microinstruction.

437

The specification for the microinstruction is

```
Register A field              XXXX                                     ⎫
Register B field              XXXX                                     ⎪
ALU Source                    XXX                                      ⎪
ALU Function                  XXX                                      ⎪
ALU Destination               001        (Mode 1)        Effectively   ⎪
Increment Control             X                          "No           ⎪
External ALU Destination      00                           Operation   ⎪
Condition Code Select         XXX        (Don't care                   ⎬
Status Register Control       1X0X         (Inhibit)                   ⎪
Shift Logic Control           XXXX       (Don't care                   ⎪
Macroinstruction Register                                             ⎪
            Strobe            0          (Don't strobe)                ⎭
Sequencer Failed Test
            Control           1X1001     (Step on)
Sequencer Pass Test
            Control           1X1111     (Microprogram jump)
Microprogram Branch Control   00         (Select source memory
External Microprogram Address                            bit)
            Select            11         (Jump field)
Register Select               X          (Don't care)
Memory Control                00X        (No action)
Microprogram Jump Address     0001 0000 0100
                                         (Next decision in
                                          Figure 18.30 104(HEX))
```

This microinstruction is on line 2 of Figure 18.31.

3) CALCULATE SOURCE OPERAND ADDRESS

This function is carried out by a micro-subroutine which
reads the memory location pointed to by the SCR, updates the
SCR, and then calculates the actual operand address. There is
one subroutine for each addressing mode and they all place the
resulting operand address in T3. The three least significant
source address bits are used to determine which subroutine is
called. The specification for the microinstruction which
calls the appropriate micro-subroutine is:

```
Register A field                     XXXX                               ⎫
Register B field                     XXXX                               ⎪
ALU Source                           XXX                                ⎪
ALU Function                         XXX                                ⎪
ALU Destination                      001      (Mode 1)      Effectively ⎪
Increment Control                    X                      "No         ⎬
External ALU Destination             00                     Operation"  ⎪
Condition Code Select                XXX      (Don't care)              ⎪
Status Register Control              1X0X     (Inhibit)                 ⎪
Shift Logic Control                  XXXX     (Don't care)              ⎪
Macroinstruction Register                                              ⎪
            Strobe                   0        (Don't strobe)            ⎭
Sequencer Failed Test Control        XXXXXX   (Don't care)
Sequencer Pass Test Control          011111   (Micro-subroutine jump)
Microprogram Branch Control          11       (Select pass condition)
External Microprogram Address
            Select                   01       (Source field)
```

```
Register Select              X        (Don't care)
Memory Control               00X      (No action)
Microprogram Jump Address    XXXXXXXXXXXX
                                      (Don't care)
```

This microinstruction is on line 3 of Figure 18.31.

4) FETCH SOURCE OPERAND

This operand has its address located in T3 and the operand
itself is to be fetched into T1. Thus T3 must be given access
to the address bus and the data appearing on the data bus
must be routed via the D input of the arithmetic unit to
register T1. This can be achieved by selecting ALU mode 2 and
specifying T1 as the ALU destination (B address). The
arithmetic unit will obtain its R input from the data bus,
zero will be on the S input and addition will be specified.

The specification for the microinstruction is:

```
Register A field             1101     (Register T3)
Register B field             1011     (Register T1)
ALU Source                   111      (S=0 R=D)
ALU Function                 000      (Add)
ALU Destination              010      (Mode 2)
Increment Control            0        (Simple Add)
External ALU Destination     01       (Address Bus)
Condition Code Select        XXX      (Don't Care)
Status Register Control      1X0X     (Inhibit)
Shift Logic Control          XXXX     (Don't Care)
Macroinstruction Register
              Strobe         0        (Don't Strobe)
Sequencer Failed Test Field  XXXXXX   (Don't Care)
Sequencer Passed Test Field  1X1001   (Step On)
Microprogram Branch Control  11       (Select Pass Condition)
External Microprogram Address
              Select         XX       (Don't Care)
Register Select              1        (From microinstruction)
Memory Control               111      (Enable read, Strobe
                                      Memory Address
                                      Register)
Microprogram Jump Address XXXXXXXXXXXX
```

This microinstruction is shown on line 4 of Figure 18.31.

5) TEST FOR DESTINATION OPERAND IN MEMORY

This is identical to microinstruction 2 above except that

   (i)   The most significant bit of the DESTINATION field
          must be selected.

   (ii)   The target address of the jump will be at
          107(HEX).

Making these simple modifications the resulting
microinstruction is shown in line 5 of Figure 18.31.

6) CALCULATE DESTINATION OPERAND ADDRESS

This is identical to the microinstruction 3 above except that the DESTINATION field specifies the addressing mode. The resulting address is again left in T3.

Making these simple modifications, the resulting microinstruction is shown in line 6 of Figure 18.31.

7) FETCH DESTINATION OPERAND

This is identical to microinstruction 4 above except that the data obtained is to be put into register T2. The resulting microinstruction is shown in line 7 of Figure 18.31.

8) JUMP TO EXECUTION MICRO-SUBROUTINE

This is identical to the two other micro-subroutine jumps (lines 3 and 6 in Figure 18.31) except that the target address for the execution subroutine will be determined by the output of the mapping ROM. The resulting microinstruction is shown in line 8 of Figure 18.31.

9) TEST FOR DESTINATION IN MEMORY

This is virtually a repeat of the microinstruction on line 5 except that the destination of the conditional jump is microprogram ROM address 10A. This test is needed because, if memory were specified as the destination address, the execute micro-subroutine wouldl have placed the result in temporary register T2 and, in these circumstances, the result must be restored to memory. The microinstruction is shown in line 9 of Figure 18.31.

10) STORE RESULT IN MEMORY

Because the memory address of the destination is still retained in the memory address latches, there is no need to issue it again. However, the memory address latch strobe, MAS, must not be activated otherwise the latches will be updated with whatever information happens to be on the ALU output.

ALU mode 1 with S=0 and the R operand from port A will make the necessary data available at the output of the ALU provided that register T2 is made available at port A.

The specification for the microinstruction is

Register A field	1100	(T2)
Register B field	XXXX	(Don't Care)
ALU Source	100	(S=A R=0)
ALU Function	000	(Add)
ALU Destination	001	(Mode 1)

```
Increment Control                 0      (No Increment)
External ALU Destination         10      (Data Bus)
Condition Code Select           XXX      (Don't Care)
Status Register Control        1X0X      (Inhibit)
Shift Logic Control            XXXX      (Don't Care)
Macroinstruction Register
                 Strobe           0      (Don't Strobe)
Sequencer Failed Test Control XXXXXX     (Don't Care)
Sequencer Passed Test Control 1X1001     (Step On)
Microprogram Branch Control      11       (Select Pass)
External Microprogram Address
                 Select          XX      (Don't Care)
Register Select                   1      (From microinstruction)
Memory Control                  010      (Write, don't latch
                                          address bus)
Microprogram Jump Address XXXXXXXXXXXX (Don't Care)
```

This microinstruction is on line 10 of Figure 18.31.

11) RETURN TO FETCH

This is required on completion of the current microprogram so
that   the   next   macroinstruction   will   be   obtained.   This
requires   an   unconditional   jump   to   microprogram   address
100(HEX).   This   is   similar to a conditional jump except that
the test is forced to pass. Except for this difference and
the target address change, the microinstruction, which is
shown on line 11 of Figure 18.31, is the same as the
conditional jumps on lines 2, 5 and 9.

The above discussion shows how microinstructions may be
constructed and the way in which the operation of a
microprogrammed device is conditioned by the initial design
of the hardware. The microprogram in lines 1 to 11 of Figure
18.31 might well have been shorter if a less general approach
to operand addressing had been chosen.

It will also be clear that microinstructions can be very wide
and yet often the majority of the bits are "don't care"
conditions.   Considerable ingenuity in both hardware and
microprogramming is needed to make the microinstructions more
efficient. Needless to say, the whole process of bit-slice
design is one of iteration and slow refinement.

No   examples   of   execution   subroutines   or   addressing
subroutines have been derived since the main objective has
been to illustrate how microprogrammed hardware may be used
to implement a sequential machine. This has been achieved
with the example thus far and little useful purpose would be
served by extending it further. Interested readers might,
however, like to prove to themselves that lines 20, 21, 22 in
Figure 18.31 comprise a micro-subroutine which will use
absolute addressing to determine an operand address while
lines 30 and 31 comprise a micro-subroutine to add together
two operands.

Microinstruction coding form

Microinstruction bits

Line no	Microinstruction coding form	Microprogram ROM address (hexadecimal)
1	Fetch	1 0 0
2	Conditional jump	1 0 1
3	Microsubroutine jump	1 0 2
4	Fetch source operand	1 0 3
5	Conditional jump	1 0 4
6	Microsubroutine jump	1 0 5
7	Fetch destination operand	1 0 6
8	Microsubroutine jump	1 0 7
9	Conditional jump	1 0 8
10	Store result	1 0 9
11	Unconditional jump	1 0 A
20	See p 441	
21	See p 441	
22		
30	See p 441	
31		

Field columns (left to right across the microinstruction bits):

- A port select: A0, A1, A2, A3
- B port select: B0, B1, B2, B3
- Source operands: I0, I1, I2
- ALU function: I3, I4, I5
- ALU destination: I6, I7, I8
- Increment ALU: I9
- External ALU destination: AD0, AD1
- Condition code: CCS0, CCS1, CCS2
- Status reg. source/dest: CS0, CS1, CS2, CS3
- Shift logic control: SC0, SC1, SC2, SC3
- IR strobe: IR
- Sequencer control for fail test: CN, S0, S1, RE, PUP, FE
- Sequencer control for pass test: CN, S0, S1, RE, PUP, FE
- Micro program branch: BCS 0, BCS 1
- External micro-program address: SDS 0, SDS 1
- Register select: RAS 0
- Memory control: R/W, MEM, MAS
- Microprogram jump address: J0, J1, J2, J3, J4, J5, J6, J7, J8, J9, J10, J11

Figure 18.31: Example Microinstructions

18.4 Development of Microprogrammed Systems

It will be apparent from the foregoing discussions that the development of microprogrammed systems is quite a different enterprise compared with the development of more conventional microprocessor systems. At least three separate phases may be identified.

(i)   Development of microprogrammed hardware

(ii)   Design and development of the microprograms for the hardware

(iii) Design and development of the macroprograms.

Consider first the hardware. Compared to conventional microprocessor systems, the hardware is very fast; consequently all test equipment used will have to have a corresponding specification. The number of integrated circuits will be greater than that for conventional systems and a significant proportion of it will be of medium scale. From the foregoing it will be appreciated that oscilloscopes and general-purpose logic analysers (as opposed to microprocessor analysers) will be the main pieces of test equipment.

In finished systems the microprograms will reside in high-speed bipolar ROMs. As with conventional microprocessors, read-only memory is not at all satisfactory for product development and they should ideally be replaced by read-write memory of appropriate speed. The usual approach is to remove the ROMs and replace them with connections to a large array of high-speed read-write memory. This memory appears as ROM to the bit-slice system but its contents may be altered using a keyboard or similar device which is connected to it. This is the so-called writeable control store. As will have been noticed from the previous section, the construction of microinstructions is somewhat tedious. This task can be made easier by the use of computer-aided design tools. These permit the designer to specify the way in which the microinstruction is to be broken into fields and permit the SYMBOLIC specification of microinstructions and microprograms in a way which is reminiscent of assemblers. The optimum solution is to combine the writeable control store with a mini or microcomputer to form a full bit-slice development system capable of editing and assembling microprograms, printing listings etc. and emulating high-speed ROM.

A number of development systems are available to support bit-slice system development along the lines outlined above. Typical of these are the 'System-29' supplied by Advanced Micro Devices to support the AMD 2900 family of devices and the 'STEP-3' system supplied by Step Engineering. This latter development tool is not restricted to a single family of components and can be configured to cope with most bit-slice processors and microprogrammed logic development tasks.

These systems support a full range of development facilities and permit the user to generate his own microcode symbolically using an editor and a microassembler (AMDASM on the System-29 and TMA on the Step-3). The resulting microcode may be loaded either into a writeable control store or into a PROM and its execution traced in a manner very similar to that used with conventional microprocessors.

Finally, when it comes to constructing the macroprograms for the system, the designer is entirely on his own. Because he has created a unique piece of sequential machinery, he has no alternative but to write the necessary support software himself. Depending on the equipment in question, this may be a more or less burdensome task. If the designer has access to a table-driven assembler, he will be able to readily generate an assembler for his bit-slice computer by simply changing the table definitions. If this option is not available, it may be possible to use the macro facilities available with some minicomputer macroassemblers in order to produce the necessary object code.

Appendix A. The Architecture and Instruction Set of the 8085 Processor

The 8085 processor is a development of the Intel 8080 and retains full software compatability with the older device. Indeed programs written for the 8080 will run on the 8085 with no modifications; they do not even have to be reassembled. Two new instructions have been added to support the on-chip serial interface but these are the only instruction-set changes.

There have, however, been important changes at the hardware level. Several new interrupts have been made available and the clock circuitry has been moved onto the same chip as the processor.

In order to obtain these advances while retaining a 40-pin package for the device has meant that some pins have to be given dual functions. Specifically the 8 data bits share the same pins as the lower 8 address bits. This mulitplexing is controlled by a strobe signal and somewhat complicates the design of interfaces for the 8085 unless the special support chips designed for use with the 8085 are used.

A–1 The Programmer's Model of the 8085

Figure A-1 shows the general layout of the processor as perceived by the programmer. As will be noted, there are seven addressable 8-bit registers in the machine (referred to as registers A, B, C, D, E, H, L). The number of registers present makes the 8085 appear superior to the 6800 (as indeed it is in some respects); however, these seven registers are not all general-purpose accumulators. Registers B, C, D, E, H and L have limited capabilities (they are all identical in this respect) and only register A has full functionality as an accumulator.

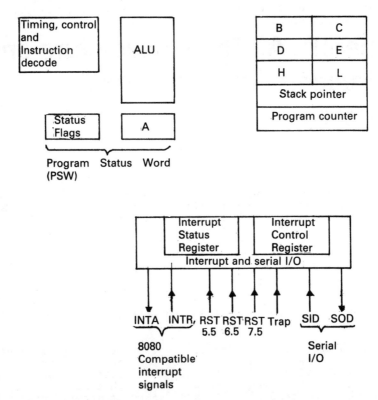

Figure A-1: Programmers model of 8085

In addition to functioning as separate 8-bit registers, the register pairs B-C, D-E, H-L may be used as 16-bit registers. Instructions which do this refer to the first-named register only.

The two other 16-bit registers are only used for the functions implied by their names and are never used for general purposes or as 8-bit registers.

Associated with the ALU is a flags register which is used to record the results of certain arithmetic and logical operations. This register, which has only five active bits, is set out in Figure A-2.

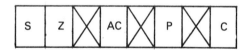

Figure A-2: 8085 Status Flags

S: Sign bit, set to 1 if the previous operations resulted in a 2s complement negative answer.

Z: Set to 1 if the previous operations produced a zero answer.

AC: Auxiliary carry used by the "decimal adjust" instruction to correct binary addition to BCD addition.

P: Indicates the parity of the result of the previous operations (1 = Even, 0 = Odd).

C: Set to 1 if the previous operations caused a carry out of the most significant bit of the accumulator. Also set during rotate instructions.

An obvious, and frequently inconvenient, omission from the above status flags is an overflow flag. As a result, the programmer must check every 2s complement operation with a suitable subroutine to determine whether the result is valid.

Although not obvious from the above discussion, it is important to note that the H-L register pair has an implied function in many 8085 instructions. It is frequently used to hold the address of a memory-resident operand and is therefore often referred to as the Data Pointer. The B-C and D-E register pairs have a very limited role as data pointers in respect of accumulator operations.

A–2 Addressing Methods in the 8085

The 8085 makes use of the folloiwing addressing methods:

    Implied addresssing
    Indirect addressing
    Absolute addressing
    Immediate addressing

The absence of indexed and relative addressing is particularly notable.

447

A-2.1 IMPLIED ADDRESSING

Because the 8085 has so many registers, there is a considerable range of implied addressing instructions which serve to move data from one register to another. Also this method is used for arithmetic and logical operations between the accumulator and the other registers.

Implied address instructions occupy one byte.

A-2.2 INDIRECT ADDRESSING

This is widely used for accessing operands held in memory. The pointer itself, however, never resides in memory but instead is placed in the H-L register pair. This data pointer can be manipulated (increment and decrement) and so this can be thought of, alternatively, as a very restricted form of indexed addressing, but without the freedom to arbitrarily specify a base address.

The B-C and D-E register pairs act as indirect address pointers only in respect of data movement to the accumulator (LDAX B, LDAX D) and from the accumulator (STAX B, STAX D).

Indirect address instructions occupy one byte.

A-2.3 ABSOLUTE ADDRESSING

This is termed direct addressing in all 8085 literature. The mode is only used in two circumstances. It is used to move 8-bit data from a specified location into the accumulator (LDA) or in the reverse direction (STA); and also to move 16-bit data from the specified memory location, and next sequential memory location, into the H-L data pointer (LHLD) or in the reverse direction (SHLD). Apart from these four data movement instructions, absolute addressing is used exclusively for control transfer instructions. These are the program 'JUMP' (and jump conditionally) and subroutine 'CALL' (and call conditionally) instructions. All absolute address instructions occupy three bytes, one for the operation code and two for the 16-bit address.

A-2.4 IMMEDIATE ADDRESSING

Immediate address instructions feature prominently in the data movement and arithmetic/logical instructions. 8-bit immediate data may be moved to any register or to memory (using the data pointer to specify the memory location) and may figure in any single-precision arithmetic, logic or comparison operation. Additionally 16-bit immediate data may be moved to any appropriate 16-bit register pair.

Immediate instructions occupy two bytes, one for the operation code and one for the data when 8-bit data is featured. Otherwise three bytes are required.

A–3 The Instruction Set of the 8085

All 8085 instructions are accommodated in one to three bytes
and execute (with a 320ns clock period) in 1.3us to 5.8us.

A-3.1 DATA MOVEMENT INSTRUCTIONS

Data may be moved around the 8085 using all of the available
addressing methods. The most general instruction in this
class is the MOV instruction which has the form

        MOV r1, r2

where r1 and r2 can specify any of the 8-bit registers A, B,
C, D, E, H, L. Data is moved from r2 to r1. The source and
destination registers may be identical, thus forming a "no-
operation".

A memory location may be involved in the data movement by
using the form

        MOV M,r (from register to memory)

    or

        MOV r,M (from memory to register)

In both cases the addressing method is indirect and the data
pointer (H-L) is used to specify the memory location.

Immediate data may be moved to a register or to memory using
the following special forms of the move instruction:

        MVI r
        MVI M

where again the memory location involved is specified by the
data pointer.

Certain additional instructions are available when the
accumulator is the source or destination of data. These have
previously been mentioned under the heading of absolute and
indirect addressing and are summarised below:

LDA \<address>	move data to accumulator from memory	Using absolute
STA \<address>	move data to memory from accumulator	addressing

                                                 Data Pointer

LDAX B	move data from memory to accumulator	B - C
LDAX D	using indirect addressing	D - E

```
                                                  Data Pointer
STAX B          move data from accumulator        B - C
                to memory

STAX D          using indirect addressing         D - E
```

16-bit data may be moved to the H-L register pair from memory using absolute addressing by the previously mentioned instruction

> LHLD <address>

The reverse is accomplished using

> SHLD <address>

16-bit immediate data may be moved to the stack pointer or any other 16-bit register using

```
                   ⎡ SP ⎤
        LXI        ⎢ B  ⎥
                   ⎢ D  ⎥
                   ⎣ H  ⎦
```

The one-of-a-kind implied addressing instruction 'XCHG' exchanges the contents of the D-E register pair with the contents of the H-L pair.

No status flags are changed by data movement instructions.

A-3.2 LOGICAL AND ARITHMETIC INSTRUCTIONS

With one exception, the arithmetic and logical instructions of the 8085 all make use of the accumulator as the source of one operand and as the destination for the result. The classes of operation provided are

> Add
> Add with carry
> Subtract
> Subtract with borrow
> Compare
> And
> Or
> Exclusive-Or

In all cases, the second source operand may be found

(i)   in a register (including the accumulator itself)

(ii)   as immediate data, following the operation code

(iii)   in the memory location pointed to by the data pointer H-L.

The various status flags are set, according to the result of the operation. The 'compare' is a special case of subtract:

the operation is carried out and the flags set, but the result is not placed in the accumulator. It is used for checking the value of operands.

The add-with-carry and subtract-with-borrow instructions are included, as outlined in 4.7, to facilitate multi-precision arithmetic. In fact, one double-precision instruction is included in the processor itself. This is called:

$$DAD \quad \begin{bmatrix} B \\ D \\ H \\ SP \end{bmatrix}$$

and it adds the contents of the specified register pair to the contents of the H-L register.

A number of other instructions exist as adjuncts to the arithmetic and logic operations. These are:

CMA: which forms the logical complement of the accumulator.

DAA: decimal adjust - corrects result of BCD addition as outlined in 4.9.

Manipulation of the carry flag is also possible using the two instructions

STC: set carry

CMC: complement carry

No "clear carry" instruction is available but the instruction 'OR' accumulator with itself ORA A is a 1-byte instruction which achieves the same without disturbing the accumulator.

A-3.3 REGISTER MANIPULATION

The contents of any of the 8-bit registers A,B,C,D,E,H,L may be incremented or decremented by 1-byte instructions which set the status flags appropriately. Likewise the 16-bit registers B,D,H,SP may be incremented or decremented by 1-byte instructions which DO NOT affect the flags.

Further operations are possible on the accumulator only. This may be rotated left or right. The bit which leaves one end of the accumulator is put back into both the other end and the carry. Figure A-3 shows the rotate right case.

A similar "rotate (left or right) through carry" exists. This includes the carry bit as a ninth bit in the accumulator as shown in Figure A-4.

The 8085 is, unfortunately, completely devoid of arithmetic shifts (in which the sign bit is replicated) or long shifts involving the 16-bit register pairs.

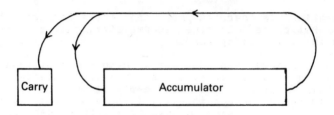

Figure A-3: Right Rotate

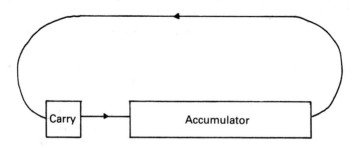

Figure A-4: Right Rotate Through Carry

A-3.4 MEMORY MANIPULATION

One byte instructions are available to increment and
decrement the memory location indicated by the data pointer,
setting the flags appropriately. This is useful for
monitoring loop counters, etc.

A-3.5 STACK OPERATIONS

The stack is an important feature of the 8085 architecture
since it is used for all subroutine and interrupt operations.

Items are placed on the stack with a 'PUSH' operation and
retrieved with a 'POP'. The stack pointer determines the
location of the stack in memory and always points to the last
item on the stack. The stack pointer is decremented during a
push and incremented during a pop so the stack grows
downwards in memory and should therefore be initialised
somewhere near the top of the existing read-write memory area
(using the LXI SP instruction).

An interesting feature of the stack operations is the fact
that only 16-bit quantities may be pushed onto the stack.

(They are, of course, stored as 2 bytes in the 8-bit wide memory). Registers B-C, D-E and H-L may be stacked in this way. For stack purposes the accumulator and the flag byte are associated as a single 16-bit processor status word (PSW).

The top item on the stack may be exchanged with the contents of the H-L register pair, and also the stack pointer may be loaded from the H-L pair. The latter of these two instructions is a means of swapping data spaces for stack-oriented programs (XCHG does the same for register-oriented programs).

A-3.6 PROGRAM CONTROL AND SUBROUTINE LINKAGE

Control may be transferred from one part of a program to another by means of a JUMP instruction, the target address of the jump being specified in the second and third bytes of the instruction.

Likewise a subroutine may be accessed by a CALL instruction. This transfers control to the first instruction in the subroutine (specified by bytes two and three of the call) and, at the same time, maintains a record of the address of the instruction immediately following the call (the return address). This return address is pushed onto the stack.

Return from a subroutine is achieved by popping the return address from the stack into the program counter. Care must be exercised by the programmer to ensure that any items placed on the stack by the subroutine are removed before the return is executed, otherwise the correct address will not be popped from the stack.

All of the above instructions: jump, call and return, may be made conditional upon:-

    Carry Set
    Carry Reset
    Zero Flag Set
    Zero Flag Reset
    Sign Flag Set
    Sign Flag Reset
    Parity Odd
    Parity Even

Program control may also be transferred by either of the following one-byte instructions

    PCHL
    RST   n   (n = 0.......7)

PCHL causes a jump to the address pre-loaded into the H-L register pair.

RST n behaves like a subroutine call and causes the return address to be put on the stack before branching to the address 8*n. In fact RST may be better thought of as a

software-induced interrupt since its operation is integrated
into the operation of the 8085 RST 5.5, RST 6.5 and RST 7.5
interrupt pins (see below). The operation of RST n proceeds
irrespective of whether interrupts are enabled or disabled.

A-3.7 INTERRUPTS, SERIAL I/O AND MACHINE CONTROL

The 8085 is distinguished, at the software level, from the
8080 by the presence of four additional interrupt levels and
an on-chip serial I/O capability. The machine control and
8080-compatible instructions will be examined first.

A-3.8 MACHINE CONTROL AND 8080 COMPATIBLE INTERRUPTS

The 8085 has a single 'NOP' instruction which may be used to
provide a short (1.3us) delay or to leave blank spaces in a
program during development.

The machine may be halted by the use of the HLT instruction.
Once this is obeyed, all of the Tri-State bus signals (see
later) are floated, and the machine enters an 'idle' state.
In a halt state the machine is not, in fact, stopped and it
continues to examine all of its interrupt lines. The
processor exits from the halt state when any enabled
interrupt occurs. In addition a hardware reset operation (see
later) will also cause an exit from the Halt. (In the 8085
there exists a completely non-maskable interrupt pin called
TRAP thus it is always possible to leave the Halt. This is
not true of the 8080 which can, therefore, go into indefinite
suspension.)

The interrupt system may be turned on and off by using the
enable interrupts (EI) and disable interrupts (DI)
instructions. This is the only way of controlling interrupts
on the INTR pin.

The 8080 has only one interrupt line and this gains access to
the processor via the INTR pin. This facility is included on
the 8085 and operates in the same way as the 8080.

If the INTR pin is at logic '1', an interrupt acknowledge
cycle is initiated at the end of the current instruction
provided that interrupts are enabled. The program counter is
not incremented. An interrupt acknowledge signal is issued
and this causes the interrupting device to place a valid
instruction code onto the data bus, typically a 'CALL' or a
'RST n'.

If an 'RST n' is placed on the bus, the processor saves the
current program counter on the stack and executes the
instructions residing at address 8*n. If a call is placed on
the bus, two further read cycles are carried out during which
time it is assumed that the interrupting device will place
the call address on the data bus. The previous program
counter contents is then saved on the stack and the
instructions residing at the address specified by the
interrupting device are obeyed.

As will be appreciated from the above discussion, the logic in the external device is fairly complex.

The occurrence of an 'INTR' interrupt turns the interrupt system off until an 'EI' instruction is obeyed.

A-3.9 8085-ONLY INTERRUPTS

The 8085 is equipped with four more interrupt lines than the 8080 and three of these (RST 7.5, 6.5, 5.5) can be individually switched on and off (masked). These interrupts are much easier to use than 'INTR' since, once the interrupt is recognised, control is automatically passed to a specified memory address and the previous value of the program counter saved on the stack. The table below shows to which address control is transferred by these interrupts, and also by the RST n instructions.

	Interrupts	Hexadecimal Address
Decreasing Priority	TRAP	24
	RST 5.5	2C
	RST 6.5	34
	RST 7.5	3C

RST n	Hexadecimal Address
n=0	00
1	08
2	10
3	18
4	20
5	28
6	30
7	38

Clearly there are not many bytes available for each service routine (only 4 between 2C and 30) and so, unless the service routine can be kept very short, an unconditional jump to the service routine proper is usually placed at the vector addresses specified above.

With the exception of 'TRAP', the recognition of an interrupt causes an automatic DI instruction to be executed by the hardware.

With the exception of RST 7.5, the interrupts are recognised as logic '1' levels. RST 7.5 is recognised on a 0 —→1 transition and sets an internal latch.

There is a clear order of priorities to the interrupts and, provided that the interrupt system has been re-enabled, a high priority interrupt can break into the service routine of a low priority one. 'INTR' interrupts are the lowest of all priorities while TRAP is the highest and does not require the interrupt system to be enabled.

The current status of the interrupt system can be determined by executing a RIM instruction. This has the effect of reading the interrupt status register into the accumulator. The layout of the bits read is shown in Figure A-5.

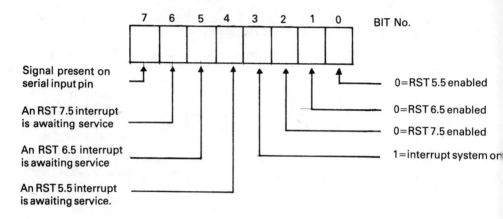

Fig. A–5: Layout of Accumulator After A RIM Instruction

The overall interrupt on-off is, of course, controlled by the EI/DI instructions. However, selective enabling of the RST interrupts is controlled by writing to the interrupt control register. This is achieved by setting the appropriate bits in the accumulator and then executing the SIM instruction. This is also used to output data to the serial output pin. Because one might wish to write serial output data without changing the interrupt mask and vice-versa, two bits are designated as access bits to control the operation of SIM. The layout of the accumulator prior to SIM is shown in Figure A-6.

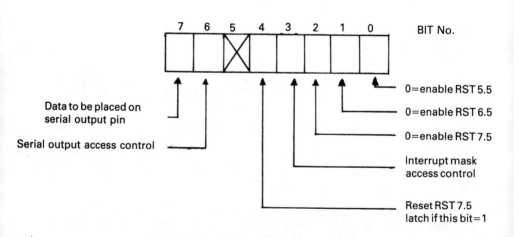

Fig. A–6: Accumulator Prior to SIM

456

Access to the serial output and interrupt masks are controlled by bits 3 and 6 as shown in the table below

Serial data access control (bit 6)	Interrupt access control (bit 3)	Action by SIM
0	0	No action
0	1	Change interrupt mask only
1	0	Change serial data only
1	1	Change both interrupt mask and serial data

The use of bits 0→2 is straightforward, but bit 4 requires a little explanation. The RST 7.5 latch is automatically reset when the interrupt is recognised. However, contact bounce might cause it to be set again during the service routine. This would cause a spurious secondary interrupt when the current service is finished. By placing a '1' at bit 4 while accessing the interrupt mask with SIM will avoid this by resetting the latch.

A-3.10 SERIAL I/O

The RIM and SIM instructions outlined above provide the basis for a very simple software controlled serial I/O channel. Provided that the necessary timing can be achieved - perhaps with a free running oscillator connected to an interrupt pin, or by a software delay loop - the state of the serial input channel can be sampled at the bit times by using RIM and likewise the appropriate output can be sent to the serial output channel using SIM.

Clearly the serial-to-parallel and parallel-to-serial conversion will have to be undertaken by software.

A-3.11 INPUT-OUTPUT INSTRUCTIONS

The 8085 utilises an integrated I/O bus approach as explained in Chapter 7. The I/O function is not, however, memory mapped. Instead the peripherals occupy a separate I/O address space having 256 addresses, or ports. The differentiation between memory and I/O accesses is achieved by the control line IO/M̄. To output data to a peripheral, the data is first loaded into the accumulator and then the following instruction is executed

OUT <Port No.>

likewise, executing the instruction

        IN <Port No.>

will read data from the specified peripheral port into the accumulator.

In conclusion, it is worth pointing out that the 8085 does not have any bit manipulating instructions. These would be very useful in certain applications.

A-4   THE BUS STRUCTURE OF THE 8085

Probably the most important single property of the 8085 bus structure is that the 8-bit data bus shares its pins with the lower 8 address lines. In this way, only sixteen pins are needed for the address and data lines thus freeing many pins for extra functions.

In order to make use of this multiplexed bus, the low-order 8-bits of address must be latched by a device such as the 8212, or special 8085-bus compatible devices must be used.

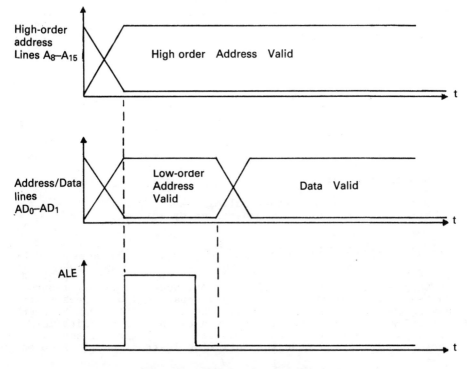

Figure A-7: 8085 Bus Organisation

During the early part of a bus cycle, the 16 address/data lines contain only address information and ALE is at logic '1'. Once the address has become stable, ALE drops to logic '0' and the low order 8 address lines become data lines and carry data into or out of the processor during the remainder of the bus cycle. The falling edge of ALE is used to latch the low order address signals (Figure A-7).

A read operation is indicated by the $\overline{RD}$ line going to logic '0'; likewise a logic '0' on the $\overline{WR}$ line indicates a write operation. The 8085 bus structure separates the memory and I/O address spaces and the particular space being referenced in any given transaction is indicated by the state of the IO/$\overline{M}$ line (logic '1' = I/O, logic '0' = memory). The generation of a 'VALID' signal as discussed in Chapter 7 is achieved by combining these signals as shown in Figure A-8.

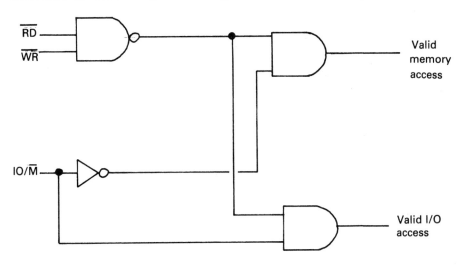

Figure A-8: Generation of "Valid" Signals

One drawback of the $\overline{RD}$ and $\overline{WR}$ signals is that they go low very late in the bus cycle, thus imposing stringent requirements on memory access times.

The 8085 bus provides encoded status information about its activities much earlier in the bus cycle via a pair of status lines S0 and S1. These become valid at much the same time as the address and IO/$\overline{M}$ signals and are encoded as shown below

S1	S0	OPERATION
0	0	Halted
0	1	Memory or I/O read
1	0	Memory or I/O write
1	1	Instruction Fetch (read)

459

The 8085 has the facility to accommodate slow memories. Within the bus structure is a READY line; if this is taken to logic '0', the current bus cycle is extended by the insertion of one or more "wait" states. The address, data, S0, S1, $\overline{RD}$, $\overline{WR}$ and IO/$\overline{M}$ lines and all other outputs are maintained unchanged. When the peripheral has had sufficient time, it takes the READY line back to logic '1' and the operation continues.

There is provision for other devices to become masters of the bus, for example DMA controllers. This is achieved via the HOLD and HLDA (hold acknowledge) lines of the bus. A hold operation is requested by taking the HOLD line to logic '1'. On completion of the current instruction cycle, the 8085 relinquishes control of the bus by floating (tri-stating) the address, data $\overline{RD}$, $\overline{WR}$ and IO/$\overline{M}$ lines. The 8085 acknowledges that it will relinquish the bus by taking HLDA to logic '1', and this signal is used by the new bus master to initiate its operations. The hold state lasts for as long as the hold line is kept at logic '1'.

HOLD is treated as a very high priority interrupt and will take over from any service routine or from a HALT instruction. Control is returned at the end of the Hold State.

There are five interrupt lines in the 8085 bus structure and these have been fully dealt with in the previous section (instruction set). There is also an interrupt acknowledge line $\overline{INTA}$ which maintains compatibility with the 8080 and which is used by devices which interrupt via the INTR line as an indication that they should force an instruction code onto the data bus.

The final two lines of the bus are the clock output line (CLK) and the RESET OUT line. The clock line carries the clock waveform generated by the 8085 to the rest of the system while the reset out line indicates that the 8085 has received a hardware reset. This signal is used to initialise all other devices in the system.

The remainaing seven pins of the 8085 do not connect to the bus but are used for its own purposes. Two supply the +5 volt power to the processor. Two are used for the connection of a crystal to the on-chip oscillator circuit. As an alternative, these latter two pins may be used for a low precision R-C oscillator circuit or may be driven by some external oscillator. The system clock frequency is one half of the frequency input at these pins. Two further pins are used for the rudimentary serial I/O capability (SID, SOD).

The final pin is used to initiate a system reset. When $\overline{RESET}$ $\overline{IN}$ is taken to logic '0' the program counter is cleared and the processor is held in this reset state until the input is taken back to logic '1'.

While $\overline{RESET\ IN}$ is at '0', RESET OUT is at logic '1'. RESET IN is usually activated by a reset switch or when power is applied to the processor via a circuit like that shown in

Figure A-9. From a program execution point of view, the action of $\overline{\text{RESET IN}}$ is like RST 0 except that the old program counter is not stacked. The program which commences at location 0000 is normally the power-on initialisation for the system, the so called "cold start".

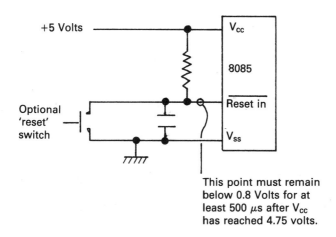

Figure A-9: Reset Circuitry

Appendix B. Support Devices for the 8080 and 8085 Processors

It will be recalled from Appendix A that the 8085 processor makes use of a multiplexed bus whereas the 8080 processor does not multiplex its bus. It is natural, therefore, that devices originally designed to operate in conjunction with the 8080 processor cannot be used directly with the 8085.

There exists therefore a range of peripherals designed explicitly for use with the 8085. These devices include logic on-chip to demultiplex the necessary information from the bus. Where it is required to use devices designed originally for the 8080 bus structure, the 8085 bus must be demultiplexed to provide separate address and data lines. In this Appendix, multiplexed-bus support chips will be discussed first, followed by those designed for the non-multiplexed bus.

B–1 Multiplexed – Bus Support Devices

Four devices will be discussed in this Section:

      (i)   the 8185 read/write memory

      (ii)   the 8355 ROM with I/O

      (iii)   the 8755 EPROM with I/O

      (iv)   the 8155 read/write memory with I/O and timer

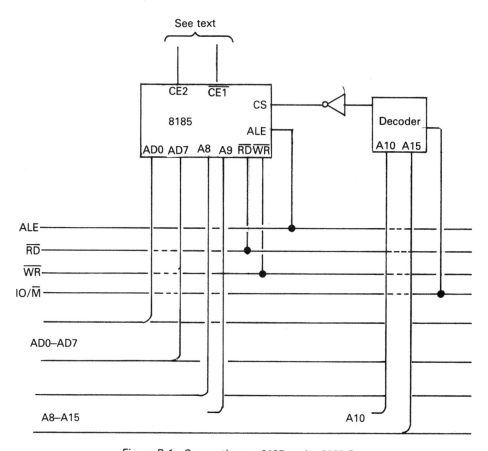

Figure B-1: Connecting an 8185 to the 8085 Bus

It will be appreciated from the above list that there is a high degree of integration in most of these devices and many small 8085 systems will consist of only three or four integrated circuits.

B-1.1 THE 8185 READ/WRITE MEMORY

This is a simple read/write memory circuit with no frills. Its capacity is 1K 8-bit words and it is designed for direct connection to the 8085 multiplexed bus (see Figure B-1).

It should be noted that, in small systems, the decoder could probably be removed if CS, CE1 and CE2 were used skilfully in a partial decoding scheme. In this connection, however, it should be noted that the state of CE1 and CE2 are latched by the falling edge of ALE and must, therefore, be correctly set up early on in the bus cycle (thus a high-speed decoder is needed). These signals also have a secondary function. Not only do they select the 8185 but they also serve to take it

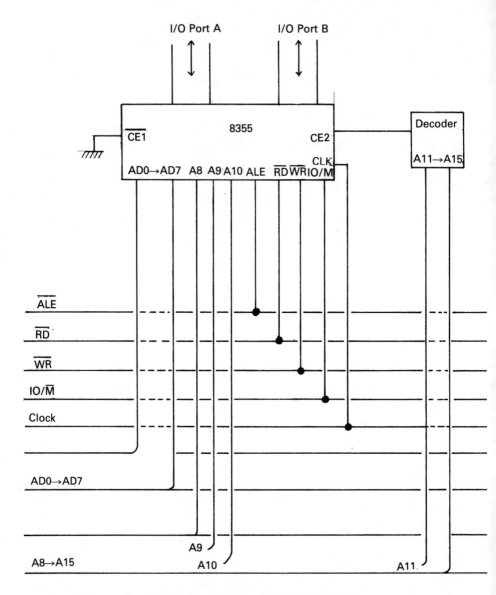

Figure B–2: Connection an 8355 to the 8085 Bus

out of its low power standby mode. If power consumption is important they should be used to ensure that the device is only powered up when needed and not connected permanently to appropriate logic levels.

If $\overline{CE1}$ is taken to the IO/$\overline{M}$ line while CE2 is permanently wired to logic '1', this will ensure that the memory is only powered up during memory access cycles.

B-1.2 THE 8355 ROM WITH I/O

This is a combined memory and I/O device on the same chip it combines two 8-bit parallel I/O ports with 2K x 8-bit words of mask-programmed ROM. The ROM section is accessed when the IO/$\overline{M}$ line is low during a read cycle while the I/O section is accessed during either a read or a write with the IO/$\overline{M}$ line held at logic one. Thus the memory and the I/O occupy separate address spaces, the I/O being accessed by IN and OUT instructions and the memory by all other instructions which transmit data to, or receive data from, the bus.

The circuit is equipped with two enable inputs $\overline{CE1}$ and CE2 both of which are latched by the falling edge of the ALE signal early in the bus cycle. Likewise IO/$\overline{M}$ is latched by ALE. Since this event occurs only about 100 ns into the bus cycle it implies that high speed decoders must be used for addressing. Figure B-2 shows the general circuit arrangement.

Very little needs to be said about the memory itself. It simply appears as 2048 locations beginning at address

$$nnnnn\ 000\ 0000\ 0000$$

where nnnnn is the combination of '1's and '0's selected on address lines A11-A15 by the decoder.

The I/O section appears as four consecutive port addresses commencing at a base address determined by the decoder (Figure B-3). This base address is not numerically identical to that for the memory section and the relationship will be explained a little later.

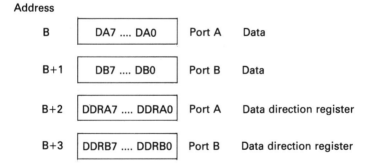

Figure B-3: Internal Registers of the 8355

The lines of each port may be selectively programmed as inputs by writing a '0' to the appropriate bit position in the corresponding data direction register. Likewise a '1' configures the line as an output. Thus writing 1110 0000 out to DDRA (using the instruction OUT B+3) will configure lines DA7, DA6 and DA5 as outputs and the remainder as inputs.

Note that data written to output pins is read back in when the relevant port is read. Also data may be written to a port which is configured as an input. This data will appear at the output pins if the relevant port is subsequently re-configured as an output. The reset function configures all I/O ports as inputs.

The derivation of the base address, B, is important. During I/O instructions (IN n, OUT n, where n = port number) the 8 bits representing the port address are output on the high order address lines (A8-A15) throughout the operation and also on the low order address lines until they are latched by ALE. Thus the address seen by the decoder is

Address lines	A15	A14	A13	A12	A11	A10	A9	A8	A7	A6	A5	A4	A3	A2	A1	A0
Data on lines	P7	P6	P5	P4	P3	P2	P1	P0	P7	P6	P5	P4	P3	P2	P1	P0

                 monitored by the decoder   latched and used for port selection

P7 .... P0 = 8-bit port code

Clearly the base address, B, is given by the five most significant bits of the base address of the ROM memory section followed by three zeros. Hence a memory configured to have addresses in the range 2000 ——→27FF will have I/O ports at port addresses 20 ——→ 23 (i.e. B=20).

B-1.3 THE 8755A EPROM WITH I/O

This device is an EPROM version of the 8355A and is, therefore, functionally equivalent. The only differences are that pin one of the device serves both as CE and also as a programming control, and pin 5 instead of being connected, has to receive a +5 volt supply during normal operation and +25 volts during programming. This virtual pin compatibility makes it very easy to use 8755A during product development and to use 8355A for production.

The programming characteristics will not be described here except to remark that they are similar to the 2716 component. The contents of the memory may be erased by exposure to ultra-violet light.

B-1.4 THE 8155 READ/WRITE MEMORY WITH I/O AND TIMER

This part contains 256 x 8-bit words of read/write memory plus three I/O ports. Two of these ports are 8-bits wide while the third (port C) is only 6 bits wide. Depending on the mode in which ports A and B are used, these bits may be allocated in groups of three, for handshaking control of I/O via the 8-bit ports.

466

In addition to these facilities, a 14-bit down-counter is also included. This may be pre-loaded with any count value under program control and may then operate in one of four counting modes.

The 8155 has seven registers within it which are accessed by reference to one of six different addresses as shown in Figure B-4.

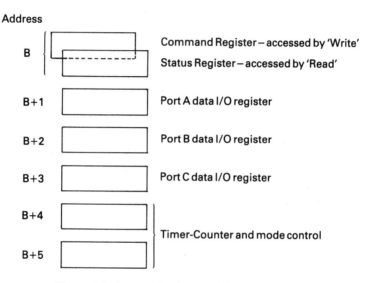

Figure B-4: Internal Registers of the 8155

The layout of the command register is as shown in Figure B-5. It will be seen that each of ports A and B can only be configured as inputs or outputs as a whole; this is achieved by bits 0 and 1 respectively.

The next two bits control how port C will be used, and in so doing also affect the way in which ports A and B are used.

It will be seen from Figure B-5 that port C may simply be configured as an input or output. Alternatively, groups of three port C lines may be allocated to the control of data flow through the other ports. In mode 10 only lines C0 —➤ C2 are used in this way, the remaining three being used as simple output lines. In mode 11 all lines are used for port control. In this case:

(C3)   (C0)
(C4) perform the same function for port B as (C1) do for A
(C5)   (C2)

The discussion will therefore be limited to lines C0 —➤ C2.

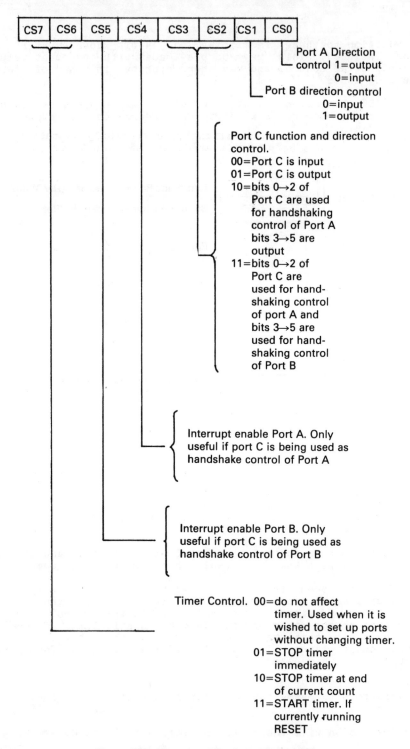

Figure B–5: Command Register of the 8155

CO is configured as an output signal in modes 10 and 11. It functions as an interrupt signal and is normally connected to one of the processor interruput lines. The operation of this line may be enabled/disabled by use of the interrupt enable for port A (bit CS4).

C1 is configured as an output called "buffer full" and C2 is configured as an input and designated as a strobe control. These two lines operate slightly differently depending on whether port A has been designated as an input or as an output.

IN INPUT MODE

The peripheral assembles the data and makes it available to port A. The strobe line (C2) is then taken low which latches the data into the buffer and raises the buffer full (C1) line to indicate to the peripheral that the transfer is in hand. The peripheral then releases the strobe and this causes the interrupt line to assert itself (if enabled). In due course the processor services the interrupt and reads the data from port A. This clears "buffer full" and indicates to the peripheral that it may strobe in new data.

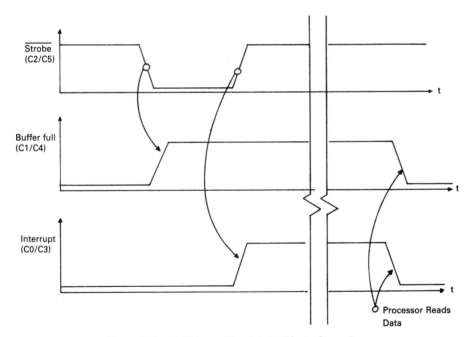

Figure B-6: 8155 Input Handshake Mode Operation

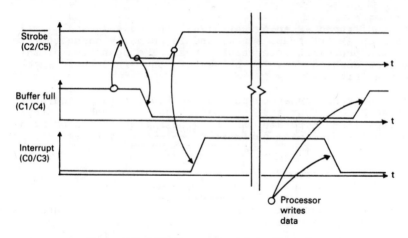

Figure B-7: 8155 Output Handshake Mode Operation

IN OUTPUT MODE

The peripheral monitors "buffer full" (C1) and when it is high, indicating that data is available, the peripheral accepts this data and takes "strobe" (C2) low to indicate this fact. This causes the buffer full signal to go low indicating that the data has been read. The peripheral then lets the strobe return high thus causing the interrupt line (C0) to assert itself, if enabled. The processor responds to this interrupt by writing fresh data to port A and, as a consequence, the buffer full line is taken high again indicating that fresh data is available (Figure B-7).

From the above discussion, it should be clear that each peripheral uses eight data lines plus two control lines. The third control line of each group is entirely internal to the processor system (Figure B-8).

The status register is read by reading the port address occupied by the command register. The layout of the status register is rather straightforward and simply reflects the status of the various control lines associated with ports A and B, namely interrupt enable, interrupt request (which is set when an interrupt is required even though the interrupt enable may be cleared hence inhibiting interrupts) which serves as a port status flag, and buffer full. Bit 6 of the register is a service request flag indicating that the timer has timed out (Figure B-9).

As shown in Figure B-4, the timer section is controlled by the contents of port addresses B+4 and B+5. The two most significant bits of port B+4 are used to specify the count mode to be used while the remaining six bits are concatenated with the 8 bits in port B+5 to form a 14-bit initial count value. The timer is started or stopped by writing to the

470

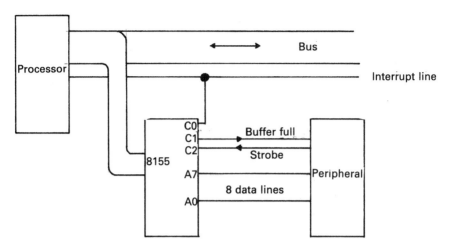

Figure B-8: Connection of an 8155 to a Peripheral

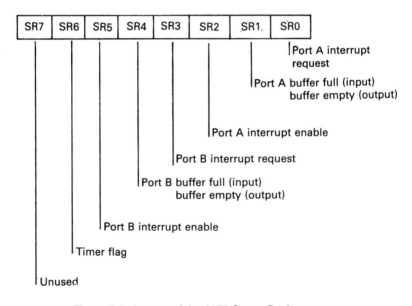

Figure B-9: Layout of the 8155 Status Register

command register as previously detailed. The count is decremented every time there is a $0 \longrightarrow 1$ transition on the timer input pin of the 8155. If a constant frequency source is used for this, the device is being used in timer mode. However, it may equally well be used as an event counter by connecting the output of an event detector to the timer-input pin. There is also a 'TIMER OUT' pin which changes level at various points in the count cycle depending on the mode of operation of the counter.

It may readily be used to stimulate some external event (such as an analogue-digital conversion), be connected to the processor interrupt line so that interrupts are generated at regular intervals, or be used to generate precise waveforms for external use. Figure B-10 shows the layout of the timer control words.

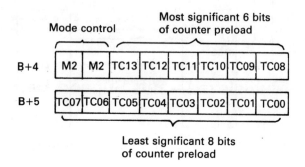

Figure B-10: Layout of Timer Control Registers

The four modes of operation of the timer are quite straightforward.

M2   M1

0   0   The timer output is logic one for the first half of the count and is logic zero for the remainder. The output is reset to logic one on termination of the count.

0   1   As for mode 00 except, that the counter is reloaded and restarted after termination. Thus a square wave is generated at "Timer Out".

1   0   The timer output is a logic one throughout the count except for a single count period immediately prior to termination. When it is taken low. The output is reset to logic one on termination.

1   1   As for mode 10 except that the counter is reloaded and restarted after termination, thus providing regular short pulses at "Timer Out".

B-1.5 COMPLETE SYSTEMS

From the above device descriptions, it will be apparent that very complete systems may be constructed by using only multiplexed-bus peripherals. Timing, read/write memory, ROM,

472

EPROM and parallel I/O are all well supported. No serial I/O support is provided but it will be recalled that the 8085 has a pair of serial I/O pins (SID, SOD) and so, at a fairly simple level anyway, serial I/O may be supported by the processor itself. Likewise, no clock support is provided because the 8085 includes full clock logic 'On-Chip'.

If more complex serial and parallel I/O facilities are required, then devices designed for use on a non-multiplexed bus must be employed and some of these will be discussed in Part II of this Appendix.

B–2 Non-Multiplexed – Bus Support Devices

The devices described in this section will operate both with the 8080 processor and also with the 8085 if the low order address information is demultiplexed from the address/data bus. As a general rule, these devices have greater functionality than the multiplexed-bus components and therefore require a more detailed treatment. However, the function of this Appendix is primarily to provide an overview of the available support and to provide an introduction to the capbilities. Therefore the full detail of some devices will not be presented and readers are urged to consult the relevant data sheets for a more exact description.

B-2.1 DEMULTIPLEXING THE 8085 BUS

The 8085 processor shares eight lines between the low order address bits (A0-A7) and the data. The address information is present on the address-data bus for a little over 200 ns at the beginning of the cycle. During part of this time "ALE" is at logic 1 and about half way through the period, when the low order address information is stable, "ALE" drops to logic 0. This 1 $\longrightarrow$ 0 transition may be used to latch the address information. A suitable device for this purpose is the 8212 I/O port (which in fact has far wider uses than this)(see Figure B-11).

While "ALE" is high, the output side of the 8212 follows the input (AD0 $\longrightarrow$ AD7) side. Once "ALE" falls to logic 0, the output information is frozen.

B-2.2 PARALLEL I/O USING THE 8255A

The 8255A is a device which provides up to three 8-bit parallel I/O ports, ports A, B and C. Port C may, in some circumstances, be used to provide "handshake" control lines for the other two ports.

The device is connected to a bus as shown in Figure B-12 where it will be noted that the two least significant address lines are taken directly to the 8255A to provide addresing for the four internal registers.

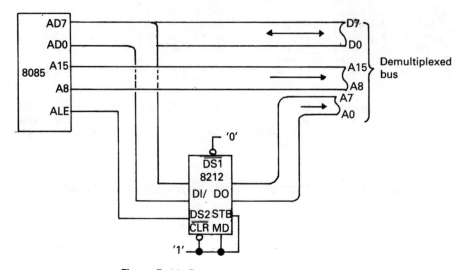

Figure B–11: Demultiplexing the 8085 Bus

As shown, the device is set up for memory mapped I/O but use of IO/M̄ or the equivalent 8080 signals (ĪOR, ĪOW) would permit separation of the I/O and memory address spaces.

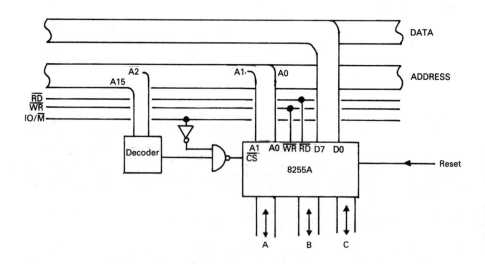

Figure B-12: Connection of an 8255A to the Bus

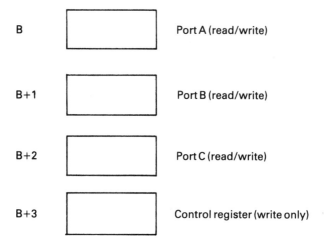

B		Port A (read/write)
B+1		Port B (read/write)
B+2		Port C (read/write)
B+3		Control register (write only)

Figure B-13: 8255A Register Allocation

The addressing structure of the device is as shown in Figure B-13 where B is the memory address determined by the design of the decoder.

The control register is used primarily to determine the direction of data flow in each port and the mode of operation. Ports A and B are treated as two 8-bit entities, but port C is divided into two halves, port C upper (C4 ⟶ C7) and port C lower (C0 ⟶ C3). This is necessary because in some modes port C upper is needed to provide handshake controls for port A and, if port B is operated in similar modes, port C lower provides the necessary control signals. Before describing the layout of the control register, the various operating modes will be outlined.

MODE 0

Mode 0 is a simple I/O mode with no handshaking controls; data is simply written to or read from the relevant port data register. Ports A and B may be individually selected to operate in mode 0 and their respective parts of port C will then also operate in mode 0. The direction of data flow may be individually assigned to port A, port B, port C upper and port C lower.

MODE 1

Mode 1 may be individually selected for either port A or port B. When selected, the lines of the corresponding half of port C are redefined as handshake lines. Ports A and B can operate as inputs or outputs in this mode.

When port A is in mode 1, port C is redefined as follows:

	A is Input	A is Output
C3 C4	Interrupt Control Strobe	Interrupt control } Simple I/O lines
C5 C6	Input buffer full } Simple I/O Lines	Acknowledge
C7		Output buffer full

When operated in this mode, the protocol is identical to that of the 8155 I/O port handshake mode illustrated in Figure B-6 for input and B-7 for output. The correspondence between the signals of the 8255 and those of the 8155 is shown below:

Line	Corresponding 8155 Singals	
	Input	Output
C3	Interrupt	Interrupt
C4	Strobe	– – –
C5	Buffer full	– – –
C6	– – –	Strobe
C7	– – –	Buffer full

Thus the only difference is the inverted significance of C7 during output operations.

When port B is configured in mode 1, the following port C lines are redefined as follows:

C0	Interrupt Control	(Similar to C3)
C1	Input buffer full/output buffer full	(Similar to C5/C7)
C2	{ Strobe (I/P) { Acknowledge (O/P) }	(Similar to C4/C6)

MODE 2

Only port A can be operated in mode 2 which is a bidirectional bus I/O mode. When port A is in this mode, port C bits C3 ⟶ C7 are assigned to provide control signals. Bits C0 ⟶ C2 are used as simple I/O if port B is still operating in mode 0, or they are used to support handshaking for port B in mode 1.

The operation of port A in mode 2 will only be briefly outlined by listing the functions of the relevant control signals.

C3   Interrupt. Designed for connection to the processor interrupt line.

C4   Strobe   ⎫ for input data
C5   Input buffer full   ⎭ handshaking

C6   Acknowledge   ⎫ for output data
C7   Output buffer full   ⎭ handshaking and bus driver enable

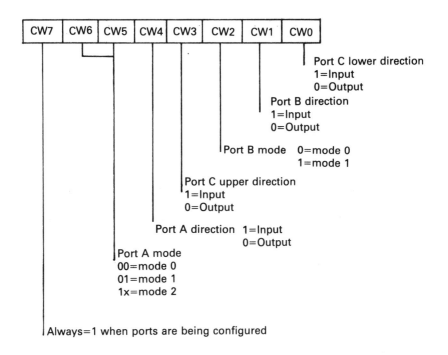

Figure B-14: Allocation of Control Word Bits During Configuration of the 8255A (CW7=1)

It is only possible to write an 8-bit word to port C when both port A and port B are operating in mode 0. In most other circumstances, the I/O lines of port C that are not used for handshake control must be written to using the "bit set/reset" function of the control word.

This is achieved by writing a data word to the control register with the most significant bit equal to zero. In these circumstances, the contents of bit CW0 is written into the bit position of port C specified by CW1⟶CW3 (see Figure B-15).

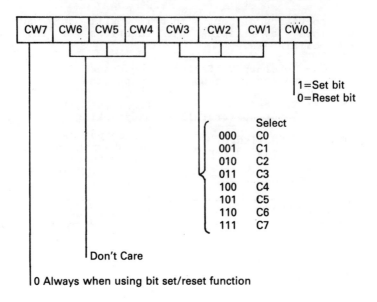

Figure B-15: Use of Control Word Bits During 'bit set' Operations (CW7=0)

If port C is read, then the 8-bit word received will represent the data input to port C (when mode 0 is selected for ports A and B). Otherwise it represents the status of the various buffer-full and interrupt request lines plus any I/O lines remaining in port C.

It will be recalled that one of the control lines used in mode 1 is an interrupt line. This can be selectively enabled or disabled by writing to C2 (port B), C4 (port A as I/P) and C6 (port A as O/P) using the bit set/reset facility.

B-2.3 THE 8253 PROGRAMMABLE INTERVAL TIMER

The 8253 contains three identical counter/timer units each of which can be programmed to operate independently in a number of modes including BCD counting. Control of all three is via a single control register. Bus interfacing follows the same principles as were outlined for the 8255A and the timer appears to the programmer as a sequence of four locations as shown in Figure B-16.

Each counter unit consists of a 16-bit down-counter which can be made to count in a straight binary or binary-coded decimal mode. Each counter is provided with two inputs and one output. The "clock" input is used to receive the output of a constant frequency source or an event detector and every $1 \longrightarrow 0$ transition on this input will cause the contents of the counter to decrement.

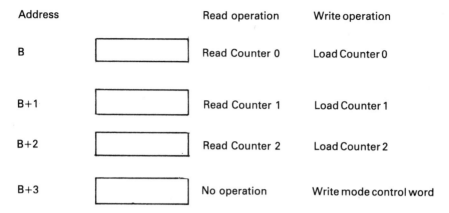

Address		Read operation	Write operation
B		Read Counter 0	Load Counter 0
B+1		Read Counter 1	Load Counter 1
B+2		Read Counter 2	Load Counter 2
B+3		No operation	Write mode control word

Figure B-16: Register Allocation in the 8253 Timer

The second, "gate" input is used to gate the input waveform or "clock" thus inhibiting counting and also, in some operation modes, causing the counter to be reloaded.

The output of each counter may be used to generate a precise waveform for external circuitry or it may be routed to the processor interrupt bus to cause interrupts on termination of counting.

It will be noticed from Figure B-16 that although each counter is 16 bits long, it is accessed by a single 8-bit port. The counter is loaded in two 8-bit bytes and the significance of each write operation is determined by the contents of bits RL0 and RL1 of the control word (Figure B-17). Depending on the way these are set, the 8253 will interpret a write to a particular counter as loading its least significant byte or its most significant byte. In one configuration, it expects two writes to occur, the first to the least significant byte and the second to the most signficant byte (e.g. using a SHLD instruction.)

The significance of RL0 and RL1 is the same when it is necessary to read the contents of a counter. There are clearly problems when reading the value of a counter which is counting since the contents could change between reading the least significant byte and the most significant byte. This is especially true if the count has reached a value such as 0100. The first read, of the least significant byte, will be 00. If the most significant byte is then read, this latter may be found to have decremented to 00 giving a total count of 0000 which is greatly in error. The solution is to inhibit counting before reading the counter. Alternatively, the special latching read mode must be selected by setting RL0=RL1=0 (in which case bits 0 ⟶ 3 of the control word, Figure B-17, are immaterial). Issuing this special control word effectively reads all 16 bits of the counter "on-the-fly" into a temporary latch from where it may be read without error using the standard counter read procedures.

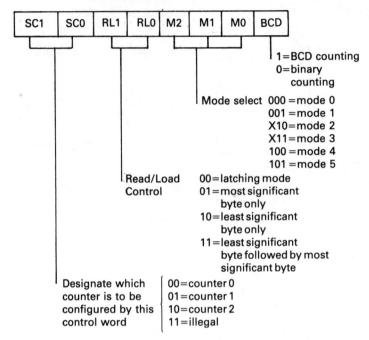

SC1	SC0	RL1	RL0	M2	M1	M0	BCD

1=BCD counting
0=binary
counting

Mode select   000 =mode 0
               001 =mode 1
               X10=mode 2
               X11=mode 3
               100 =mode 4
               101 =mode 5

Read/Load   00=latching mode
Control   01=most significant
                 byte only
           10=least significant
                 byte only
           11=least significant
                 byte followed by most
                 significant byte

Designate which   00=counter 0
counter is to be   01=counter 1
configured by this   10=counter 2
control word   11=illegal

Figure B–17: Layout of 8253 timer control word

In order to complete discussion of this counter, it only remains for the modes of operation to be discussed.

MODE 0

The output goes to logic 0 after the counter is set running and goes high when the count terminates. It only returns low when the counter is reloaded. Completion of counter loading sequence initiates the operation of the counter. The count may be held at any time by using the gate control.

MODE 1

This mode is initiated by a rising edge on the gate input. At this point the output goes low for the duration of the count. Taking the gate low stops the count without resetting the output. When the gate goes high again, the count is restarted from the beginning.

MODE 2

In this mode the counter counts down to 0, then automatically reloads and starts counting down again. The output goes low for one clock period at the completion of each count, thus providing regular time markers for a system. The gate input, when low, stops the counter and leaves the output high. Once the gate goes high the count restarts from the beginning.

MODE 3

This mode provides a continuous square wave at the output with a total period equal to the duration of one count sequence. Gate operation is similar to mode 2.

MODE 4

This mode causes the output to go high after a delay equal to the time taken for the counter to count down to 0. The output is taken low for one clock period and then returned high. Thus a logic 0 strobe pulse is generated a fixed time after the count is started by software. The gate acts as a counter enable/disable.

MODE 5

This is similar to mode 4 except the start of the pre-strobe delay is determined by a 0⟶1 transition on the gate.

These modes are indicated diagramatically in Figure B-18.

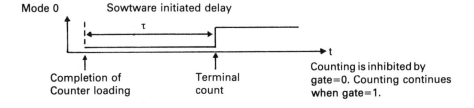

Mode 0 — Sowtware initiated delay

Completion of Counter loading — Terminal count

Counting is inhibited by gate=0. Counting continues when gate=1.

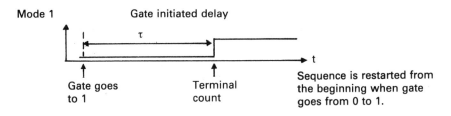

Mode 1 — Gate initiated delay

Gate goes to 1 — Terminal count

Sequence is restarted from the beginning when gate goes from 0 to 1.

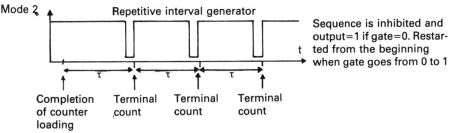

Mode 2 — Repetitive interval generator

Completion of counter loading — Terminal count — Terminal count — Terminal count

Sequence is inhibited and output=1 if gate=0. Restarted from the beginning when gate goes from 0 to 1

481

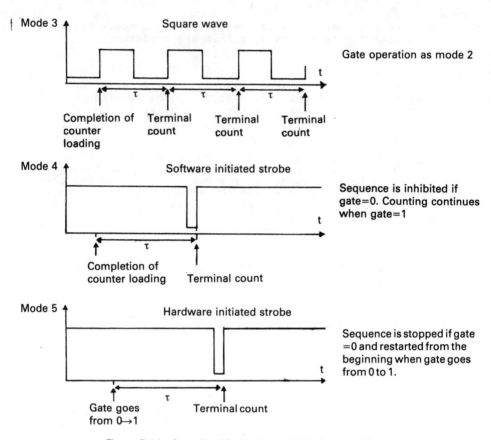

Figure B-18. Counting Modes in the 8253 Counter/timer

B-2.4 THE 8251A PROGRAMMABLE COMMUNICATIONS INTERFACE

This device supports both synchronous and asynchronous communications. It is connected into a system in a manner similar to the 8255A except that address line A1 is taken to the decoder. The 8251A, therefore, appears to the programmer as a pair of read/write locations as shown in Figure B-19.

Address	Read	Write
B	Data in	Data out
B+1	Status	Command

Figure B-19: Register Allocation in the 8251A Communications Interface

The 8251, once configured by setting up the command register appears to the programmer as a single read/write location. In order to transmit a character, the required data is simply written in parallel from the data port from whence it will be transmitted serially under the full control of the 8251A. Likewise serial input data is received and checked by the 8251A before the programmer reads it, stripped of all synchronisation and parity bits, in parallel into the processor.

B-2.4.1 SYNCHRONOUS TRANSMISSION AND RECEPTION

It will be recalled that synchronous transmission requires special synchronising characters to be sent followed by a continous stream of data. If data is temporarily absent then the synchronisation characters must be inserted into the transmission stream to maintain synchronism between the transmitter and receiver. This is done automatically by the 8251A. The following options are available to the user who utilises the 8251A as a synchronous communications device.

(i)   Single/double synchronisation character

(ii)   Enable/disable parity generation

(iii)   Odd/even parity

(iv)   5, 6, 7 or 8-bit character length

(v)   Internal or external synchronisation. In internal synchronisation mode the 8251A inspects the received data stream for synchronisation characters. If external synchronisation is selected, other circuitry is assumed to be present and the 8251A does not commence reception until this circuitry informs it that synchronisation has been achieved.

In order to initiate the 8251A for synchronous operation, a stream of three or four 8-bit words must be written to the command port, in the correct order, immediately following a reset operation. The words, in order are:

1. MODE INSTRUCTION

2. SYNCHRONISATION CHARACTER 1

3. SYNCHRONISATION CHARACTER 2*

4. COMMAND INSTRUCTION

* This will be omitted if the mode instruction specifies only one synchronisation character.

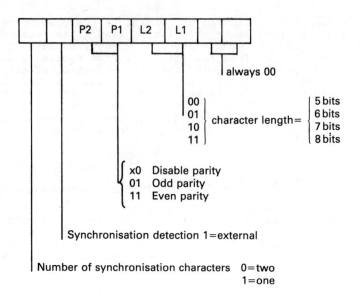

| | | P2 | P1 | L2 | L1 | | |

always 00

00			5 bits
01	character length=		6 bits
10			7 bits
11			8 bits

x0	Disable parity
01	Odd parity
11	Even parity

Synchronisation detection 1=external

Number of synchronisation characters 0=two
1=one

Figure B-20: 8251A mode instruction for synchronous operation

Transmission and reception are at the rate defined by the separate transmit and receive clocks. That is, reception is at 9600 Baud if the receive clock is 9600 Hz. The format of the mode instruction is shown in Figure B-20 and the format of the command instruction is shown in Figure B-21.

The 8251A supports various modem control functions. The control of two of these ("request to send" and "data terminal ready") and of other operations is governed by the command instruction as shown in Figure B-21. The word written at the end of the initialisation stream has the significance of a "command" instruction as do any subsequent write operations to the command port. A reset of the device (and hence full re-initialisation) may be forced via the command instruction facility.

B-2.4.2 ASYNCHRONOUS TRANSMISSION AND RECEPTION

It will be recalled that asynchronous transmission requires that the transmitted data be surrounded by synchronisation bits so that the synchronisation is re-established for every character.

The transmit side of the 8251A adds the necessary start and stop bits to the character loaded into the transmit data buffer. Likewise these bits are checked and · then removed during reception.

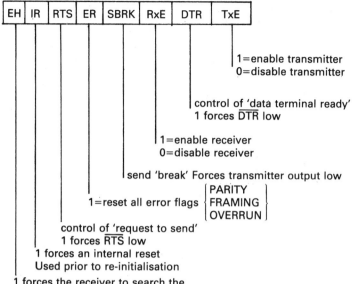

| EH | IR | RTS | ER | SBRK | RxE | DTR | TxE |

1=enable transmitter
0=disable transmitter

control of 'data terminal ready'
1 forces $\overline{DTR}$ low

1=enable receiver
0=disable receiver

send 'break' Forces transmitter output low

1=reset all error flags { PARITY / FRAMING / OVERRUN }

control of 'request to send'
1 forces $\overline{RTS}$ low

1 forces an internal reset
Used prior to re-initialisation

1 forces the receiver to search the
incoming data stream for synchronisation
characters. (Must be included in the first
command instruction if internal synchronisation
is selected.)

Figure B-21. Layout of the 8251A Command Instruction

The transmit and receive baud rates are governed by separate clocks. Unlike synchronous transmission, it is possible to use a baud rate which is 1/16th or 1/64th of the raw clock rate, the actual selection being under the control of the mode instruction as shown in Figure B-22. The options available for asynchronous operation are:

(i)   Baud rate division ratio
(ii)   5, 6, 7 or 8-bit characters
(iii)   Parity enable/disable
(iv)   Parity odd/even
(v)   1, 1.5 or 2 stop bits

Note that, in the last instance, the receiver only REQUIRES one stop bit.

The post reset initialisation sequence is only two words long when the mode instruction indicates asynchronous operation. The first write to the command port following a reset is interpreted as the mode instruction (Figure B-22 for asynchronous operation), the second word is a command instruction as illustrated in Figure B-21. The only difference in the command instruction compared with the synchronous case is that the "EH" bit has no meaning for asynchronous operation.

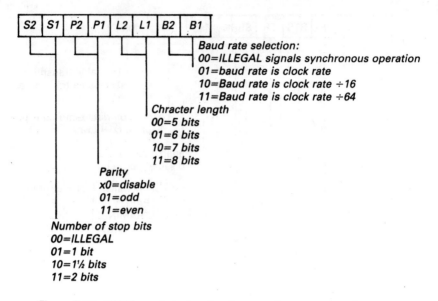

| S2 | S1 | P2 | P1 | L2 | L1 | B2 | B1 |

Baud rate selection:
00=ILLEGAL signals synchronous operation
01=baud rate is clock rate
10=Baud rate is clock rate ÷16
11=Baud rate is clock rate ÷64

Chracter length
00=5 bits
01=6 bits
10=7 bits
11=8 bits

Parity
x0=disable
01=odd
11=even

Number of stop bits
00=ILLEGAL
01=1 bit
10=1½ bits
11=2 bits

Figure B-22: 8251A mode instruction for asynchronous operation

B-2.4.3 MODEM CONTROL

The 8251A provides two modem control output signals, namely RTS (inverse request-to-send) and DTR (inverse data-terminal-ready). These can be controlled by software via the command instruction (Figure B-21). Similarly two signals generated by modems may be received by the 8251A, namely DSR (inverse data-set-ready) and CTS (inverse clear-to-send). The DSR input may be inspected by a software read of the status register.

CTS does not appear in the status register but is used internally to inhibit the generation of the "transmitter ready" signal. The layout of the status register is shown in Figure B-23.

B-2.4.4 ERROR CONDITIONS

Three receiver error conditions are detectable via the status register.

(i)   Parity error

If the parity of an incoming character does not match that programmed into the 8251A, then this bit will be set.

486

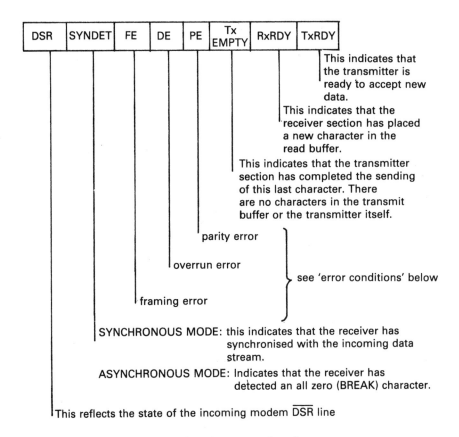

Figure B-23: 8251A status register layout

(ii)   Overrun error

If the receiver has a new character to be placed into
the read buffer when the previous character has not
been read, then data must be lost. In this situation,
the overrun error flag is set.

(iii) Framing error

This is only relevant for asychronous operation. If
the receiver fails to find at least one stop bit after
the received character, synchronisation may have been
lost. The framing error flag is therefore set.

B-2.4.5 INTERRUPT CONDITIONS

In order to service the communications link, a processor must
know when the receiver has data available and also when the

487

transmitter can accept new data. This information is given by
the RxRDY and TxRDY status bits shown in Figure B-23. These
can be read by polling the status register but in many
systems it may be preferable to permit these conditions to
cause interrupts. To this end, these two status flags are
brought out to pins on the 8251A package. These may then be
joined to an appropriate interrupt line.

The TxRDY flag is not joined directly to its output pin
however. It is conditioned by $\overline{CTS}$ so that an interrupt will
only be raised if the transmitter is ready and the modem is
indicating that it is "clear-to-send".

B-2.5 THE 8214 INTERRUPT CONTROLLER

It will be recalled that the 8085 supports both three levels
of vectored interrupt (RST 5.5, 6.5, 7.5) and also the 8080
compatible non-vectored interrupt. The 8214 chip is designed
to provide a vectored interrupt facility for both the 8080
and 8085 processors using the normal non-vectored INTR/$\overline{INTA}$
protocol described in A-3.8. It will be seen from this
section that once an interrupt has been generated the
8080/8085 enters an acknowledgement cycle during which it
obeys an instruction which has been placed on the data bus by
the external circuitry. This instruction may be a three byte
"JUMP" or a one byte "RST n" instruction. The 8214 may be
used to support the latter option.

The facilities provided by the 8214 may be summarised as
follows:

(i)   arbitrates between up to eight simultaneous
        interrupt requests and issues a code
        corresponding to the successful request.

(ii)   can selectively lock out interrupts below a
        certain level.

(iii)   may be daisy-chained with other 8214s to provide
        more levels of priority.

To achieve these results, the 8214 incorporates priority
encoding and decoding circuitry similar to that shown in
Figure 12.11b. Thus three of the outputs "($\overline{A0} \longrightarrow \overline{A2}$)" from
the 8214 contain a binary coded indication of the highest
priority request present on the eight input interrupt lines
($\overline{R0} \longrightarrow \overline{R7}$). Note that the $\overline{R0}$ is the LOWEST priority.

Before an interrupt is indicated by the INT output of the
8214, the priority level of the successful request is
compared with the contents of the status register in the 8214.
If the priority of the request exceeds the limit value loaded
into the status register then the interrupt is allowed.
Otherwise it is not. It will be recalled that the binary
instruction code for an "RST n" instruction is

11 xxx 111

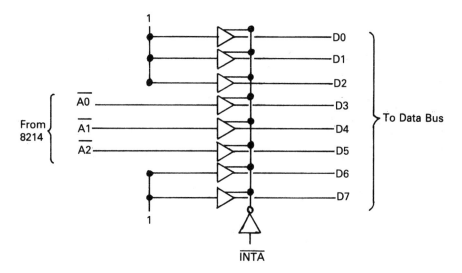

Figure B-24: Generation of an RST n instuction

where the three bits xxx indicate the value of n. The outputs ($\overline{A0} \longrightarrow \overline{A2}$) of the 8214 may be used to insert these bits and hence force a different restart instruction for each priority level as shown in Figure B-24.

Notice that the "RST n" instruction is gated onto the data bus only when the processor is acknowledging an interrupt request. Table B-1 summarises the instructions issued and the start address of the service routine for each priority level. In most cases, this "routine" will be a simple 'JUMP' to some other more convenient location.

Priority level	R	A2	A1	A0	RST n	Start Address (hexadecimal)
Highest	n=7	0	0	0	RST0	0000* same as hard-ware reset
	6	0	0	1	RST1	0008
	5	0	1	0	RST2	0010
	4	0	1	1	RST3	0018
	3	1	0	0	RST4	0020
	2	1	0	1	RST5	0028
	1	1	1	0	RST6	0030
Lowest	0	1	1	1	RST7	0038

Table B–1

The interrupt request issued by the 8214 must be maintained until it is acknowledged by "INTA". This means that the interrupt request from the peripheral must be maintained until serviced. Furthermore, it must be removed immediately

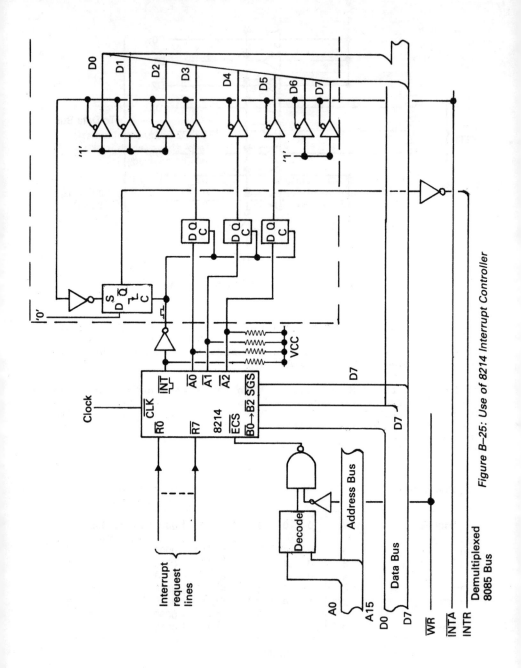

Figure B–25: Use of 8214 Interrupt Controller

Configuration defined
by connections to data
bus in Figure B–25

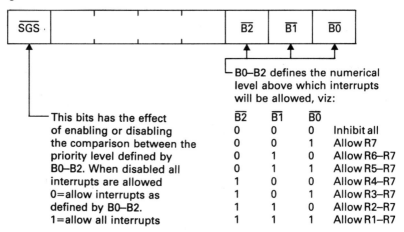

SGS				$\overline{B2}$	$\overline{B1}$	$\overline{B0}$

B0–B2 defines the numerical
level above which interrupts
will be allowed, viz:

This bits has the effect
of enabling or disabling
the comparison between the
priority level defined by
B0–B2. When disabled all
interrupts are allowed
0=allow interrupts as
defined by B0–B2.
1=allow all interrupts

$\overline{B2}$	$\overline{B1}$	$\overline{B0}$	
0	0	0	Inhibit all
0	0	1	Allow R7
0	1	0	Allow R6–R7
0	1	1	Allow R5–R7
1	0	0	Allow R4–R7
1	0	1	Allow R3–R7
1	1	0	Allow R2–R7
1	1	1	Allow R1–R7

Figure B–26 : Status Word for 8214 as used in Figure B–25.

the interrupt is acknowledged in order to avoid repeated
interrupts.

These requirements are most easily met if the OUTPUT of the
8214 including its interrupt request line are latched by
external circuitry, as shown in Figure B-25.

The only register within the 8214 is a status register which
is used to define the priority level at, and below which,
requests should be inhibited. The status register is clocked
by the $\overline{ECS}$ input which should therefore be connected to the
output of a suitable decoder. The design of the latter will
determine the memory address or I/O port address at which the
status register resides. The use of the status register is
defined in Figure B-26.

It should be noted that the circuitry included in a dotted
line in Figure B-25 may be provided with a single 8212 device
used in "interrupting instruction port" mode.

A number of signals present on 8214 have been omitted from
Figure B-25. These are:

(i)   The daisy-chaining signals: an 8214 is inactive if it
        receives a "0" on its ETLG input. This input is
        connected to the "ENGL" output of the next highest
        priority 8214 in a daisy-chain. The "ENGL" output is
        held at logic "1" if:

(a) the 8214 has no interrupts

and

(b) the 8214 has a logic "1" on its "ETLG" input.

The highest priority 8214 will have its "ETLG" input permanently wired to its logic 1 as shown in Figure B-27.

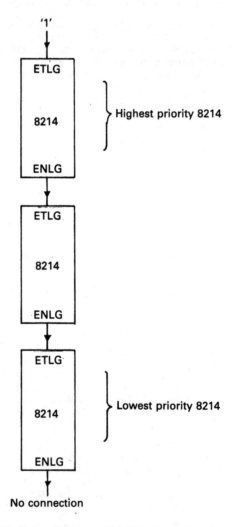

Figure B–27: Daisy-chaining of Multiple 8214 Devices

(ii)   The interrupt enable input "INTE". This is designed to be connected to the corresponding control bus signal of the 8080 and serves to enable the 8214 interrupt output. This signal has been eliminated from the 8085 bus as it is of little use. "INTE" will be wired to logic "1" in 8085 systems.

(iii)   The $\overline{ELR}$ control serves as an enable for $\overline{A0} \longrightarrow \overline{A2}$. It is normally taken to logic "0".

The 8214 provides simple but adequate vectored interrupt support for many 8080 and 8085 systems. If more sophisticated prioritising schemes are required, these may be obtained by using the far more complex 8259 part.

Appendix C. Digital Systems Components

It has been necessary in previous Chapters to draw diagrams of various logic circuits using standard symbols for the various components. In this Appendix, the functions of each of these basic components will be defined. It is intended that this Appendix will be used solely as a reference while studying the various diagrams in the main text and no attempt has been made to extend the treatment to a discussion of logic design techniques. Likewise no claim of completeness is made for this Appendix; only those components used in the main text will be discussed.

Many components will be described by what is known as a TRUTH TABLE. This is a table which presents all possible input combinations on one side with the corresponding outputs written on the other. Thus if there is any doubt as to how a particular component will operate under any given circumstances, it is merely necessary to determine the state of each of its inputs and then find the line of the truth table containing this combination. The output of the circuit will then be on the right-hand (output) side of the truth table.

On some occasions the signal level on an input line may be irrelevant to the operation of the component. This is called a "don't care" condition and is represented in the tables by an "X". When the signal level is important, it is represented in the tables either as

1 for logic "1"

or

0 for logic "0"

C–1 Logic Gates

These are components which combine multiple input signals to produce a single output signal. Although, in general, there are a large number of inputs, the following discussions will be illustrated by reference to gates with only two inputs. Where extension to more than two inputs is possible, the operation of the larger capacity gate should be self-evident.

C-1.1 THE 'AND' GATE

This is a circuit which produces a logic "1" at its output if, and only if, all of its inputs are at logic "1". Otherwise it remains at logic "0".

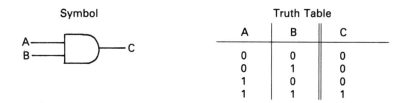

Symbol		Truth Table		

A	B	C
0	0	0
0	1	0
1	0	0
1	1	1

The logic equation for the gate is $C = A \wedge B$.

C-1.2 THE 'NAND' GATE

Nand is a contraction for not-and. This gate performs similarly to the AND gate except that its output is the logical inverse of the corresponding AND gate. Thus the output of a NAND gate is at logic "0" if, and only if, all of its inputs are at logic "1". Otherwise its output is logic "1".

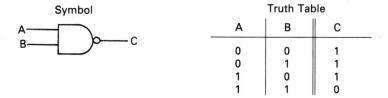

Symbol		Truth Table		

A	B	C
0	0	1
0	1	1
1	0	1
1	1	0

The logic equation for the gate is $C = \overline{A \wedge B}$.

Notice that the only difference between the symbols for AND and NAND is the small circle on the output. This circle is always taken to mean that the signal to which it applies is logically inverted.

C-1.3 THE 'OR' GATE

This is circuit the output of which is logic "1" if any one
or more of its inputs is logic "1".

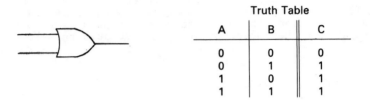

Truth Table

A	B	C
0	0	0
0	1	1
1	0	1
1	1	1

The logic equation for this gate is C = A $\vee$ B.

C-1.4 THE 'NOR' GATE

NOR is simply not-or. The output of a NOR gate is the logical
inverse of the corresponding output for an OR gate. The
output is logic "0" if one or more of the inputs are at logic
"1".

Symbol

Truth Table

A	B	C
0	0	1
0	1	0
1	0	0
1	1	0

The logic equation for this gate is C = $\overline{A \vee B}$.

C-1.5 THE 'EXCLUSIVE-OR' GATE (XOR)

This is sometimes called the "not equivalent" gate which is a
far more apt title. The output of this gate is logic "1" if,
and only if, the two inputs are different. The comparison
with the "OR" function (sometimes called the inclusive-OR) is
interesting.

Symbol

Truth Table

A	B	C
0	0	0
0	1	1
1	0	1
1	1	0

The logic equation for this gate is C = A $\oplus$ B.

496

C-1.6 THE 'EQUIVALENCE' GATE

This is sometimes called the exclusive-NOR gate because its output is the logical inverse of the exclusive OR. The output of the equivalent gate is a logic "1" if, and only if, the two inputs are in the same logic state.

Symbol   Truth Table

A	B	C
0	0	1
1	1	0
1	0	0
1	1	1

The logic equation for this gate is $C = \overline{A \oplus B}$.

C-1.7 BUFFERS AND INVERTING BUFFERS

It is sometimes necessary to increase the electrical power in a logic circuit. This is done with a buffer, which has no effect on the logic values in the circuit.

$y = x$

Some types of buffer introduce a logic inversion into the system. This type of buffer has the symbol:

$y = \overline{x}$

Inverting buffers may, in fact, not increase the electrical power at all and may be used simply for their inverting property. In this case they are referred to just as inverters. A NAND gate or a NOR gate with both inputs connected together will function as an inverter.

C–2 Bus Interface Components

It will be recalled that there are many occasions when it is necessary to physically connect together the outputs of several systems via a bus structure. There are very clear

497

dangers in doing this since if two of the sources of logic signals are active on the bus at the same time, and are trying to force different levels onto the bus, severe damage could be done.

Two solutions to this problem are possible.

(i)   Arrange that circuits can only force one level (usually "0"). The other level being achieved by letting the bus "float", for instance, when no devices are trying to force a "0" level. Thus the "1" level is more of an "absence of '0'" than anything positive. The bus is pulled to "1" by a load resistor called a BUS LOAD or a PULL-UP resistor.

This is the "wired-or" solution and it is implemented using gates having special "open-collector" outputs. This means that no load resistor is included in the circuit and the output of the logic gate appears to be a simple switch. Figure C-1 shows a bus with three open-collector devices connected.

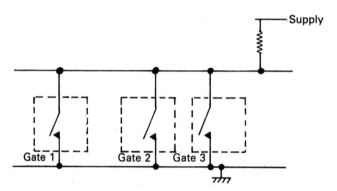

Figure C-1: A wired -OR bus configuration

It will be clear from Figure C-1 that since all gates force the same level (switch closed) or acquiesce to the bus level prevailing (switch open) no conflict can occur. The disadvantage of this arrangement is that, while the bus can be brought to logic "0" quite quickly because of the active pull-down exerted by the switches, it only rises to logic "1" relatively slowly. This is overcome by the second solution.

(ii) Arrange that the bus drivers are actively selected and that when they are not selected they have very little effect on the bus. This is known as a tri-state logic because three possible states exist for each output:

498

```
(a) driver disabled - no influence on the bus
(b) driver enabled - logic "1" on the bus
(c) driver enabled - logic "0" on the bus
```

These states may be understood by reference to
Figure C-2, which represents the effective
circuitry at the output of a tri-state driver.

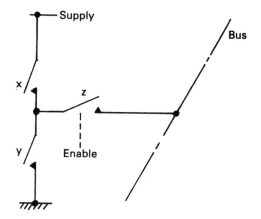

Figure C-2: Effective output circuity of a tri-state buffer

State (a) exists when switch Z is open. This is usually
referred to as the "high impedence", "hi-Z" or "disabled"
state.

State (b) exists when switch Z is closed and when switch X is
closed (switch Y is open).

Switches X and Y never open or close together. Because the
bus is actively pulled to each of the logic levels, the
switching performance is very nearly the same for both
transitions "0" ⟶ "1" and for "1" ⟶ "0".

The symbol for a tri-state buffer is

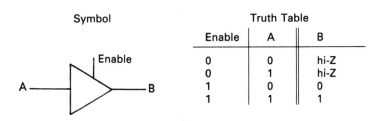

A tri-state driver which is enabled by a logic "0" would have
the symbol and the truth table shown below.

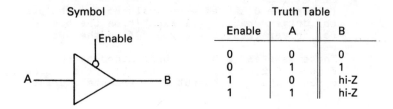

Symbol

Enable

A ———▷— B

Truth Table

Enable	A	B
0	0	0
0	1	1
1	0	hi-Z
1	1	hi-Z

C–3 Decoders

Decoders are devices which monitor a set of logic inputs and produce an output at logic "1" if, and only if, a particular combination occurs on the input lines. They are essentially combinations of gates. Figure C-3 shows a decoder which monitors the lines $A(0) \longrightarrow A(2)$ for the particular combination.

$$A_2 \quad = \quad 0$$
$$A_1 \quad = \quad 0$$
$$A_0 \quad = \quad 1$$

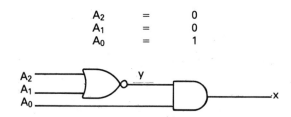

Figure C-3: An Example Decoder

An analysis of Figure C-3 will be a useful illustration of how the truth tables in Section C-1 may be used.

The decoder output X can only be "1" if both Y and A0 are "1" (because the output gate is an AND gate).

However, Y will only be "1" if both A2 and A1 are "0" (because the input gate is a NOR gate). Thus to get the decoder output to logic "1" requires

$$A_2 \quad = \quad 0$$
$$A_1 \quad = \quad 0 \qquad \text{as required}$$
$$A_0 \quad = \quad 1$$

Commercial decoder circuits are available which produce outputs for all possible combinations of input. The 74S138 is one such device which has eight outputs, only one of which is active at any given time. Which particular output is active is determined by the combination of "1"s and "0"s on the three input lines. It is termed "one-out-of-eight" decoder.

500

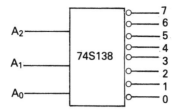

Figure C-4: A Proprietary 1-out-of-8 Decoder

Notice that the outputs are "active low" as shown by the small circles on the output lines. To use this device in a decoding circuit, the designer merely selects the output corresponding to the desired input combination; for instance, output line 3 will go low if, and only if, the input combination is

$$A_2 \quad = \quad 0$$
$$A_1 \quad = \quad 1 \quad \bigg\} \quad = \text{Binary 3}$$
$$A_0 \quad = \quad 1$$

Often it is necessary to decode more than three lines. This, is possible because most decoders have "enable" inputs which permit them to be cascaded.

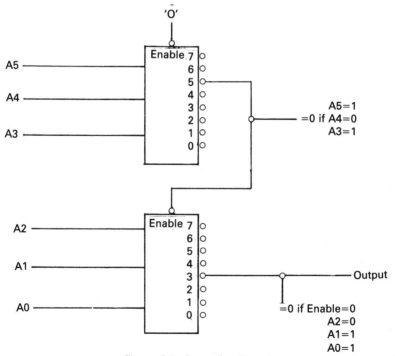

Figure C-5: Cascading Decoders

501

Notice that the enable input is active low and that one of the decoders is permanently enabled.

The output goes to logic "0" if A5⟶A0 have the combination 101011.

C–4 Bistable Latches

Latches are devices which may be set to a particular logic state and which will remain in that state until changed. Various types exist such as R-S, J-K and D-type latches. For the purpose of this Appendix, only the D-type will be discussed.

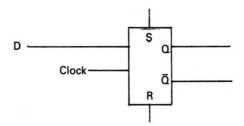

Figure C-6: A D-type Latch

The device has two outputs Q and $\bar{Q}$. $\bar{Q}$ is the logic inverse of Q.

The latch operates as follows: a logic level exists on the D input. When the clock input changes level, the logic level on the D input is locked into the latch and is available at the Q output. It remains locked in the latch until another clocking operation occurs. Various types of D-latch exist, some are latched by '0'⟶'1' transition of the clock while others are sensitive to the '1'⟶'0' transition and yet others are sensitive to one particular level of the clock.

In addition to the D input, many D-type latches have preset (S) inputs and preclear inputs (R). These are used to establish a particular level on the latch output irrespective of D or the clock. When S is asserted, Q becomes logic "1". While if R is asserted, Q becomes logic "0".

A set of D latches may be grouped together to form a register.

When used in this way, a special two-stage D-type latch called a master-slave D-type is used. The reason for this may be seen by inspection of Figure C-7.

502

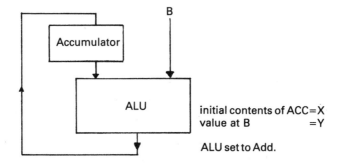

initial contents of ACC=X
value at B   =Y

ALU set to Add.

Figure C-7:Computer Arithmetic Unit During the Operation (ACC)+ B→ ACC

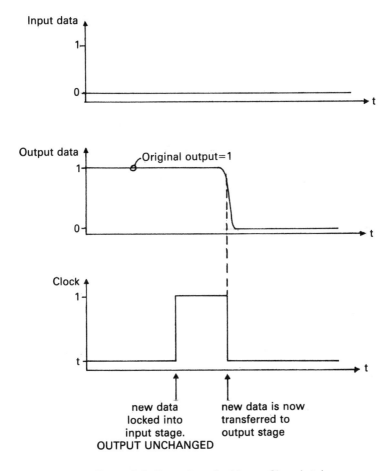

Figure C-8: Operation of a Master-Slave Latch

The result expected to be returned to the accumulator is X + Y. But consider what happens if this result appears at the output of the accumulator during latching. The ALU will see the new input X + Y and add Y to it again, giving the wrong answer X + 2Y.

This could happen several times depending on the speed of the ALU and the time taken to complete the latch. To avoid this unpredictability, a master-slave latch is used as shown in Figure C-8.

It will be appreciated from Figure C-8 that there no longer exists an unbroken feedback path, ALU $\longrightarrow$ Accumulator $\longrightarrow$ ALU, and so the problem cannot arise.

Appendix D. Semiconductor Fabrication Techniques

The purpose of this Appendix is to provide a very brief introduction to the way in which semiconductor components are manufactured and then to summarise the principal performance characteristics which result from the various manufacturing processes. The objective of this exercise is to aid readers in the selection of an appropriate microprocessor within their design constraints (e.g. speed, power consumption, etc.).

Microprocessors and their associated devices are manufactured from semiconductor materials - germanium, silicon and gallium arsenide. The first transistors were germanium devices but for the past twenty years silicon has been the dominant material. Research is currently proceeding to construct devices from gallium arsenide and other materials with a view to achieving performance improvements, but as yet no microprocessors have been produced with this technology.

Semiconductors are a class of materials in which conduction of electricity does not occur as readily as in metals. However, conduction may be achieved in a controlled way by the application of relatively low voltages. Insulators by contrast do not conduct electricity unless very large voltages are applied and the flow which results when these high voltages are applied is usually uncontrolled and results in the destruction of the insulator.

Conduction of electricity occurs when carriers of charge move about within a material. In semiconductors, this conduction may be either by carriers of positive charge (p-type) or by carriers of negative charge (n-type). The n-type carriers are less massive and more mobile than p-type carriers. It is important that the crystal structure of the semiconductor material is very pure and defect free so that the movement of the charge carriers is impeded as little as possible. In fact, the initial silicon material used for most semiconductor work has to be purified to such a degree that there are less than one part in 10^9 impurities remaining in it.

A device manufactured from silicon with a defect in it will not function correctly. Depending on the complexity of the device, the yield of good products may be anywhere in the range 5% to 20% and since these cannot be detected until late in the manufacturing process, the cost of producing 80% to 95% "junk" has to be carried in the selling price of the good product. The chance of eliminating semiconductor defects is improved

(i)   if the raw material is well refined

(ii)   if the physical size of each device is small so that the chance of including a fault is correspondingly small.

In addition, failures can occur due to faulty handling during manufacture so a third way of improving yield is:

(iii)   simplification of the manufacturing process.

D–1 The Manufacture of Semiconductor Devices

The manufacture of all semiconductor devices involves the introduction, in closely controlled quantites, of impurities into defined areas of a geometric pattern in the semiconductor. These impurities produce either p-type or n-type current carriers and the whole arrangement is interconnected as appropriate with conducting tracks of aluminium or polysilicon.

The geometry is determined by photographic masks. These are made up in quite large sizes and then reduced to the required final size photographically. These photographic patterns are transferred to the surface of the silicon by a kind of contact printing process during manufacture. The photographic emulsion used is one that is selectively hardened by light and, after printing, the softer emulsion is removed leaving a hard protective film over some areas and exposed silicon in others. The exposed silicon is then treated in various ways which result in the introduction of impurities etc. into the defined areas.

The more complex the geometric structure of the finished device, the greater the number of masking stages needed and, of course, the greater the chance of a mistake being made. The number of masks used ranges from five to eleven.

Developments in the optical techniques used permit smaller transistors to be fabricated. Apart from the obvious benefits of increased yield and circuit density, this development leads to circuits which operate more rapidly. There is therefore considerable pressure to reduce device dimensions and this has resulted in the use of electron beams for the exposure of the masks instead of visible or ultra-violet light. The shorter wavelengths associated with electron beam radiation enable finer detail to be resolved. Currently dimensions of the order of two micrometres are commonly used.

D–2 Performance Characteristics of Various Technologies

Two radically different types of transistor may be fabricated as the basic building block for logic circuits. These are the BIPOLAR transistor and the MOS (metal-oxide-silicon transistor). The former makes use of the special properties which are associated with the junction of p-type and n-type silicon, while the latter relies on the interaction between an electric field and silicon material. Generally bipolar transistors operate more rapidly than MOS transistors but require a more complex manufacturing process and take up a relatively large area of silicon. However, intensive research over the last ten years has resulted in dramatic improvements in MOS transistor performance.

The principal properties of a semiconductor fabrication technology that are of interest to a circuit designer are:

    (i)   speed of operation

    (ii)   power consumption

    (iii) transistor size.

The first two characteristics are of self-evident interest and are sometimes combined into a single "figure-of-merit", the SPEED-POWER PRODUCT.

The third characteristic is of interest because it affects the circuit complexity that is possible and also influences product yield, and hence price. Table D-1 lists the important parameters for a number of types of device technology.

The speed of the technology is measured by the time it takes for a logic signal to propagate from the input of a typical logic gate to its output. The size factor is measured by the number of typical logic gates that can be accommodated in a square millimetre of silicon.

TECHNOLOGY		SIZE gates/mm^2	SPEED gate delay ns	SPEED-POWER PRODUCT PJ
Transistor-Transistor logic (TTL)	BIPOLAR TECHNOLOGY	18	8	15
Emitter-Coupled logic (ECL)		25	1.5	50*
Collector Diffusion Isolation (CDI)		60	20	5
Integrated Injection logic (I^{2}L)		250	12	8*
VMOS	MOS TECHNOLOGY	250	2	1
CMOS		60	10	20*
PMOS		100	50	250*
NMOS Standard+		150	4	4$^\mp$
NMOS HMOS+		225**	1	1
NMOS HMOS II+		350**	0.4	0.5

* This parameter is very variable. A mean value has been given.

$^\mp$ This parameter is very variable. The figure given is for Intel devices.

+ All figures given are for the Intel process

** Estimate

Table D–1

Table D-1 shows how the intensive research into MOS processing has brought the technology close to the speeds achieved with bipolar technology but with enhanced power and size figures. What is not obvious is that MOS (except for CMOS) requires relatively few masking stages. CMOS is regarded as a low-power technology although the table does show it to have been somewhat overtaken by the NMOS processes. CMOS requires a large number of masking stages which makes it expensive, but it can be designed to work with high voltages which makes it suitable for operation in electrically noisy environments. It can also be designed for very low power, low voltage circuits making it very suitable for battery operated equipment.

V-MOS is a proprietary process which fabricates MOS transistors by forming a deep "silicon sandwich" rather than spreading the various components of a transistor around the surface of the silicon wafer. This three-dimensional approach results in a high packing density and also circumvents some of the dimensional limitations of the photo-lithographic process.

Finally, comparison between microprocessors in 1972 and those available now is of interest.

Processor	Date	Size of silicon	No. of Transistors	Clock speed
Intel 8080	1972	4mm × 7mm	4,000	500kHz
Motorola 68000	1980	7mm × 7mm	68,000	8mHz

Where the component layout is more regular than in processors, in applications such as memory arrays, even greater component densities have been achieved. For instance, the Toshiba 16K CMOS static read/write memory is reported as having 100,000 transistors on a 6mm x 6mm die.

Appendix E. Modulo–2 Arithmetic

Modulo-2 arithmetic is frequently used in error checking circuitry because it can be implemented very simply.

Modulo-2 addition is carried out in the usual way except that when a carry is generated in one column of the summation it is not propagated to the next most significant column. This is easily illustrated by an example.

First ordinary addition				
1	1	0	1
1	0	1	1
1	1	0	0	0

1✔1✔1✔1✔ ←——————— carry terms

Secondly modulo 2 addition			
1	1	0	1
1	0	1	1
0	1	1	0

↓   ↓ ←——————— carry terms ignored

It will be noted that the result of modulo 2 addition is simply the "exclusive-or" of each pair of terms.

In the same way, modulo 2 subtraction is obtained by subtracting numbers in the usual way but forgetting to "pay back" any "borrows" used. This, too, is simply illustrated by an example.

510

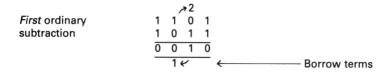

First ordinary
subtraction

```
    ↗2
1  1  0  1
1  0  1  1
0  0  1  0
      1↙      ←——————————— Borrow terms
```

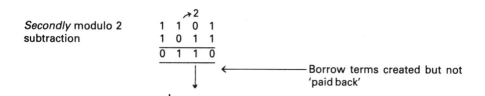

Secondly modulo 2
subtraction

```
    ↗2
1  1  0  1
1  0  1  1
0  1  1  0
      │       ←——————————— Borrow terms created but not
      ↓                     'paid back'
```

Notice that subtraction is also a term-by-term exclusive-or operation on the data.

Notice also that addition and subtraction are therefore indistinguishable operations and so one has the strange situation that

$$A + B = A - B$$

provided that A and B are binary numbers and that the arithmetic is carried out "modulo 2".

References

OTHER BOOKS COVERING A SIGNIFICANT PROPORTION OF THE MATERIAL
PRESENTED IN THIS WORK, ESPECIALLY CHAPTERS 1 TO 8 (the level
of detail and emphasis may, however, be significantly
different).

1. DOTY, K.L., "Fundamental Principles of Microcomputer
    Architecture", Matrix Publishers, Portland, Oregon,
    1979 (ISBN 0 916460 13 4).

2. LEVENTHAL, L.A., "Introduction to Microprocessors",
    Prentice-Hall International, Englewood Cliffs, New
    Jersey, 1978 (ISBN 0 13 487876 0).

3. KRUTZ, R.L., "Microprocessors and Logic Design", John
    Wiley & Sons, New York, 1980 (ISBN 0 471 02083 4).

4. LIPPIAT, A.G., "The Architecture of Small Computer
    Systems", Prentice-Hall International, London, 1978
    (ISBN 0 13 644768 4).

5. BYWATER, R.E.H., "Hardware/Software Design of Digital
    Systems", Prentice-Hall International, Engelwood
    Cliffs, New Jersey, 1981 (ISBN 0 13 383950 8).

6. HEALEY, M., "Minicomputers and Microprocessors",
    Hodder and Stoughton, London, 1976 (ISBN
    0 340 20588 1).

7. LEWIN, D., "Theory and Design of Digital Computers",
    Thomas Nelson & Sons, London, 1972 (ISBN
    0 17 761014 X).

8. BARTEE, T.C., "Digital Computer Fundamentals (5th edition)", McGraw-Hill Book Co, New York, 1981 (ISBN 0 07 003894 5).

THE FOLLOWING REFERENCES CONTAIN MATERIAL OF PARTICULAR RELEVANCE TO SPECIFIC CHAPTERS:

CHAPTER 5

9. NELSON, J.C.C., "Tabular Method for Evaluation of Incomplete Address Decoding in Microprocessor Systems", PROC IEE on Computers and Digital Techniques, Vol 2(6), 260-262, Dec 1979.

10. CLEMENTS, A., "Address Decoding Techniques for Microprocessors", IEE Colloquium on Hardware Design Techniques, Digest No 1980/11, Savoy Place, London, 6 March 1980.

11. HOLLAND P.M., "Memory System Design", IEE Colloquium on Hardware Design Techniques, Digest No. 1980/11, Savoy Place, London, 6 March 1980.

CHAPTER 8

12. DAGLESS E.L., "I/O and Apparent Concurrency", IEE Colloquium on Hardware Design Techniques, Digest No. 1980/11, Savoy Place, London, 6 March 1980.

CHAPTER 9

13. --, "M6800 Microprocessor Programming Manual", Motorola Inc, Phoenix, Arizona, 1975.

14. --, "M6800 Microcomputer System Design Data", Motorola Inc, Phoenix, Arizona, 1976.

15. OSBORNE, A. and KANE J., "An Introduction to Microcomputers (Vol 2)", Osborne-McGraw-Hill, Berkeley, California, 1978 (ISBN 0 931988 15 2).

CHAPTER 10

16. HEBDITCH, D.L., "Data Communications - An Introductory Guide", Paul Elek (Scientific Books), 1975 (ISBN 0 236 31098 4).

17. PEATMAN, J.B., "Microcomputer-Based Design", McGraw-Hill Book Co, New York, 1977 (ISBN 0 07 049138 0).

18. GORDON, J.A., "Recent Trends in Cryptology", Electronics and Power, 162-165, February 1980.

19. BEKER, H. and PIPER, F., "Cifer Systems - the Protection of Communications", Northwood Books, London, 1982 (ISBN 0 7198 2571 7).

20. DENNING, D.E., "Cryptography and Data Security",

Addison-Wesley, 1982 (ISBN 0 201 10150 5).

21. KONHEIM, A.G., "Cryptography - a Primer", Wiley, 1981 (ISBN 0 471 08132 9).

22. --, "Speech Synthesis: Devices and Applications", Electronic Engineering, 41-57, January 1981.

CHAPTER 11

23. GIBSON, A.T., "Magnetic Bubble Memory Systems", Electronic Engineering, 36-37, January 1977.

24. MARKHAM, D.C., "Magnetic Bubble Memories". Electronic Engineering. Vol 51 Part 1 no 624 (June 1979, 85-99), Part 2 no 625 (July 1979, 39-51), Part 3 no 627 (September 1979, 43-58).

25. --, "TIB 0203 Magnetic Bubble Memory - Systems Application Manual", Texas Instruments Ltd, 1979.

26. OSBORNE, A. and KANE, J., "An Introduction to Microcomputers (Vol 3)", Osborne-McGraw-Hill, Berkeley, California, 1978 (ISBN 0 931988 18 7).

CHAPTER 12

27. DAGLESS, E.L., "Interconnection Taxonomies" in "Advanced Techniques for Microprocessor Systems", F.K.HANNA (ed), Peter Peregrinus, 1980 (ISBN 0 906048 31 1).

28. DAGLESS, E.L., "Introduction to Distributed Processing" in "Advanced Techniques for Microprocessor Systems", F.K.HANNA (ed), Peter Peregrinus, 1980 (ISBN 0 906048 31 1).

29. ESCUDER, M., "Hardware Standards" in "Advanced Techniques for Microprocessor Systems", F.K.HANNA (ed), Peter Peregrinus, 1980 (ISBN 0 906048 31 1).

30. HOPPER, A., "The Cambridge Ring - A Local Network" in "Advanced Techniques for Microprocessor Systems", F.K.HANNA (ed), Peter Peregrinus, 1980 (ISBN 0 906048 31 1).

31. BASS, C., "Local Area Networks - A Merger of Computer and Communications Technologies", Microprocessors and Microsystems, Vol 5(5), 187-192, June 1981.

32. --, "Tutorial Description of the Hewlett-Packard Interface Bus", Hewlett Packard, 1980.

33. BARTHMIER, J., "Intel Multibus Interfacing", Intel Application Note AP28A, Intel Corporation, Santa Clara, California, 1979.

34. BURSKY, D., "The S100 Bus Handbook", Hayden Books, 1980.

35. LEVINE, K. and BACON, J., "Interprocess Communication", Computer Systems Group, Hatfield Polytechnic, 1980.

36. SCARISBRICK, J., "Large-Scale Multi-Ported Memories Permit Asychronous Operation", Electronic Engineering, 27-30, mid-March 1981.

37. --, "The Ethernet, a Local Area Network", Digital Equipment Corporation/Xerox Corporation/Intel Corporation, 3065 Bowers Avenue, Santa Clara, California 95051.

CHAPTER 13

38. STEVENSON, D., "An Introduction to Memory Management", Electronics and Power, 317-323, Apr 1980.

39. STEVENSON, D., "An Introduction to the Z8010 MMU Memory Management Unit", Zilog Inc., Cupertino, California, 1979.

CHAPTER 14

40. --, "M6800 Microprocessor Applications Manual", Motorola Inc, Phoenix, Arizona, 1975.

see also references (13), (14), (15) and (26)

CHAPTER 15

41. BULL, G.M. and PACKHAM, S.F.G., "Time Sharing Systems", McGraw-Hill, London, 1971 (ISBN 0 07 094161 0).

42. BARRON, D.W., "Computer Operating Systems", Chapman and Hall, London, 1971.

43. WEEMS, C., "Designing Structured Programs", Byte, 143-153, August 1978.

44. HEARN, A.D., "Some Words About Program Structure", Byte, 68-76, September 1978.

45. MUSA, J.D., "The Measurement and Management of Software Reliability", Proc IEEE, Vol 68(9), 1131-1143, September 1980.

46. CARRE, B.A., "Software Validation", Microprocessors and Microsystems, Vol 4(10), 395-406, Dec 1980.

47. GOODENOUGH, J.B., "Software Quality Assurance: Testing and Validation", PROC IEEE, Vol 68(9). 1093-1098, September 1980.

CHAPTER 16

48. LEE, S.E., "Microprocessor Analysers in the Development and Support of Microprocessor-Based Systems", Electronics and Power, 47-49, January 1978.

49. LOWE, L., "Designing for Testability", Microprocessors and Microsystems, Vol 3 no 7, January/February 1979.

50. --, "The Hewlett-Packard Digital Symposium and Exhibition" - Papers, Hewlett-Packard Ltd., 1979.

51. LELIEVRE, D. and SMITH, K., "Designing Digital Circuit Boards for Testability", Application Report MP129, Membrain Ltd., Wimborne, Dorset, 1980.

52. BENNETTS, R.G., "Techniques for Testing Microprocessor Boards", Proc IEE, Vol 128 Part A No 7, 473-491, October 1981.

CHAPTER 17

53. --, "MCS-48 Users Manual", Intel Corporation, Santa Clara, California, 1980.

54. --, "UPI-41A Users Manual", Intel Corporation, Santa Clara, California, 1980.

55. --, "Peripheral Design Handbook", Intel Corporation, Santa Clara, California, 1980.

56. --, "2920 Analog Signal Processor Design Handbook", Intel Corporation, Santa Clara, California, 1980.

57. --, "MCS-51 Users Manual", Intel Corporation, Santa Clara, California, 1981.

see also reference (15)

CHAPTER 18

58. MICK, J.R. and BRICK, J., "Bit Slice Microprocessor Design", McGraw-Hill, New York, 1980 (ISBN 0 07 041781 4).

59. MYERS, G.J., "Digital System Design with LS1 Bit Slice Logic", John Wiley, (Wiley Interscience), (ISBN 0 471 05376 7).

60. CLEMENTS, A., "An Introduction to Bit Slice Microprocessors", Electronics and Power, 230-235, March 1981.

61. HIRD, D.J. and ELLIOT, D.M., "Bit Slice Microprocessors - Their Use and Application in Minicomputers", Electronics and Power, 179-184, March 1979.

62. IBRAHIM, D., SIMMONDS, W.H. and DAVIES, A.C., "The Use of Microprogrammable Processors in Industrial Instrumentation", Sira Institute Ltd., Chislehurst, Kent, 1981.

63. --, "The AM2900 Family Data Book", Advanced Micro Devices Inc., Sunnyvale, California, 1978.

64. MICK, J.R. and BRICK, J., "Microprogramming Handbook", Advanced Micro Devices Inc., Sunnyvale, California, 1976.

65. --, "A Microprogrammed 16-Bit Computer", Advanced Micro Devices Inc., Sunnyvale, California, 1976.

66. SHAVIT, M., "An Emulation of the Am9080Å", Advanced Micro Devices Inc., Sunnyvale, California, 1978.

67. IBRAHIM, D., "Design of Microprogrammable Computer with Bit Slice Devices", Microprocessors and Microsystems, Vol 4 Part 1 no 2 (March 1980, 57-62), Part 2 no 3 (April 1980, 95-100).

68. IBRAHIM, D., "Designing Digital Sequence Controllers with Microprogramming Techniques", Electronic Engineering, 41-51, May 1980.

69. DIMOND, K.R., "Development Aids for Microprogrammable Microprocessors", IEE Colloquium on "Development of Bit Slice Systems", Digest No 1980/50, 24 October 1980.

    see also reference (15)

APPENDIX A

70. --, "MCS-85 Users Manual", Intel Corporation, Santa Clara, California, 1978.

    see also reference (15)

APPENDIX B

71. --, "Intel Component Data Catalog", Intel Corporation, Santa Clara, California, 1979.

    see also references (15), (26), (70)

APPENDIX C

72. TOCCI, R.J., "Digital Systems - Principles and Applications", Prentice-Hall International, Englewood Cliffs, New Jersey, 1980 (ISBN 0 13 212357 6).

APPENDIX D

73. MILNE, A.D., "A Survey of Present and Future Device Technologies" in "Advanced Techniques for Microprocessor Systems", F.K.HANNA (ed), Peter Peregrinus 1980 (ISBN 0 906048 31 1).

74. --, "MOS Products Catalog", Appendix B, American Microsystems Inc., Santa Clara, California, 1980.

Index

Computer Science books from Chartwell-Bratt/Studentlitteratur

Bacon, Stokes and Bacon: Computer Networks – Fundamentals and Practice
Bartholomew-Biggs M C: The Essentials of Numerical Computation
Becker J (ed): Information Technology and a New International Order
Birtwistle G et al: Simula Begin
Boyd A: Techniques of Interactive Computer Graphics
Brown M: Computers from First Principles
Bubenko jr J A (ed): Information Modeling
Freese J: International Data Flow
Gilb T: Software Metrics
Hamelink C J: Transnational Data Flows in the Information Age
Ingevaldsson L: JSP – A Practical Method of Program Design
Janning M, Nachmens S, Berild S: CS4 – An Introduction to Associative Data
  Bases and the CS4 – System
Jääskeläinen V: Linear Programming and Budgeting
Langefors B: Theoretical Analysis of Information Systems
Lawson H: Understanding Computer Systems
Lewis J W: Introduction to Data Structures
Naur P: Concise Survey of Computer Methods
Robinson H: Database Analysis and Design
Sundgren B: Data Bases and Data Models
Westh Å: Measurement and Control with a Small Computer System – some
  applications of the ABC 80 microcomputer
Witting P A: Fundamentals of Microprocessor Systems